PRACTICAL
FINGERPRINTING

BY
B. C. BRIDGES

REVISED BY
CHARLES E. O'HARA

WITH A FOREWORD BY
AUGUST VOLLMER

FUNK & WAGNALLS COMPANY

NEW YORK

Library of Congress Catalog Card Number: 63-16338
Printed in the United States of America by H. Wolff

FOREWORD

THIS WORK clarifies many doubtful definitions and presents to its readers a simple and lucid explanation of all the details involved in the classification and filing of fingerprints. Most important, from the criminal investigator's point of view, is the intensive and extensive treatment of latent fingerprint impressions found at crime scenes; never before has this subject been adequately covered by writers in the field of identification. Added to these worth-while objectives, the author has furnished a general description of the Vucetich system of fingerprint classification, which will prove useful to all fingerprint students and experts as well, especially since the Vucetich, together with the Henry system, serves as a basis for most of the other methods of fingerprint classification. The author also has included brief outlines of the majority of these other fingerprint systems, both foreign and domestic. In this book will be found a concise outline of the history and biological significance of fingerprints. These inclusions, omitted from other publications, have distinctive value to all who are interested in the field of personal identification. The book will be found most helpful to students in police-recruit training schools, and in colleges where pre-employment training is offered to those who contemplate entering police service. The work is authoritative, and is written by an experienced identification expert who for a number of years has served as an instructor in this branch of science.

AUGUST VOLLMER

PREFACE TO THE SECOND EDITION

It is hoped that the present edition will further serve to secure the position long held by Mr. Bridges' text as a standard reference work in fingerprint identification by bringing within its scope the various changes in the conventions of classification and the more recent contributions to the technical aspects of latent impressions.

In view of Mr. Bridges' past contributions to the classification methods adopted by the Federal Bureau of Investigation, it was considered appropriate to include the modifications subsequently introduced by that agency to meet its special needs for practicable and efficient extensions of the Galton-Henry system.

A most significant development in identification work—namely, the application of electronic data-processing methods to classifying, filing, and searching—is presently in a state of transition. A brief review of representative methods and practicable approaches to identification problems has, nevertheless, been presented here, together with an attempt to adumbrate the possibilities of the near future.

—C. E. O'H.

CONTENTS

ACKNOWLEDGMENTS

WE ARE deeply indebted to many sources. We wish to express our gratitude to Mr. T. Dickerson Cooke, Director of The Institute of Applied Science, for his many valuable suggestions in all aspects of this work. We are indebted to Mr. Harris B. Tuttle, Consultant in Law Enforcement Photography, Eastman Kodak Company, for his illustrations and counsel in the photographic aspects of the book. We are grateful, also, to Dr. Paul Kirk, Professor of Criminalistics, University of California; Mr. Edwin C. Conrad of Madison, Wisconsin, formerly Professor of Law at Syracuse University; Mr. William C. Cashin, Identification Consultant for the U. S. Department of State and former Director of the Division of Criminal Identification, Albany, New York; Mr. Victor A. Shamas, former consultant and identification expert for several agencies; and the representatives of Faurot Incorporated, the Polaroid Corporation, International Business Machines Corporation and Remington Rand Systems Division of the Sperry Rand Corporation.

We are grateful, too, for the assistance received from the members of the New York Police Department. For their unfailing spirit of cooperation we wish to thank Police Commissioner Michael J. Murphy, Assistant Chief Inspector Robert R. J. Gallati, Chief of Planning, Assistant Chief Inspector Walter F. Henning, Commanding Officer of the Central Office Bureaus and Squads, Captain John J. O'Neill and Lieutenant Benjamin Beigal of the Bureau of Criminal Identification, Captain Henry Guttenplan, Commanding Officer of the Police Laboratory, and Detectives John J. McGuire and Edward Meagher of the Police Laboratory.

Special thanks are due Detective Cullen Cregan, whose counsel and expertise proved invaluable in the various aspects of fingerprint classification and filing. Our thanks are also due another member of the Bureau of Criminal Identification—Detective Arthur Mandella whose research and experience provided us with the information on the identification of infant footprints.

BIOLOGICAL AND HISTORICAL DATA

BIOLOGICAL SIGNIFICANCE OF SKIN PATTERNS

ALTHOUGH popularly considered as a modern utility, the study of fingerprints and skin patterns is probably the oldest of all sciences, since its importance featured significantly many millions of years ago when tiny life forms first left the water to move about upon land. In creeping through the tidal silt, each left its informative trail which other creatures might avoid or follow at the dictates of necessity, and it is a well-established fact that down through the evolutionary development of earth life, each animal has survived only as it could recognize the traces of its friends and enemies.

The feet of early ground animals developed pads to support their weight and cushion their tread, and in some mammals the pads bore clusters of small, epidermal warts, arranged circularly around an elevated apex, and each carrying the tiny opening of a sweat gland. These warts tended to fuse together, forming transverse lines across the pad, thus providing a friction surface that prevented slipping. Skin folds surrounded the pads, each resting in a slight depression, and where the skin folds met, a delta was formed. As habits grew to be arboreal, and climbing became a part of the creature's existence, these clusters of warts or pads became somewhat flattened, and a pattern appeared. Flattening reduced the third dimension, and the design, which had been in high relief, became more like a drawing.

Survival continually depended upon the certainty of grasp, and the friction-ridge patterns were large in proportion to the size of the animal. The entire friction surface became covered with ridges, but instead of running from side to side, they retained the direction of the folds that originally surrounded the pads, while the pads themselves assumed patterns of the whorl type, affording maximum traction for a given surface. Doubtless, the hands and feet of aborigines had this same appearance. However, in the great apes and primitive man, body weight became too great for successful climbing, and the friction surfaces no longer played so important a part. The whorls then began to change to other forms, those of loops and arches.

In the hands and feet of modern man, the papillary ridges still supply friction to increase security in grasping. The corrugations strengthen the dermal structure, and facilitate the process of exudation by lifting the sweat-duct openings above the surrounding surface. They also have a sensory office in their aid to touch.

The skin is made up of two superposed layers, the epidermis and the dermis. The epidermis, or surface layer, is the one which is inked in making fingerprints. The dermis, or corium, is the deeper layer, within which are included the structures that determine the characteristics of fingerprint patterns. The thickness of the epidermis varies in the different parts of the body, showing more pronounced development toward the extremities.

The epidermis, from the surface inward, is composed of five layers: first, the corneous layer; second, the transparent layer; third, the granular layer; fourth, the Malpighian layer; and fifth, the basal or generating layer. These five layers constitute a semitransparent cuticle which molds itself like a varnish to all the configurations of the underlying tissue (Fig. 1).

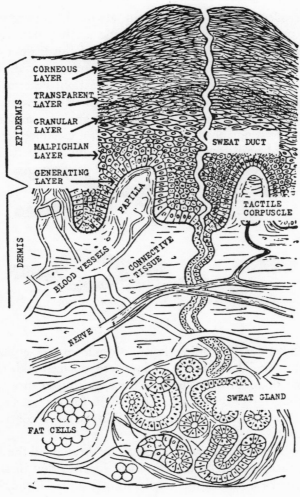

Fig. 1

All epidermal cells are originally identical, and the varied forms which they successively assume as they pass farther from the level of their origin, correspond to the distinct stages of their evolution. The cells of the basal or generating layer, which are prolonged in a vertical direction, become fore-shortened in passing into the Malpighian layer. Later, they are flattened still more in forming the granular and trans-parent layers, and in the corneous layer, are reduced to tiny scales, hard and very thin. Finally, the more superficial of

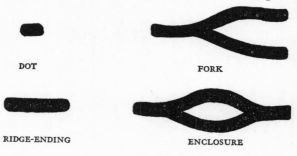

DOT   FORK

RIDGE-ENDING   ENCLOSURE

Fig. 2

these flakes in the scaling layer, drop from the epidermis as dead tissue. The cells of each layer are replaced with newer cells, which adopt their characteristics, passing in turn to the succeeding layers in order to leave room for yet newer cells. In this manner, the epidermis is the site of a continuous renovation.

The epidermal cells pass consecutively through all the stages which change them from cylindrical form to that of simple scaly particles, just as the whole animal passes through the successive evolutionary stages; but notwithstanding this cellular evolution within the epidermal layers of the skin, the pattern forms presented by the vascular and nervous papillae are perennial, immutable, and individual.

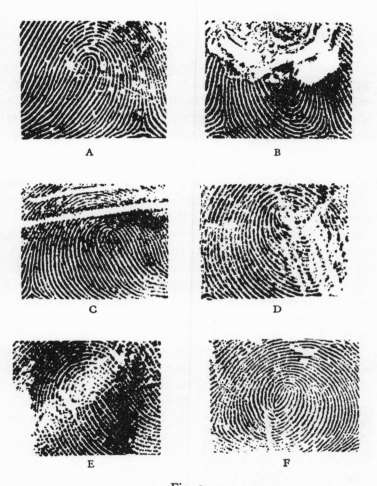

A   B

C   D

E   F

Fig. 3

Examples of skin damage caused by occupation

Ridge Formation

Personal identification by fingerprints is possible, due to the fact that normally the friction surfaces of the human hands and feet are covered with skin structure that takes the form of ridged patterns. The ridges composing these designs are in four major types of minutiae: dots, forks, ridge-endings, and enclosures (Fig. 2).

These details comprise the fundamental parts of fingerprints. The skin patterns are present on normal hands and feet some months before birth, and are constant until decomposition after death, remaining the same, except for accidental damage, as long as the body survives. The ridges may be impaired temporarily by certain occupations involving the handling of rough objects or corrosives, or in pursuits wherein the hands are kept wet for long periods (Fig. 3). Ordinary manual labor causes the friction skin to become thicker and heavier; consequently, the skin structure of men is usually coarser than that of women.

Warts, cuts, infections, burns, skin diseases, and similar blemishes are also causes of temporary skin disfigurement, but the ridges will again assume their original appearance after healing, that is, if the glands in the lower skin levels have not been attacked.

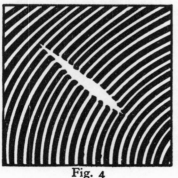

Fig. 4

Permanent ridge destruction may be caused by disease or injury that damages the aforementioned glands; by ulcers that have eaten through the skin and into the flesh, or by deep cuts and burns. (Figs. 4 and 5.) Occasionally, public of-

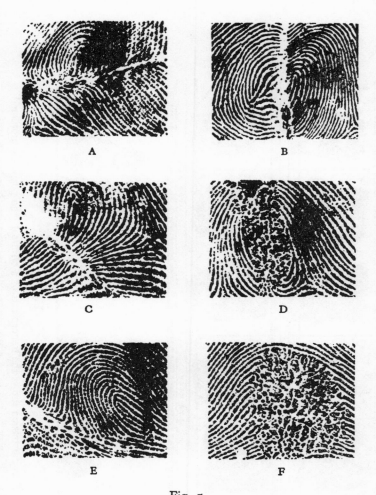

A B

C D

E F

Fig. 5

Examples of permanent scars

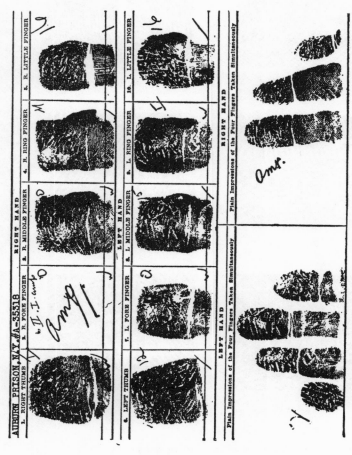

Fig. 6

This illustration shows the fingerprints of a criminal who purposely mutilated his own fingers in an effort to prevent identification. Needless to say, the patterns were still classifiable

fenders have contrived to have some of the ridges of their patterns permanently destroyed through the cooperation of unscrupulous doctors, or have purposely mutilated their own fingers in an effort to prevent recognition (Fig. 6). Such operations are not only extremely painful, but are also futile, since tell-tale scars from tissue disruption are visible to arouse suspicion, and constitute a more definite means for future identification.

Normal ridge structure is frequently broken at intervals by creases in the skin. These may result from illness, age, occupation, and other natural causes, and show in a fingerprint as small, white lines (Figs. 7 and 8). It is usually easy to distinguish between natural creases and accidental scars, since the crease leaves the ridges ending evenly, and a scar leaves the ridge endings puckered.

HISTORICAL DATA

It is conceded that early man appreciated the differences in skin markings, as indicated by numerous rock carvings and paintings featuring hand designs and fingerprints, that have been discovered in widely scattered places. The Spanish Pyrenees cave pictures, petroglyphics found on the Island of Gavr'inis off the northern coast of France, the numerous digital relics left by the American Indians—all these and many others constitute striking examples.

Nearly every country in the world holds some recorded traces of hand- and finger-impressions and their various

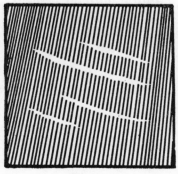

Fig. 7

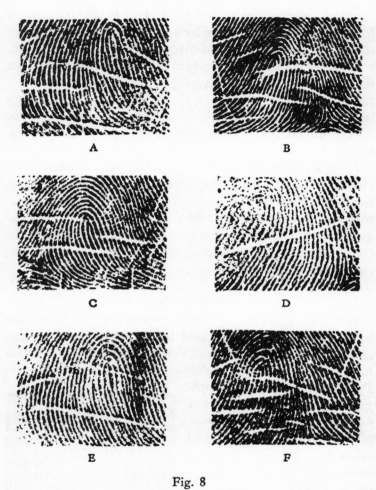

Fig. 8

Examples of skin creases resulting from age and illness
and other causes

uses. When civilization was emerging from the shadows of savagery, many superstitions were current. It was thought that inanimate objects, such as rocks and trees, were the dwelling-places of spirits; and it was a popular practice to offer prayers to these supposed deities of nature. Accompanying this gesture, the devotee would frequently place his hands upon the object of veneration, and thus produce fingerprints, which came to be considered as an indispensable part of the ritual. It is interesting to note that modern man still echoes that ancient superstition in the facetious habit of "touching wood" to avert some threatened misfortune, just as the early savage once prayed for protection with his hand upon a tree.

Somewhat more practical uses of fingerprints are recognized in the many digital impressions to be seen upon the clay tablets that display writings from ancient Assyria and Babylonia. The British Museum holds one significant relic in which the witness, a Babylonian officer, testifies that he was sent by a superior executive, ordered to make property confiscations and arrests, and also to secure the defendants' fingerprints.

It is a noteworthy circumstance that the Bible holds many direct and indirect allusions to fingerprints and skin patterns. The Apostle Paul used his own fingerprints to sign his letters (II Thessalonians 3:17). The following are also significant quotations: Job 37:7 and 13:27, Revelations 13:16 and 17, Daniel 5:5, Isaiah 2:8, Jeremiah 13:23, and Deuteronomy 9:10.

Some of the earlier practical uses of fingerprints are credited to the Chinese, who were successfully applying this facility in their daily business and legal enterprises while the Western World was still in that period known as the Dark Ages.

Kia Kung-yen, a Chinese historian of the Tang period, in his writings of A.D. 650, made mention of fingerprints in commenting on an older method of preparing legal documents. His notation reads as follows: "Wooden tablets were inscribed with the terms of the contract, and notches were cut in the sides at identical places so that the tablets could later be matched, thus proving them genuine. The significance of the notches was the same as that of the fingerprint (*hua chi*) of the present time."

The Chinese Law Book of Yung-Hwui of about the same period, in describing the code of domestic relations in China, states: "To divorce a wife the husband must give a document setting forth which of the seven reasons was assigned for the action. . . . All letters should be written in the husband's own handwriting, but in case he is unable to write, he must sign with his fingerprints."

Early in the twelfth century, a Chinese author, Shi-naingan, wrote a series of crime novels, entitled *The Story of the River Bank,* dealing with the cruel deeds of pirates. In this work, allusion is made to the use of fingerprints in criminal identification. The translation reads as follows: "Wu Sung captured the two women who had killed his brother. . . . He compelled them to ink their fingers and to record their fingerprints." From this it is safe to conclude that the science of fingerprinting had already found its place in Chinese criminal procedure.

PIONEER WORKS ON FINGERPRINTS

One of the earliest known European publications of fingerprint observation was offered in 1684 by Dr. Nehemiah Grew, Fellow of the College of Physicians and Surgeons of the Royal Society, England. Two years later, in 1686, another scientific paper appeared under the name of Marcello Malpighi, Professor of Anatomy at the University of Bologna, Italy. The research work of this latter contributor was of such outstanding importance that one of the layers of the human skin now bears his name.

A salient event in fingerprint history was marked by a treatise published in 1823 by Johannes Evangelist Purkinje, who offered the essay as his thesis for a doctor of medicine degree at the University of Breslau. In this writing Purkinje described the fingerprint types and classified them in nine major groups. The following is a brief quotation from his paper:

Our attention is next engaged by the wonderful arrangement and curving of the minute furrows connected with the organ of touch on the inner surface of the hand and foot, especially of the last joint of each finger. Some general account of them is always to be found in every manual of physiology and anatomy, but in an organ of such importance as the human hand, used as it is for every varied movement and especially serviceable to the sense of touch, no research, however minute, can fail to yield some gratifying addition to our knowledge of that organ. After numberless observations, I have thus far met with nine principal varieties of curvature according to which tactile furrows, or furrows susceptible to touch, are disposed upon the inner surface of the last phalanx of the fingers.

Another pioneer in the science of fingerprinting is recognized in Sir William Herschel, an assistant employed by the Old East India Company of Bengal, India. As a collector for the British Government, in 1858 he began fingerprinting the natives with whom he had business dealings. At that time it so happened that he requested bids for some material needed for the construction of a road in Jungpoor. Selection was made, and an agreement drawn with a native named Rajyadhar Konai. Knowing undependability to be a basic characteristic of his business associate, Herschel conceived the idea of demanding an imprint of the signer's hand in lieu of his signature, as being much more impressive and effective in forestalling any attempt toward future trickery. The fingerprints had precisely the anticipated result, and the success of that first digital signature led to similar agreements. Herschel later modified his procedure, using only the imprint of the last finger joint instead of the entire hand.

DR. HENRY FAULDS

A name honored in fingerprint history is that of Dr. Henry Faulds, an Englishman, who spent many years in Japan, where he was connected with the Tsukiji Hospital in Tokyo. Contemporaneous with Herschel, but apparently quite independent of him and without any knowledge of Herschel's work, Faulds also made valuable discoveries and contributions to the field.

While lecturing to medical students on the subject of physiology, during an inspection of some prehistoric pottery, he noted certain finger markings which apparently had been made before the clay had hardened. This incident aroused Faulds' academic interest, and he subsequently discovered other more clearly defined markings of fingerprints on pottery of later origin. These findings inspired an exhaustive study of the different designs displayed by the friction surfaces of the human hands. After collecting numerous fingerprints of other nationalities as well as the Japanese, he made comparison of their ethnological differences. His investigations were later extended to the prints of monkeys in an attempt to throw some light on possible generical relation.

One of the most valuable suggestions offered by Faulds was his contention that fingerprints found at the scene of a crime might serve to identify the criminal. In a letter dated 1880, Faulds wrote as follows:

If bloody fingerprints or impressions on clay, glass, etc., are present, the scientific conviction of the perpetrator may be effected. I have already met with two practical cases in my experience, and was able to use such fingerprints as very necessary evidence. In one case someone had left greasy fingerprints on a drinking glass. The pattern of the papillary lines was quite peculiar. Fortunately I had previously made a print of the person in question. The two patterns agreed with microscopic fidelity. In the other case, the sooty fingerprints left by a person when he climbed over a white wall, were of great value as exonerating evidence. Still other uses will occur in the field of medical jurisprudence when, for example, only the hand of a dismembered corpse is found. If the fingerprints that have been taken are known, they certainly offer stronger proof than the customary "birthmark" of the dime novel.

Faulds also wrote a textbook on fingerprint procedure in which he advocated printing all ten fingers, a practice not developed by Herschel.

Juan Vucetich, a noted Argentine criminologist, carried on extensive fingerprint research prior to 1900; and his methods are still used in most Latin countries at the present time. In the course of his activities, he collected a file of fingerprint records which was then the largest of its kind in the world.

Sir Francis Galton

Sir Francis Galton, probably the greatest British scientist of his time, published his first book on fingerprints in 1892. Prior to that date, he had given careful consideration to the discoveries of his predecessors and contemporaries, supplementing their work with a great deal of personal investigation. In his first textbook, he discussed the anatomy of finger patterns and offered practical methods for recording them. His work also included methods for classifying fingerprints, which he divided into three groups, arches, loops, and whorls. In 1894, Galton's system was officially established in England, and his basic principles are still included in many of the modern methods of classification.

When Galton first attacked the problem of fingerprint science with the thought of adapting it to use in police registration, he realized that at least three facts would have to be established in order to demonstrate the method as practical. First, it had to be proved that the skin patterns remain constant throughout the life of the individual. Second, their variability must be such that each person's prints constitute a unique characteristic. And third, it was needful to devise a method of classification that would permit of determining whether or not an especial set of patterns was that of a person who had been registered previously. He succeeded in collecting sufficient proof to answer all of these questions in the affirmative, and his system of registration became known as the A-L-W method, each letter representing a fingerprint type, that of arches, loops and whorls.

In London in 1894, Galton's system was combined with the methods of Alphonse Bertillon, and after 1895, criminals were both measured and fingerprinted. The previously employed Bertillon *signalment* was based upon eleven measurements of the human anatomy, and used the metric system for recording the data. The measurements of the body included the height (standing), the reach or spread from fingertip to fingertip with the arms outstretched, and the height of the body (seated) from the base of the spine to the top of the head. The head was measured as to length, width, length of the right ear, and the width of the face across the cheek bones. The measurements of the limbs described the length of the left foot, length of the left middle finger, length of the left little finger, and length of the left forearm.

Each of these primary groups was divided into three subgroups. The head widths were classified as narrow, medium, and broad, according to arbitrary numerical limits. Other measurements were described as being either small, medium, or large. Thus the classifications were broken down into comparatively small divisions to facilitate search. However, with large accumulations of records, the system was not infallible for various reasons. Different operators might secure differing sets of figures from their measurements, owing to varying pressure exerted on the measuring instruments. Also, the individual's dimensions were certain to alter with time and bodily condition, and obviously the system would be of little utility in cases of persons who had not attained their full growth.

It has been a popular but wrong opinion that Bertillon was one of the "originators" of fingerprinting. Contrary to this belief, he was for many years strongly opposed to the system, which was not officially adopted in France until after his death in 1914. However, despite these circumstances, Bertillon must be recognized as one of the outstanding contributors to the field of criminology, since his methods were timely and useful, constituting the temporary solution to a major problem then confronting law-enforcement officers, that of effectively describing and classifying lawbreakers.

Sir Edward Richard Henry

Following in Galton's footsteps, and basing much of his data on the great scientist's discoveries, Sir Edward Richard Henry published his *Classification and Uses of Finger Prints* in 1900, at which time he was head of the metropolitan police forces in London. The "Henry" system, with some modifications, is still in general use in most English-speaking countries, and, together with the Vucetich method, forms a basis for practically all fingerprint systems in use throughout the civilized world today.

On June 5, 1903, fingerprinting was officially adopted for identification purposes in Sing Sing Prison, and later at

Napanoch, Auburn, and Clinton Penitentiaries. When the World's Fair was celebrated at St. Louis, Missouri, in 1904, the crown jewels of the British Empire were loaned for exhibition. Those valuable objects were sent to the United States in the care of officers from Scotland Yard, who were pupils of Sir E. R. Henry, and as a result of friendly contact, a fingerprint bureau was started in the St. Louis Police Department. On November 2, 1904, the office of Attorney-General of the United States granted permission to Warden R. W. McCloughry, of the Federal Penitentiary at Leavenworth, Kansas, to purchase the necessary material and equipment for the installation of a fingerprint bureau at that prison.

It is quite possible that fingerprints were used in police procedure elsewhere in the United States prior to 1903; it has been authoritatively stated that they were first utilized in this country for noncriminal registration on December 19, 1902, by Dr. Henry P. de Forest, in the Municipal Civil Service Commission of the City of New York. Even before Galton's participation, a San Francisco photographer, Isaiah West Taber, was engaged in the study and promotion of the system, and advocated its use for the registration of the immigrant Chinese. Another early instance was furnished by Gilbert Thompson, a geologist in charge of a government survey in the Territory of New Mexico in 1882, who used his own thumbprint as a protection, to prevent tampering with the pay orders issued by himself.

The Federal Bureau of Investigation had its inception at Washington, D. C., in 1908, and in 1924 an Act of Congress officially established an identification unit therein. The fingerprint records from Leavenworth Penitentiary and the International Association for Chiefs of Police were combined and added to the Federal Bureau, which now includes the largest single collection of fingerprints in existence.

II

PROCEDURE FOR TAKING FINGERPRINTS

A LTHOUGH the present utility of fingerprint identification
has gained recognition largely through application in
criminal procedure, this method is now being adopted
in numerous civil branches of social and business activities.
One of its advantages is simplicity, little equipment being
necessary for taking fingerprints. The chief requirements are a
tube of ink, a roller, an inking plate, some simple device for
holding the record cards, and the blanks upon which the impressions are to be printed.

Ordinary printer's ink gives the best result as a pigment,
since it dries so rapidly that fresh work may be handled immediately with little danger of smudging. Also, the consistency of this material may be regulated by warming or by
using a reducing agent, should the ink be too thick. Prints
made with other substances, such as writing fluid or stamp-
pad ink, are usually unsatisfactory.

The roller best adapted to fingerprint work is known as a
brayer, and used by printers in making galley proofs, a convenient size being about six inches long and two inches in
diameter.

An inking plate may be made from a piece of thick glass;
six or seven inches wide and twelve or fourteen inches long
is an appropriate size. This should be mounted at an elevation

that will allow the subject's arm to assume a horizontal position while the fingers are being inked. Some types of inking equipment are provided with an adjustment that raises or lowers the shelf holding the pad and the fingerprint card, a desirable convenience insuring good results regardless of the subject's height. The level of the inking pad and printing equipment should be such that there is no strain or pressure on the fingers; it should also be placed at the edge of the table upon which it is mounted, so that the subject's fingers which are not being printed will not interfere with the manipulation of the other fingers in the printing process.

Solvents are important in the equipment, since it is often necessary first to clean a subject's fingers, and it is always imperative to cleanse the roller and inking plate thoroughly after each using. Denatured alcohol, gasoline, and benzine are well suited to this purpose. Any laxity in preparation may result in imperfect impressions, devoid of identifying characteristics, or with false markings caused by lint, dust, or gummed ink.

The conventional card for recording fingerprint impressions is 8″ x 8″ square; this size was finally adopted to facilitate filing and to establish a uniform medium of exchange. The 8″ x 8″ card was first designed and introduced in 1908 by P. A. Flak, a Straits Settlements fingerprint expert employed by the Library Bureau Company of Chicago. He prepared this card at the suggestion of the firm for which he was working, as best adapted for filing purposes.

The accompanying illustration (Fig. 9) shows a set of fingerprints on the type of card used by the Federal Bureau of Investigation. From this illustration it will be noted that there are two kinds of fingerprint impressions on the same card. The upper ten prints are taken individually of the thumb, index, middle, ring, and little fingers of each hand in the

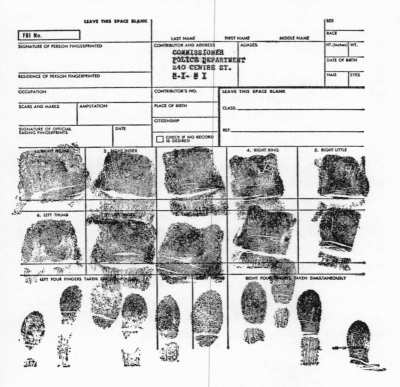

Fig. 9

order named, and are known as "rolled" impressions. The smaller prints at the bottom of the card are taken simultaneously, printing all the fingers of each hand, and are known as "plain" or "flat" impressions; their purpose is to serve as a check on the sequence of the rolled prints, thus determining whether or not the latter have been recorded in their correct order.

Classification of the prints involves the consideration of a number of factors included in the pattern, and requires ridge

counting, ridge tracing, and the clear recognition of certain
focal points. It is, therefore, important that all of the pattern
be imprinted in the rolled impressions. Fig. 10, *A* and *B*,
shows an example of this; *A*, being fully rolled, reveals the
entire pattern and shows the fingerprint to be a composite
of the "whorl" type; *B*, being but partly rolled, discloses only
a portion of the pattern, and leads the classifier to believe that
the impression is a "tented arch," a quite different pattern
falling in another group. In addition to establishing accurate
classification, it is plain that the larger surface of a fully rolled
impression also affords the investigator a greater number of
points for comparison.

When a set of impressions is to be taken, a small daub of
ink is placed on the inking slab and thoroughly rolled until a
thin and even film of pigment covers the entire surface. The
subject to be printed should stand in front of and at forearm
length from the inking plate. In taking rolled impressions,
the bulb of the finger is placed at right angles to the surface
of the plate. The finger is then turned or rolled until the
bulb faces in the opposite direction (Fig. 11). In inking the

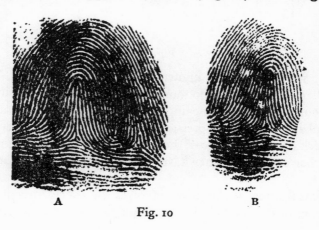

A   B

Fig. 10

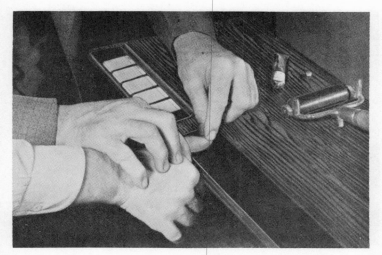

Fig. 11

Fig. 12

Procedure for Taking Fingerprints
(For continuation see next page)

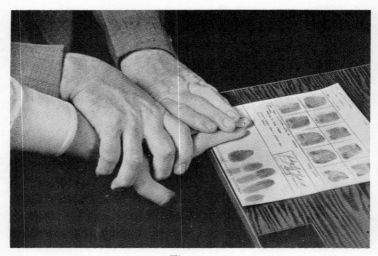

Fig. 13
Procedure for Taking Fingerprints

finger, the ink should be applied evenly from the tip to below the first joint. By pressing the finger lightly on the card and rolling in the same manner, a clear, rolled impression of the finger-pattern surface is obtained (Fig. 12). The degree of pressure applied to the finger in inking is not as exacting as that exerted in printing. It will be found that a comparatively light pressure on the paper will produce a suitable result. Many poorly recorded fingerprints are the consequence of too much pressure on the paper. The best results may be expected by inking and printing each finger separately, beginning with the right thumb, and then in order, the index, middle, ring, and little finger.

When taking rolled impressions, if consideration is given to the anatomical structure of the forearm, more satisfactory prints will be secured. The two bones of the forearm, extending from the elbow to the wrist, are known as the ulna and the radius, the radius being the bone on the upper or thumb side of the arm, and the ulna on the lower or little-finger side. As its name suggests, the radial bone swings back and forth in a partial circle about the ulna. In making fingerprints, advantage may be taken of this natural movement, and with the motion of rolling the finger, the radius should always be made to revolve about the ulna from the tensed position to the relaxed position. This requires that the thumb and fingers be *always rolled away from the body of the person who is being printed*. This starts the motion with the elbow slightly lifted, and the arm more or less tensed in supporting its weight, and concludes the movement with the arm and fingers relaxed. Figs. 11 and 12 illustrate the correct position and method of holding the fingers for inking and printing when making a rolled impression.

As stated, the degree of pressure exerted in taking fingerprints is an important factor, but it will vary with different subjects. Experience and observation will determine the requirements; no fixed rule can be established in this connection. However, it is important to see that the subject's hand and arm are relaxed, and that he submits to the operator's manipulations, since any willful resistance, or even attempted aid, on the part of the subject, prevents the operator from correctly gauging the pressure, and hinders his operations, thus resulting in unsuitable prints.

Physical condition, occupation, or accident may so modify the skin structure as to render the taking of fingerprints difficult even under ordinary circumstances. Here the operator must experiment with the amount of ink and degree of pressure in order to effect his purpose. In certain cases, should the subject be held in custody for as long as ten to fourteen days, it is often possible to secure good prints after the troublesome conditions have become less pronounced.

The plain impressions shown on the lower portion of the card in Fig. 9, are made by pressing all the fingers of the hand on the inking slab, and then on the paper, the right hand being impressed on the right side of the card and the left hand opposite, as shown in the illustration. The thumbs are then inked and pressed without rolling, in the designated spaces. Fig. 13 illustrates the correct procedure in recording the plain or unrolled impressions.

It sometimes happens that a subject has lost one or more fingers, and in such a case the space on the card where the missing digit would ordinarily be impressed, should be marked "AMP," indicating amputation. This is done in order to make the necessary allowance when the print is classified. Should any of the fingers be temporarily damaged or otherwise unprintable due to bandages, etc., the finger's condition should be briefly described in the space provided on the card for that especial finger. Should this be neglected, the empty space may

FEDERAL BUREAU OF INVESTIGATION, UNITED STATES DEPARTMENT OF JUSTICE
WASHINGTON, D. C.

CURRENT ARREST OR RECEIPT

DATE ARRESTED OR RECEIVED	CHARGE OR OFFENSE (If code citation is used it should be accompanied by charge)	DISPOSITION OR SENTENCE (List FINAL disposition only. If not now available, submit later on FBI Form R–84 for completion of record.)

If COLLECT wire reply or COLLECT telephone reply is desired, indicate here

☐ Wire reply   ☐ Telephone reply   FOR INSTITUTIONS USE ONLY

Telephone number   Sentence expires ....

INSTRUCTIONS

Please Paste Photograph In This Space

Since photograph may become detached indicate name, FBI number, and arrest number on reverse side whether attached to fingerprint card or submitted later.

1. FORWARD ARREST CARDS TO FBI IMMEDIATELY AFTER FINGERPRINTING FOR MOST EFFECTIVE SERVICE.
2. TYPE or PRINT all information.
3. Note amputations in proper finger squares.
4. REPLY WILL QUOTE ONLY NUMBER APPEARING IN THE BLOCK MARKED "CONTRIBUTOR'S NO."
5. Indicate any additional copies for other agencies in space below—include their complete mailing address.

SEND COPY TO:

FD-249 (Rev. 1-24-61)   U.S. GOVERNMENT PRINTING OFFICE   o48—10—72020-2

Fig. 14

lead the classifier to conclude that the finger is no longer on the hand.

In the various identification bureaus throughout the country, a variety of card forms is provided for recording fingerprints. Unfortunately, this type of record has not as yet been standardized. However, in nearly every instance, the size at least is uniform, 8″ x 8″ generally having been adopted. Furthermore, although the arrangement may differ slightly, in nearly all cases, spaces are designated for the data relating to the subject's description, the charge or offense for which

Fig. 15

he is arrested, his criminal history, and other details; and care should be exercised to inscribe this information legibly, together with the subject's name, aliases, color, and sex, in the spaces provided, as inaccuracies in these items may lead to future uncertainty and confusion.

The Federal Bureau of Investigation employs a form as illustrated in Fig. 14. Should a fingerprint record feature later in court procedure, which is not infrequently the case, a legal question will very likely be raised as to who recorded the especial prints in evidence. Here the operator's signature is indispensable. It is important also that the card be inscribed legibly with the name of the police department or other organization under whose authority the fingerprints were taken. Fig. 15 shows a fingerprint-card form designed by the writer. It includes a number of novel features that have proved useful and convenient. A detail deserving special mention is that of the space wherein the subject is required to furnish his address and the exact date and place of his birth, in addition to his signature. At the top of the card, spaces are indicated for inscribing the subject's record numbers (if they exist) for the identification of files of the state bureau and for the Federal Bureau of Investigation (DCI and FBI). Another useful innovation in this fingerprint-card form is the inclusion of the subject's motor vehicle operator's license number and his Social Security number, if available. These latter items will be certain to prove most important and helpful in numerous requirements.

III

CLASSIFICATION BY THE HENRY SYSTEM

AFTER a set of fingerprints has been properly placed on the conventional record card, it is then necessary to give the patterns a numerical identity that will permit not only of filing the prints with similar records, but also of referring to them by their card formulae, should such future reference be necessary. To accomplish this purpose, there has been devised a variety of so-called classification systems in which numbers, letters, and other symbols are selected to indicate certain pattern characteristics. There are over fifty such methods in use throughout the different countries of the world. The method in almost universal use in the United States is known as the "Galton-Henry Method," or the "Henry" system, its name being derived from its originators, Sir Francis Galton and Sir Edward Richard Henry, already mentioned.

At this point a condensed résumé of the Galton-Henry, or so-called Henry method, is offered, in order to furnish a clearer understanding of such discussion as may follow relating to the more intimate details of the system.

Under the Henry system, fingerprints are in two classes, those which are given numerical value, and those which are not. The patterns having value are Whorls and Composites (see definition), and those having no value are Loops and Arches (see definition).

All patterns are divided as follows:

(A) Patterns having no numerical value

	Subdivided	Symbol
1. Arches	Plain Arches	A
	Tented Arches	T
2. Loops	Radial	R
	Ulnar	U

(B) Patterns to which numerical values are assigned

	Subdivided	Symbol
3. Whorls (plain)	Inner	I
	Meet	M
	Outer	O
4. Composites:		
Central Pocket Loops	Like Whorls	CP
Twinned Loops	" "	TL
Lateral Pocket Loops	" "	LP
Accidentals	" "	AC

Fig. 16 shows diagrammatic and actual illustrations of the various fingerprint types. In this group of patterns will be noted a design described as an "Exceptional Arch." This pattern, now classified with Tented Arches, was not included in the description of pattern types under the Henry system, but was added subsequently, as explained later in the text.

1. In Arches, the ridges run from one side to the other without backward recurvature. In plain arches there is no delta ordinarily. Should there be the appearance of a delta, no ridges must intervene between the delta and the core; that is, if even one uninvolved ridge recurves and there is a count of one, the pattern is no longer an Arch, but becomes a Loop. In Tented Arches, the ridges at the core or center have an upward thrust in the shape of a tent, arranging themselves on both sides of a spine or axis, toward which the adjoining ridges converge.

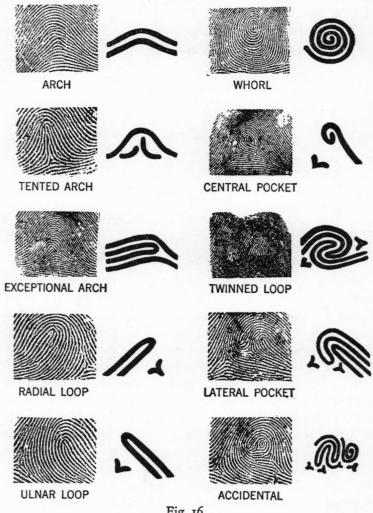

ARCH

WHORL

TENTED ARCH

CENTRAL POCKET

EXCEPTIONAL ARCH

TWINNED LOOP

RADIAL LOOP

LATERAL POCKET

ULNAR LOOP

ACCIDENTAL

Fig. 16

Diagrammatic and actual illustration of the various finger print types

2. In Loops, the ridges enter and exit on the same side of the pattern. There must be at least one ridge that follows or tends to follow this course, and there must be at least one ridge between the delta and the core. Radial Loops slant toward the thumb, and Ulnar Loops slant toward the little finger.

3. In Whorls, at least one ridge must recurve and make a complete circuit around the core, and there are two deltas ordinarily. (See group classification for subdivisions of I, M, and O.)

4. Composites have characteristics of two or more of the foregoing patterns. In Central Pocket Loops, the majority of the ridges take the form of a loop, but one or more ridges recurve at the core to form a pocket. If a line drawn up the line of exit of the ridges meets a recurving ridge at right angles, it is a Central Pocket; otherwise it is a Loop. (This is the Galton-Henry test for all Whorl types.) Twinned Loops and Lateral Pocket Loops are composed of two distinct loops, one overlapping the other. In Lateral Pocket Loops, the ridges forming the cores of the loops pass out (or have their exits) without being divided by either of the deltas. In Twinned Loops, these lines (called the Core Lines) are divided by one of the deltas, either right or left. This factor is of little importance except in singleprint classifications, since both types of pattern have value and are given no special consideration under the Henry system. Accidentals are patterns which are too irregular to be classed in any of the foregoing groups.

The classification, or Formula, is composed of figures and letters, usually placed in the upper right-hand corner of the fingerprint card, for the purpose of filing and searching the record. It is made up of Primary, Secondary, Group or Sub-Secondary, and Final or ridge count of the right little finger.

Primary: This is expressed in the form of a fraction from

1 over 1 to 32 over 32, and is the numerical value of the Whorls in a set of prints, with one extra point added to both numerator and denominator. The values are assigned by pairing the fingers, beginning with the right thumb, in the order in which they occur on the fingerprint card (see Fig. 17). Thus: First pair, right thumb and right index, are given values of 16 each; Second pair, right middle and right ring, values of 8 each; Third pair, right little and left thumb, values of 4 each;

In Fig. #17, the Chart and simple rule as devised by the writer, will be found very helpful in securing the primary classification under the Henry system.

R. Thumb	R. Index	R. Middle	R. Ring	R. Little
16	16	8	8	4

L. Thumb	L. Index	L. Middle	L. Ring	L. Little
4	2	2	1	1

The combined values of the Whorls showing in the white squares, plus one, will equal the numerator of the primary classification.
The combined values of the Whorls showing in the dark squares, plus one, will equal the denominator.

Fig. 17

Fourth pair, left index and left middle, values of 2 each; and Fifth pair, left ring and left little, values of 1 each. Only Whorls (the term here is meant to include Composites and Accidentals) are given these values when they appear in the specified locations. Thus: the sum of the numerical values of the Whorls, if any, in fingers 1, 3, 5, 7, and 9, with 1 added, is the denominator of the primary classification. The sum of the numerical values of the Whorls, if any, in fingers 2, 4, 6, 8, and 10, with 1 added, is the numerator of the primary classification. Where no Whorls appear in a set of impressions, the primary would be 1 over 1. One thousand and twenty-four (1,024) possible primaries may be attained from 1 over 1 to 32 over 32, which latter would be the primary when Whorls appear in every finger.

Secondary: Arches, Tented Arches, Radial and Ulnar Loops occurring in the index fingers, constitute the Secondary, and are indicated by capital letters, the right index being considered the numerator and the left index the denominator. When Whorls appear in the index fingers, they may be indicated by a dash. An Arch in the right index and a Tented Arch in the left index would be expressed by *A* over *T*.

Group, or Sub-Secondary: The ridge tracing of Whorls (*I, M,* and *O*) and the count of Loops (*I* and *O*) of the index and middle fingers of both hands compose this group. In ridge-tracing Whorls, trace from the lower branch of the left delta, following it toward the right delta. If it passes inside the right delta by three or more ridges, it is considered an Inner. If it meets the right delta or passes inside or outside by less than three ridges, it is designated as Meeting. If it passes outside by three or more ridges, it is an Outer. In the indexes (should the patterns be Loops), if the count of ridges between the delta and the core be less than ten, it is designated as an Inner; if ten or more, it is an Outer. In the middle finger, if the count is less than eleven, it is designated as an Inner; eleven or more, as an Outer. Fingers of the right hand in this division of the formula are considered as the numerator, and the left hand the denominator.

In the earlier period of fingerprint classification, large collections of prints were nonexistent, and it was not necessary to subdivide extensively for filing and searching. Consequently, in the Henry textbook, further division of the Group, or Sub-Secondary, was described as follows: If different patterns occur in the digits composing the numerator or the denominator, then only the pattern in the index is considered. Thus, if the index is a Loop, counting inner, and the middle is a Whorl, only the inner is noted in the formula, and vice versa. If an Arch or Tented Arch occurs in either index, there is no Group, there being no count in Arches. This procedure was quite satisfactory when the Henry system was first introduced; however, since present-day requirements demand inclusive consideration, the sub-secondary group may designate all patterns appearing in the index and middle fingers, regardless of any dissimilarity of type. Furthermore, additional extension of the ridge counting will be helpful with the inclusion of the ring and little fingers, should they be Loops, and their tracings should they fall in the Whorl division. Here the loop-count of the ring finger is thirteen or less for an inner, fourteen or more for an outer. The little-finger count is nine or less for an inner, and ten or more for an outer.

Lettered Group: Arches, Tented Arches, and Radial Loops are of such relative infrequency that when they appear in any of the digits other than the index fingers, they are designated by small letters (the index fingers are indicated by capitals). Thus, if all ten fingers contain Arches, the formula would be *aA3a* over *aA3a*, the *3a* meaning that there are three Arches after the index finger. The first small *a* indicates an Arch in the thumb. If the thumbs contain Radial Loops, and all other fingers are Arches, the lettered classification would be *rA3a* over *rA3a*.

In addition to the above divisions of the formula, under the Henry system the ridge count of the right little finger was noted, when the pattern was a Loop, this count being placed at the extreme right of the formula. When an Arch, a Tented Arch, or Radial Loop appeared in any finger other than the index of either hand, there was no Group. For current requirements, the treatment previously described is advocated for this step in the procedure as well. Also, the ridge count of both little fingers may be added in all cases, and should these digits display Whorls, the whorl patterns may be "counted" like Loops, if so desired. In "counting" a Whorl pattern for this purpose, the count should be made from the left delta to the core in Whorls on the right hand, and from the right delta to the core should the Whorl design be on the left hand.

Type-Lines, Cores, and Deltas

Following an establishment of the Henry system's fundamentals, as described in the preceding paragraphs, it is necessary to give attention to a discussion of these elements in more detail.

In the technical analysis of fingerprint patterns, three basic factors feature importantly: namely, type-lines, cores, and deltas; it is needful to become familiar with the procedure in recognizing and placing them. The underlying principles are simple, and subsequent illustrations will serve to clarify them.

The type-lines are the innermost ridges that bound the pattern area (see Fig. 18). These ridges run parallel, then diverge or separate, and surround or tend to surround the pattern area, which is that portion of the fingerprint wherein are included the characteristics that determine its pattern type. In Fig. 18, which shows a loop pattern, the type-lines are designated by the letters X and Y. Letter A indicates the point where the type-lines diverge, and denotes the location of the delta. Fig. 19 illustrates how the type-lines surround the pattern area. The upper type-line, indicated by the letter X, turns upward, bounds the top of the pattern area, then curves downward, and passes out on the opposite side of the impression. The lower type-line, marked Y, runs parallel with X where

Fig. 18

Fig. 19

Fig. 20

Fig. 21

Fig. 22

Fig. 23

it enters the pattern, but diverges at the place marked *A*. After turning downward, it passes out on the opposite side of the pattern.

In patterns where type-lines are present, the delta is located midway at their place of divergence, or just in front of that point, and may be represented by a dot, a fork, a ridge ending, a ridge fragment, or a recurving ridge. With the exception of some forms of arch, type-lines are present in all fingerprint patterns. In order to locate the delta correctly, establishment of the type-lines is absolutely necessary, and since in some cases they are but fragmentary, it is important to study the impressions to determine their precise location. As previously indicated, the type-lines enclose the pattern area, and outline the portion of the design that is considered in the procedure of classifying.

Type-lines may not be continuous, and are frequently broken; therefore, when tracing a broken ridge, the ridge just outside the point of fracture is considered as the continuation of the traced ridge. Examples of broken and unbroken type-lines are given in Figs. 20 and 21 respectively.

Most fingerprint patterns include certain focal points described as the core, or inner terminus, and the delta, or outer terminus. Their correct location in all cases is one of the material requirements in the science of fingerprinting. As its name suggests, the core is located at the approximate center of the pattern. Although the subject of deltas will be discussed at greater length presently, at this point it is necessary to offer some introductory data on deltas, to insure a better understanding of cores. Furthermore, it would seem appropriate to mention the "line of count," which is an imaginary straight line from the delta to the core, the core and delta representing its "inner" and "outer" terminus (Fig. 27). This line indicates the ridges to be "counted" as explained in a following section of the text.

The delta is the first fork or bifurcation (—<), abrupt ridge-ending (—), meeting of two ridges (<), island or enclosure (-○-), dot (•), ridge fragment (〜), or any ridge formation of any nature, at or nearest the center of the divergence of the two type-lines, or directly in front of that point. This rule remains constant even if such ridge, meeting of ridges, fork, or other ridge formation, is or appears to be joined to either or both of the type-lines, or to ridges converging upon it within the pattern area.

As used in connection with the procedure of fingerprint classification, the term "delta" requires some explanation. The dictionary gives the following definition: Delta—(1) the fourth letter in the Greek alphabet (△), corresponding to the English letter D; (2) a triangular alluvial deposit in the mouth of a river; (3) anything triangular; etc.

The significance of the term "delta," as used in physical geography, is similar in its relation to fingerprints. The alluvial deposit that sometimes forms where the waters diverge at a river's mouth, is comparable to the delta in a skin pattern, where the dot, fork, recurvature, or other ridge structure found midway between the diverging type-lines, marks the focal point under consideration. The general appearance of a delta in physical geography is illustrated in Fig. 22, while Fig. 23 depicts the type-lines in a fingerprint enclosing the pattern area, and with the delta located at their point of separation. The type-lines are indicated by $X — X$, while letter D marks the delta.

In the terminology of fingerprint procedure, certain words find frequent use, two of which are "bifurcation" and "divergence." To avoid confusion, a clear understanding of these terms is necessary. Bifurcation is the dividing or forking of a single ridge into two or more branches. Fig. 24 shows a single bifurcation, while examples such as shown in Fig. 25 are considered as two bifurcations, although the divisions are at the same point.

Divergence is the separation or spreading apart of two ridges that previously were running parallel or nearly so, as illustrated in Fig. 26. Thus it will be recognized that a single ridge may bifurcate, but cannot diverge.

In the classification of fingerprints, certain focal locations, considered as fixed points in the pattern, are known as the "inner terminus" and the "outer terminus." The inner terminus is the core, or approximate center of the pattern, while the outer terminus is the delta; and connecting them is the "line of count," as previously outlined. These fixed points are indicated in Fig. 27, which illustrates a loop pattern. The core is designated by the letter C, while D marks the delta. The type-lines are marked $X — X$. It will be seen that the delta is located midway between the diverging type-lines, as already described.

In Fig. 27, the dotted line indicated by letter B marks the "shoulder" of the innermost loop. The shoulder is the turning-point of the ridge that forms the central loop. This is a feature of importance. Should the core of the pattern be formed by a loop that includes no ridge structure, the core is located at the shoulder of this loop that is farthest from the delta, as shown in Fig. 28. If the central loop surrounds a single rod, the tip of this ridge is the core, and if there is an uneven number of rods present, the central spine is the core (see Fig. 29). When the central loop surrounds an even number of rods, the central two are considered as being joined in an imaginary loop, and the rod farthest from the delta is the core, as indi-

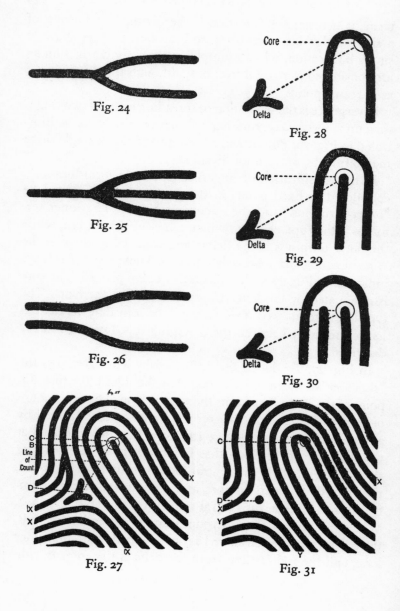

Fig. 24

Fig. 25

Fig. 26

Fig. 27

Fig. 28

Fig. 29

Fig. 30

Fig. 31

Core

Delta

Core

Delta

Core

Delta

C
B
Line
of
Count

D

IX

X

IX

C

D
XI

Y

X

Y

cated in Fig. 30. This principle is more explicitly illustrated in the following diagrams, in which the type-lines are indicated by the letters X and Y, the core and delta being designated in each instance.

In Fig. 31, the core is located at the shoulder of the loop farthest from the delta, as described above, the delta in this instance being a dot. Fig. 32 shows a pattern in which the core is formed by a single rod that rises as high as the shoulder of the surrounding loop. In this pattern, the delta is represented by a fragment of a ridge. In Fig. 33, the central loop surrounds two rods, both of which rise as high as the loop's shoulder. Here the core is placed at the tip of the rod which is farthest from the delta. In this design, the delta is represented by a small ridge bifurcation midway between the diverging type-lines.

The central loop in Fig. 34 surrounds three rods, all of which rise as high as the loop's shoulder, and the tip of the central rod is the core. Here the delta is placed at the lower end of a short ridge, the bottom extremity of which is the only ridge structure nearest the point where the type-lines separate.

In Fig. 35, the central loop encloses four rods which all rise as high as the shoulder of the loop. In this case, the two middle rods are considered as being joined, and the core is at the tip of the rod that is farthest from the delta, which in this design is the first of several bifurcations, and is selected because it is nearest the point where the type-lines diverge.

The pattern depicted in Fig. 36 includes a central loop surrounding five rods, all of which rise as high as the loop's shoulder. The rule here is to place the core at the tip of the central rod. The delta in this pattern is at the end of a downward-pointing ridge, the same being the most central point where the type-lines diverge. The circumstance of the bifurcation at the point marked B, where the ridge forks from the

Fig. 32

Fig. 33

Fig. 34

Fig. 35

Fig. 36

Fig. 37

upper type-line, is of no significance, since this forking is too far from the point of separation to constitute a delta.

In the design shown in Fig. 37, the central loop encloses six rods which all rise to the loop's shoulder. Here the core is at the tip of the fourth rod from the delta; the delta is the outer ridge of an enclosure at the point of type-line divergence.

Fig. 38 illustrates a type of fingerprint pattern which is frequently encountered, and which sometimes causes confusion. Here are found two overlapping loops and, according to the established rule, the shoulder of either might be considered as the core. However, since a common loop pattern can have but one core, it is necessary, in such cases, to make further distinctions. With patterns similar to that shown, the ridges E and F are considered as a surrounding loop, although they are in reality only portions of two distinct loops, and are treated as if they enveloped ridges A and B, ridge A being selected, and the core established at the point indicated in the diagram. The delta in this illustration is the upper tip of a short ridge, the point indicated being the most centrally located ridge structure at the point of type-line divergence.

In all the diagrams shown in Figs. 32 to 37 inclusive, pattern types are illustrated in which the rods enclosed by the central loop rise as high as the loop's shoulder in every instance. However, this condition is not always the case. The following drawings depict examples of patterns in which the enclosed rods are of decidedly unequal lengths, and in which some of the rods do not rise as high as the shoulder of the enclosing loop. Unequal-length rods are commonly encountered in fingerprint cores; consequently, the following rule must govern all cases falling in such a category: Only ridges that rise as high as the shoulder of the enclosing loop are considered in establishing the core of a pattern.

The drawing shown in Fig. 39 has a central loop which encloses two rods of unequal length, one of which, ridge *A*, rises as high as the loop's shoulder, while the other, ridge *B*, is too short to be considered in the core formation, since it does not reach the shoulder of the loop. A similar example is shown in Fig. 40. Here are three rods, *A*, *B*, and *C*, surrounded by a central loop. Ridge *C* is the only one of the three that rises as high as the loop's shoulder, and consequently is considered as the core of this pattern.

The central loop in Fig. 41 encloses four rods, *A*, *B*, *C*, and *D*. Ridge *C*, being the only one that rises as high as the loop's shoulder, forms the core of this pattern. Fingerprints sometimes display examples of multi-rod inclusions such as that shown in Fig. 42. Here six rods are present, *A*, *B*, *C*, *D*, *E*, and *G*. It will be noted that ridge *G*, which forks at *F*, alone rises to the necessary height, and is therefore deemed the pattern's core.

Although often discussed but superficially, the subject of deltas is one of vital importance in the mechanics of fingerprint classification, since the correct technical description of a pattern frequently depends upon the precise location of the delta, or outer terminus. Also, the terms "open" and "closed" deltas must be well understood. The "open" delta is represented by an isolated dot, fragment, or other ridge formation, located midway where the type-lines separate, and in no manner attached to the neighboring structure. A "closed" delta is formed when a ridge bifurcates or forks at this point, with the two resultant lines spreading in opposite directions across the space where the type-lines separate, thus obstructing or "closing" the opening. The variance in fingerprint formation displays this latter condition in many manifestations.

Fig. 43 illustrates a design in which the delta is the frag-

Fig. 38

Fig. 39

Fig. 40

Fig. 41

Fig. 42

Fig. 43

ment of ridge indicated where the type-lines X and Y diverge. The ridge marked $A — A$ is the first ridge to be counted, while that marked $B — B$ is the second. If the ridge fragment which constitutes the delta were not present, the delta would then be located at the point marked E on ridge $A — A$, and the ridge marked $B — B$ would be the first to be counted. In Fig. 44, the delta is a fork just in front of the type-lines' divergence. Although it is not exactly at the central point of separation, it is the first bit of formation nearest that point. The fact that the bifurcating ridge is attached to the lower type-line $Y — Y$, does not prevent the forking from being considered as the delta. In this pattern, the ridge $A — A$ is the first ridge to be counted. The circumstance that the two bifurcating forks from the delta are joined to ridge $A — A$ is of no importance.

In Fig. 45, the delta is formed by a forking that is not attached to either of the type-lines, but is attached to the ridge $A — A$, which constitutes the first ridge to be counted, ridge $B — B$ being the second. Fig. 46 is similar to Fig. 44, with the exception that the bifurcating ridge that forms the delta ·is attached to the upper type-line $X — X$ instead of the lower.

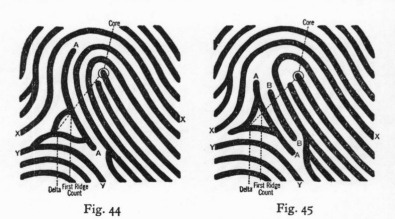

Fig. 44   Fig. 45

Here ridge $A - A$ is the first ridge count, $B - B$ being the second.

The design illustrated in Fig. 47 should receive careful attention. Here the delta is placed at the lower extremity of a short ridge that is not in alignment with the line of count. It will be noted that the line of count from the delta to the core passes an open space between the tip of the ridge that constitutes the delta and the ridge marked C, of which the delta is a part. This makes ridge C the first ridge to be counted Fig. 47 should be compared with Fig. 48. The delta in Fig. 48 is similar to that in Fig. 47, with the exception that the short ridge, the lower end of which forms the delta, is in alignment with the line of count, and therefore no ridge count may be found at this point, ridge $A - A$ being the first ridge to be counted.

The delta indicated in Fig. 49 is a V-shaped ridge formation, and the continuation of the structure is attached to the upper type-line. This latter circumstance is of no significance, since the line of count traverses an open space between the delta and the ridge that is indicated as the first ridge count.

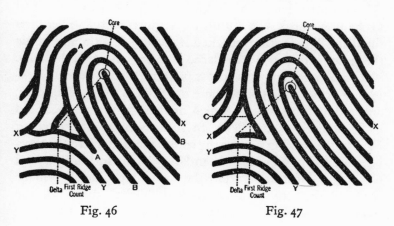

Fig. 46   Fig. 47

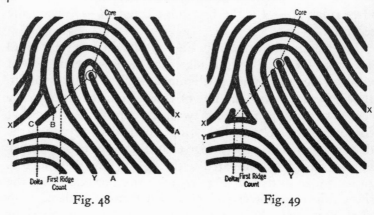

Fig. 48   Fig. 49

In this and in similar instances, the attachment of a type-line to ridge structure constituting the delta is of no importance.

The design shown in Fig. 50 illustrates an example of ridge formation that sometimes occasions confusion, since here is a forking from the lower type-line Y, at the point marked A. However, it is not at the midway point where the type-lines $X-X$ and $Y-Y$ separate, and consequently can not be considered as the delta. The forking of ridge structure attached to the type-line $X-X$ fulfills the requirement, and becomes the delta. The forkings marked A, B, and C, although inside the pattern area, are not so placed as to be considered the delta.

It sometimes happens that a pattern displays several forkings at or near the point where the delta is to be established, and a doubt arises as to which of these bifurcations should be recognized as the delta. In such cases, as illustrated in Fig. 51, the forking nearest the core is selected. Here the type-lines are indicated as $X-X$ and $Y-Y$, the forking marked C being a bifurcation from the lower type-line. It will be observed that the forking marked "Delta" meets all the requirements, as it is situated just in front of the point where the type-lines diverge. In similar cases displaying multiple forking, it is advisable to exercise care in selecting the correct forking as the delta; and in this connection the rule demands that the delta be located at or near the point where the type-lines diverge, and in order to qualify as a delta, the ridge structure must meet this requirement regardless of its distance from the core of the pattern. This point is well illustrated in a previous example, Fig. 35, wherein a series of forkings exist. In this case, the forking nearest to the core is plainly not the delta.

The important factor just mentioned is also illustrated in Fig. 52, which shows a design in which the fork marked *B* is much nearer the core than the bifurcation marked *A*, which is the delta. With recognition of the diverging place of the type-lines, which are marked $X-X$ and $Y-Y$, it will be noted that fork *A* is just in front of the point of separation, thus answering the requirements of a delta.

Examples of forking and interrupted type-lines are illustrated in Figs. 53 and 54. Here the delta is "open," being represented in both figures by a dot that is quite free from all surrounding ridge structure. It must be understood that the

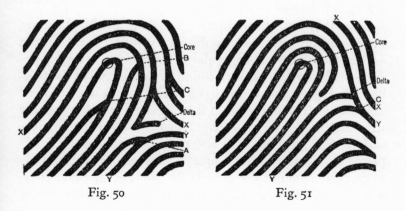

Fig. 50   Fig. 51

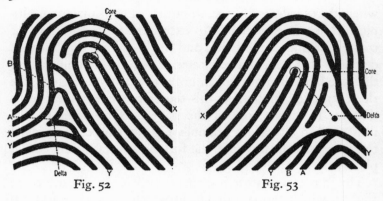

Fig. 52   Fig. 53

type-lines indicated by $X-X$ and $Y-Y$ in both of these drawings, are considered as continuous despite the fact that forkings and interruptions, respectively, occur in the two instances. This latter condition (Fig. 54) is sometimes caused by enlarged glands or other abnormalities, that prevent portions of a ridge from inking in the fingerprint-recording process. These complications demand extreme care in the procedure of correctly locating the delta, since type-lines may be so broken as to offer a deceptive appearance, and suggest wrong conclusions in placement.

Although dots are frequently found in all skin patterns, their mere presence is not sufficient to justify their selection as deltas in all cases. Fig. 55 shows an example of such a circumstance, in which a dot is found in the vicinity of the type-lines' divergence, but is not so placed that it may be considered as the delta. The upper tip of the ridge marked A is the only structure that answers the requirements for a delta. Another ending ridge, marked B, is also present, but is not favorably placed for a delta. Such examples as this require careful study to properly establish the delta at the point of type-line divergence. In this illustration, too hasty judgment might consider

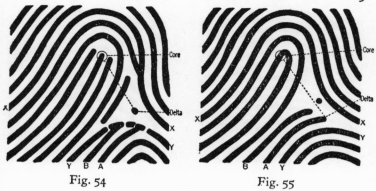

Fig. 54   Fig. 55

one of the ridges *A* or *B* as the lower type-line, and to view the dot as the delta. However, the type-lines in this instance are indicated by the customary letters $X—X$ and $Y—Y$.

Although determination of the delta, as indicated by the diverging type-lines, is an exacting requirement in the procedure of fingerprint classification, if the correct rules are applied, as illustrated in the included examples, there will be no difficulty in properly establishing the delta, regardless of any involving factors that may be included.

ARCHES

As already mentioned, under the Henry system, fingerprint patterns are in two divisions, those to which arbitrary values are given, and those which carry no value (see data on page 29). Of the latter group, the first pattern to be more fully considered will be. that of arches.

The configuration of this design shows the ridges flowing from one side to the other, usually with a noticeable rise near the center, but having no definite or pronounced upward thrust, and no backward looping or recurving of ridges. No

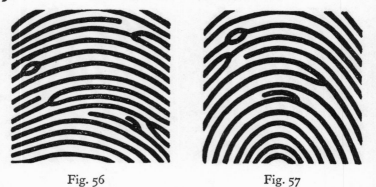

Fig. 56   Fig. 57

core or delta is found in plain arches, which derive their name from the slight central elevation assumed by their ridge structure. Figs. 56 and 57 show line drawings, while Fig. 58 illustrates actual patterns of the plain-arch type.

This type of pattern is the easiest to identify, as it is the simplest, and represents about 5 per cent of all fingerprint patterns. This, and certain subsequent approximations, apply more appropriately to the white race only. The arrangement of the ridge flow in a plain arch suggests strands of rope lying over a barrel. Although the ridge structure of plain arches may display all the component parts of finger patterns, namely, dots, forks, ridge-endings, and enclosures, there are no recurvatures or other complicating factors such as we encounter in all other fingerprint types. A careful study of the representative patterns here included will convey just what is to be expected in the fingerprint type that is classified as a plain arch.

TENTED ARCHES

Following plain arches, the next pattern is that of tented arches (see page 29), in which design the included formations

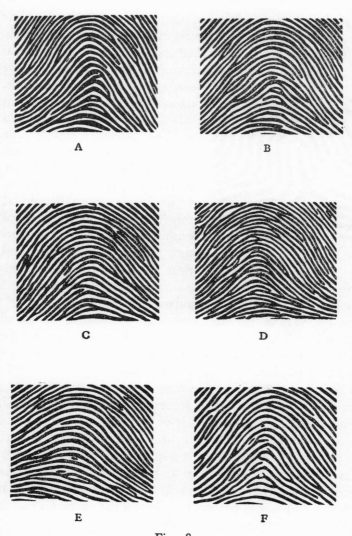

Fig. 58

Plain arches

present a more diversified appearance. Fig. 59 shows a line drawing, while Fig. 60 illustrates examples of the tented arch. In this design there is a marked suggestion of the plain arch; the ridges usually flow from one side of the pattern to the

other, having their exit, as a rule, upon the opposite side from which they entered. However, a marked difference exists in the presence of a ridge displacement in which the central ridges have a decisive upward thrust, and in which one or more of the central ridges have the appearance of pushing the surrounding structure upward. The ridges bend near the core to arrange themselves on each side of the central spine or series of spines, and converge on either side in angular formation.

Fig. 59

In the various pattern compositions classified as tented arches, it will be noted that the ridge or ridges forming the spine or tent, need not be of any specific or fixed length, nor need they be placed vertically in all cases.

Confusion sometimes arises with certain other pattern types that closely resemble tented arches, but which in reality fall in another group, usually that of loops. Some examples of this situation are shown in Fig. 61. When the subject of loops has been more fully covered at a subsequent point in the text, it is recommended that Fig. 61 be reconsidered, since the distinguishing characteristics will then be more apparent. It is deemed advisable, however, to present the examples shown in Fig. 61 in conjunction with the data on tented arches.

In addition to the conventional tented-arch-type patterns, there are certain other designs which are also classified as

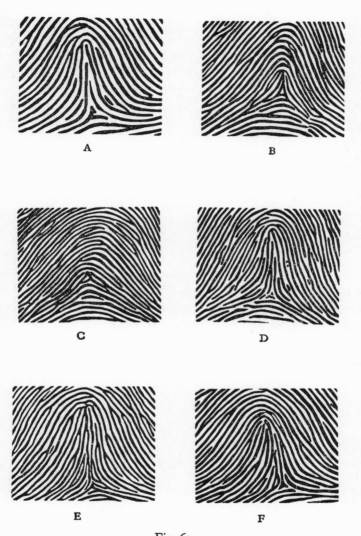

Fig. 60

Tented arches

Fig. 61

Tall loops resembling tented arches

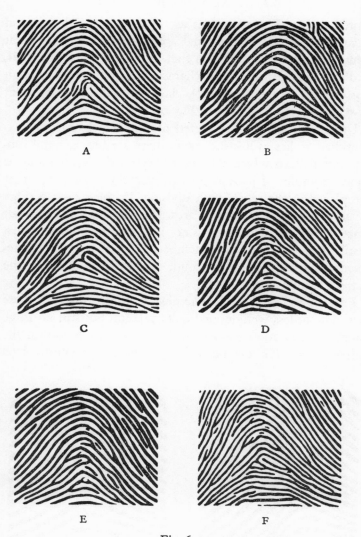

Fig. 62

Exceptional arches

tented arches. These patterns are of a transitional type and have been termed "exceptional arches" (see Fig. 16). Their structure is more varied than that of ordinary tented arches, and may include some of the characteristics of a loop, although not enough to give them loop classifications. An assortment of such patterns is offered in Fig. 62.

Under the heading of tented arches, which includes exceptional arches as just indicated, there are four general subtypes of pattern which may be so classified. Figs. 63 and 64 show examples of patterns of the exceptional-arch type that are placed in the tented-arch division. In these cases a ridge recurves within the pattern area, thus forming a loop; but since there is no delta, there is no ridge count, and the pattern is still an arch. It must be remembered that one of the requirements of a loop is a ridge count of at least one, before the pattern can be so classified.

Figs. 65 and 66 illustrate the next example, in which there is a more-or-less well-defined delta present, but still no ridge count. One or more rods or spines may intrude within the pattern area at the core, but as long as there are no uninvolved

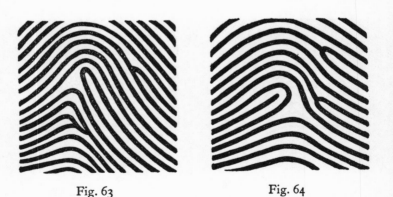

Fig. 63   Fig. 64

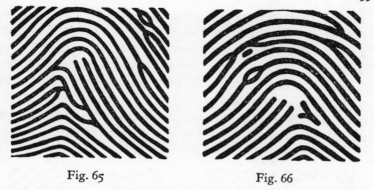

Fig. 65   Fig. 66

recurving ridges between the core and the delta, the pattern
is considered a tented arch.

In Figs. 67, 68, and 69, a slightly different situation is pic-
tured, in which a delta is present and also a ridge that
recurves in front of it. However, in these cases the recurving
ridge is not uninvolved, but is attached to other ridge structure. Here the FBI classification procedure separates two
cases: a loop with an involvement which seems to flow from

Fig. 67   Fig. 68

another ridge, abutting at about a right angle outside the
recurve between the shoulders; and a tented arch having
an appendage abutting the recurve also at a right angle.
These patterns are always cross-referenced to avoid error.

The most easily recognized form of tented arch is that in
which the ridges have a plainly angular formation as previously described. Figs. 70 and 71 illustrate this. Fig. 72 is a
typical tented arch.

Fig. 69   Fig. 70

Fig. 71   Fig. 72

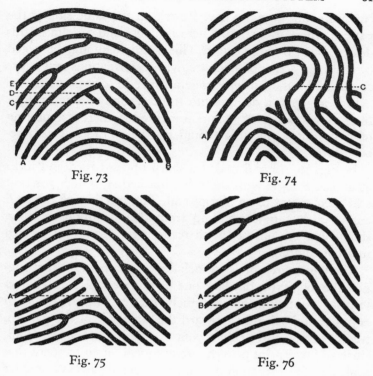

Fig. 73

Fig. 74

Fig. 75

Fig. 76

Fig. 73 shows another variation of the tented-arch-type pattern. Here ridge *A* enters on one side of the pattern and has its exit on the other. It rises sharply, and alters its course at the point marked *E*. In this design, the spine of the tent is represented by ridge *B*. At the point marked *D*, ridge *C* branches from ridge *A*, but should not be considered as a recurving ridge.

Fig. 74 illustrates a type of pattern often questioned by classifiers. It has the suggestion of a loop, but is in reality a tented arch. It will be noted that ridge *A* has a definite recurvature, but does not have its exit on the same side of the pattern where it entered. There is a core and a delta in this design, but no ridge count. This example should be noted carefully; in actual practice, many such formations may cause confusion by their marked resemblance to loop patterns.

Fig. 75 shows a design with three abruptly ending ridges, but no recurvature. At the point marked A, there is a meeting of two ridges; but this should not be considered as a recurvature.

In Fig. 76, ridge B makes a sharp upward turn and forks at an acute angle with the ridge marked A, which passes it and then comes to an abrupt end. The meeting of ridges B and A at an angle resulting from their running together, should not be confused with recurving ridges. This pattern in a tented arch.

The tented-arch division includes certain patterns that suggest the loop type, but lack one or more of the four characteristics required in loops, namely, the recurving ridge, with entrance and exit on or toward the same side of the pattern, a core, a delta, and a ridge count of at least one. Nevertheless, since all fingerprint patterns are unique, it often happens that some especial formation may include such details as to render its accurate classification difficult. In such cases the preferred procedure employs a "reference" classification; that is, the most plausible classification is recorded, and following, another formula that may be considered as second choice. In certain difficult instances, several such references may be necessary in order to describe adequately the prints in question. In looking through the files for any such questionable classification, search will be made under all possibilities of the formula, both for "first choice" and all possible "references."

In order to consider a pattern as a tented arch, it is not absolutely necessary that a central spine or spines be present.

If such detail should be included, it is, of course, considered as a tented-arch characteristic; but many tented-arch types approximate the loop pattern, and here a central spine or rod is not essential. Nor is it necessary that the ridges be thrust upward vertically. As already indicated, some patterns may have a central spine or spines curved and pointing downward, the print still being classified as a tented arch. Fig. 88 approximates this situation, but since there is a delta and a ridge count of one, the pattern is classified as a loop. However, with the delta absent, this pattern would be a tented arch.

The accurate establishment of the core and delta, when present, is a vital factor in distinguishing between loops and tented arches. This is especially true in cases where some ridge may recurve and tend to terminate on the same side of the pattern from which it entered; but in so doing it does not cross the "line of count," or the imaginary line between the core and delta.

In many patterns the design will be in nearly a vertical position, having the suggestion of a tented arch, but with close examination, it will be discovered that at least one of the ridges recurves between the core and some delta formation, thus giving the print the characteristics of a loop (see Fig. 61). This similarity is, of course, true of actual tented arches with the general formation that suggests a loop.

An example of the tented-arch type falling in this class is illustrated in Fig. 77. Here may be seen the semblance of a loop, but it will be noted that the type-lines X and Y separate near the center after running parallel, their divergence enclosing a single loop within the pattern area. It would be possible to judge a delta as being present at the point marked A upon the ridge that recurves near the place where the type-lines separate. However, in that case there would be no intervening ridges between the core and the delta, and consequently no ridge count. Therefore, this especial pattern must be considered as a tented arch and not as a loop.

A loop pattern is shown in Fig. 78. It is quite similar to the design shown in Fig. 77, but in this case there is a ridge count between the core and delta, which is indicated by the letter D, and located at the separation of the type-lines X and Y. This illustration shows the minimum requirements for a loop pattern; namely, core, delta, recurving ridge, and a ridge count.

Another tented-arch pattern is shown in Fig. 79. In this design a recurving ridge, indicated by letter A, encloses three rods that rise to the shoulder of the loop. A core could be established at the summit of the central rod, but since the recurving ridge does not go beyond the line of count, the design is not a loop.

A recurving ridge is shown in Fig. 80, but here also the ridge, marked A, does not exit on the same side of the pattern where it entered, although it tends to do so; and since the recurving ridge does not reach the line of count, the pattern is still a tented arch.

Fig. 81 illustrates another example of the pattern type that requires careful consideration. In this instance the design is that of a loop that approximates a tented arch. Ridge A recurves, and although it does not terminate on the side of the pattern where it entered, it does intersect a line drawn between the delta and the core, thus giving the pattern the needed requirement to be classified as a loop.

The need for close analysis is emphasized in Fig. 82, which closely approximates the design in Fig. 81, with the exception that the pattern is a tented arch and not a loop. Here ridge A passes the point marked C, and continues on to make an exit on the side of the pattern from which it entered. In this design a core is present as well as a clearly defined delta, but since

Fig. 77

Fig. 78

Fig. 79

Fig. 80

Fig. 81

Fig. 82

there is no ridge that recurves and passes between these two focal points, the pattern is classified as a tented arch.

Loops

As stated in the summary of the Henry system, a loop is a pattern in which one or more ridges enter on either side of the design, recurve in the form of a staple or hairpin, pass between the delta and the core, and finally terminate on or toward the same side of the pattern from which entrance was made. A loop must have at least one uninvolved ridge that follows this course. It must also have a core, a delta, and a ridge count of at least one, in order to qualify as a loop. Thus it will be noted that there are four basic loop characteristics. The loop is the most frequently encountered of pattern types, and represents approximately 65 per cent of all fingerprints.

As previously indicated, loops are considered as being either radial or ulnar, according to the direction in which they slope. The two bones in the forearm are the radius and the ulna, the radius being the one on the thumb-side of the hand, and the ulna being on the opposite or little-finger side. Therefore, loops that slope toward the little finger are considered as ulnar loops, while those that slope in the opposite direction, or toward the thumb, are classified as radial loops. Ulnar loops appear most frequently, although radial loops are often found in the index fingers.

In connection with radial and ulnar loops, it will be necessary to recognize the fact that fingerprints recorded upon a fingerprint card show the loop patterns sloping to the right when they are ulnar, and to the left when radial, should the impressions be those of the right hand. In a recording made from the left hand, the opposite is the case, the ulnar loops sloping to the left and the radial loops to the right. This

explanation will clarify the fact that fingerprints are considered as being either radial or ulnar, depending upon the
direction in which they slope on the subject's fingers rather
than their appearance upon the surface where they may be
recorded.

Fig. 83

Fig. 83 shows a typical loop design, while Fig. 84 offers
various examples of actual loop patterns. Fig. 85 shows the
ridge marked *A* entering on the right side of the impression,
recurving, and making its exit at the point marked *B*, which
is on the same side of the pattern where it entered. The letters
X and *Y* indicate the type-lines in this pattern, which includes
all the essentials of a loop, and consequently is classified accordingly.

Fig. 86 illustrates a distinctive design in which the ridge
marked *A* is surrounded by an enclosure or elongated pocket
at the center of the pattern. Although this ridge does not
begin or terminate at the outer edge of the fingerprint, it
still is within the pattern area and forms a recurvature, passing across the line of count between the core and delta, and
tends to terminate toward the same side of the pattern where
it began. This pattern is also a loop.

In Fig. 87, the ridge marked *A* enters the pattern area and

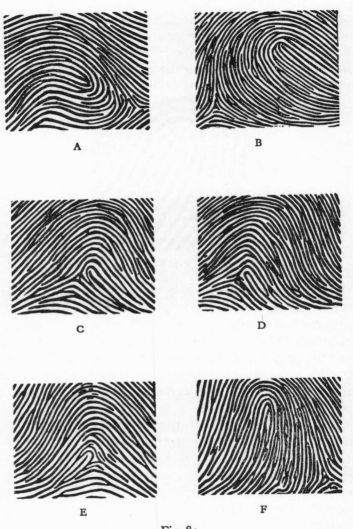

Fig. 84

Loops

terminates in an enclosure shaped like a tennis racket. This illustrates another type of loop pattern.

Fig. 88 shows a type of pattern which sometimes becomes confusing. Ridge *A* has its entrance and exit on the same side of the design; this backward curvature is not enough of itself to justify a loop classification, but the presence of a well-defined delta identifies the design as a loop with a ridge count of one. In the absence of a delta, this pattern would be classified as a tented arch.

Fig. 89 illustrates another design that approximates a tented arch, but is still classified as a loop. In this instance, the ridge

Fig. 85

Fig. 86

Fig. 87

Fig. 88

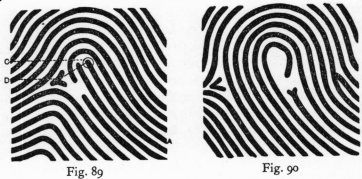

Fig. 89   Fig. 90

marked *A* does not terminate on the same side of the pattern where it entered, but recurves in that direction with sufficient continuation to pass between the core and delta, and crosses the line of count. This example has the minimum requirements of a loop, and is classified as such.

A type of pattern that is sometimes classified incorrectly is shown in Fig. 90. Here is found the suggestion of a central pocket loop, since the innermost ridge tends to recurve at the core. However, the recurvature is not enough to form a right angle with the exit line; therefore the pattern is that of a plain loop.

Fig. 91 shows a commonly encountered type of pattern having a converging design. This formation is also sometimes mistaken for a central pocket, but as there is no recurvature, the design is still a plain loop.

A ridge arrangement that is even more frequently mistaken for a central pocket loop is shown in Fig. 92. Here several ridges assume a circular formation at the core, but as they are all connected by a ridge that runs up the line of exit to the core, the design is still classified as a plain loop. These last two examples should be noted carefully, as both types are often encountered, and may sometimes cause confusion.

Fig. 91

Fig. 92

WHORLS

Fingerprint patterns of the whorl type display ridge formation in which one or more ridges make a complete recurvature or circuit about the core of the print. The general design of whorls may be either circular, spiral, oval, or in some other variant of the rounded form. The conventional whorl-type pattern has two deltas, and may have either a single or a double core. About 30 per cent of all fingerprint patterns are in some variation of the whorl.

Fig. 93 shows a design of whorl formation, while Fig. 94 illustrates representative examples of actual whorl types. Since recurvature is so essential in determining the whorl type, the Galton-Henry system provides a test for its recognition. Fig. 95 shows the rule of procedure in which an imaginary line is drawn parallel with the exit ridges and in the direction

Fig. 93

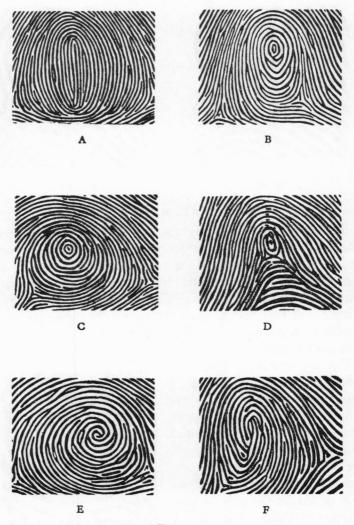

Fig. 94

Whorls

of the core of the pattern. Should this line encounter another ridge at right angles, which will be possible only when recurvature is present, the pattern then falls in the whorl division.

Fig. 95

Ordinarily, patterns of the whorl type include two deltas, and this inclusion is considered by some authorities as indispensable. However, since whorl patterns are essentially more dependent upon recurvature than upon the presence of a fixed number of deltas, which are often so situated that their certain inclusion in the recorded fingerprint is problematic, it would seem more appropriate to designate as whorls those patterns which exhibit recurvature, regardless of whether or not two deltas may be readily recognized in all cases.

Additional grounds for such contention exist in the fact that patterns are sometimes encountered which are undeniably whorls, but in which the exact location and even the existence of one or both deltas is impossible to establish. Several such examples are shown in Fig. 96, wherein it will be noted that the ridge structure toward one or the other or both sides of the print, in the several cases, "merges" into the non-friction skin with no sign of a clearly defined delta. These particular patterns extend from the ball of the finger entirely around the side and well over the top or "nail" area of the digit, as indicated in the illustrations. Fig. 96-A shows a whorl with no left delta, while in Fig. 96-B, the right delta is missing. It would be plainly impossible to place two deltas in these patterns with any degree of exactitude, although without

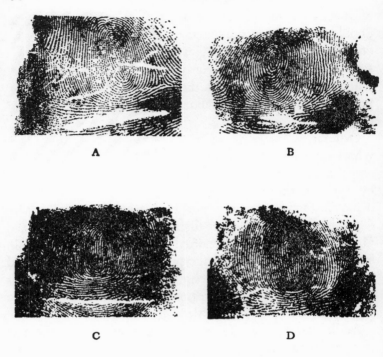

Fig. 96

Whorl patterns with one delta and with no deltas

question the designs are whorls, and consequently must be considered as whorls with but one delta. In Figs. 96-C and 96-D, *both* deltas are absent, and here there is little choice but to consider the patterns as whorls with *no deltas whatever*. It should also be added that patterns such as those shown in Fig. 96 are by no means uncommon.

The contention that fingerprint patterns must have at least two deltas in all cases in order to be placed in the whorl division and given arbitrary value, in the opinion of some, may continue to be a matter of personal decision. However, as the Henry system is still recognized as a standard, at least in the United States, it would seem reasonable to abide by the method's rule which values recurvature in whorl patterns as a more essential requisite than the exact number and precise location of the deltas.

CENTRAL POCKET LOOPS

The central pocket loop design has been classified as a pattern in which a majority of the ridges have the appearance of a loop, but in which one or more of the ridges within the pattern area recurve about the core, thus forming a pocket. To this description additional distinction is added with the rule that establishes an imaginary straight line between the two deltas of the pattern; if such a line does not cross or touch any of the recurving ridges that lie between the delta and the core, the pattern may be classified as a central pocket (see Fig. 97).

Figs. 97 and 98 illustrate the fundamental requirements

Fig. 97   Fig. 98

for central pocket loops, while Fig. 99 presents examples of actual central-pocket-loop patterns. Fig. 100 depicts a number of plain-loop patterns of the type that is sometimes confused with true central pocket loops. It is suggested that careful study be given to Figs. 99 and 100.

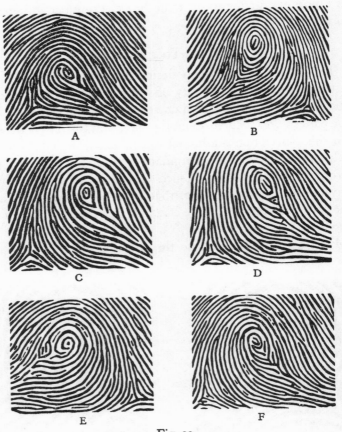

Fig. 99
Central pocket loops

In procedure that deals with ten-finger classification, the identifying characteristics which distinguish central pocket loops from other whorl forms are of less importance, since such designs fall in the whorl division and are treated accord-

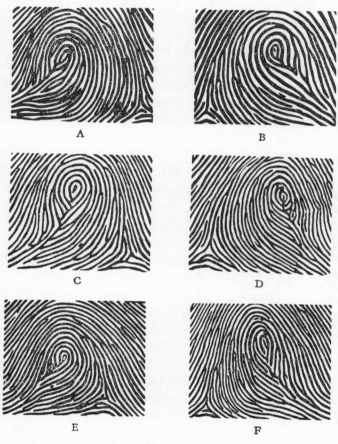

Fig. 100

Plain loops resembling central pocket loops

ingly, with no mention of any intimate details other than a subnotation, in some instances, stating whether the print is "inner," "meeting," or "outer," as explained later. However, this does not mean that the distinguishing features should be disregarded, since they are important in single-print classification and in many other connections as well.

Twin Loops

This formation is so named because herein are presented two distinct loops, one surrounding or overlapping the other, and having the termination or outlet of the ridges representing the core of each loop separated by, or on opposite sides of, one of the deltas, either right or left. The ridges in question, conventionally described as the "core lines," are those that originate at the respective core of each loop (see Fig. 101). As explained, in cases where these core lines are separated by either delta, right or left, the pattern is classified as a twin loop. Fig. 101 illustrates a twin-loop design, while Fig. 102 presents actual examples of twin-loop patterns.

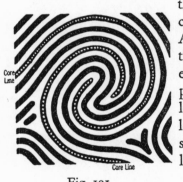

Fig. 101

Fig. 103 shows examples of certain pattern designs that are sometimes mistaken for twin loops. All these are classified as plain loops, but their formation is described as converging, thus giving them the resemblance to actual twin loops (also see Fig. 91). This same condition is present in the designs shown in Fig. 100. Figs. 102 and 103 should be studied carefully.

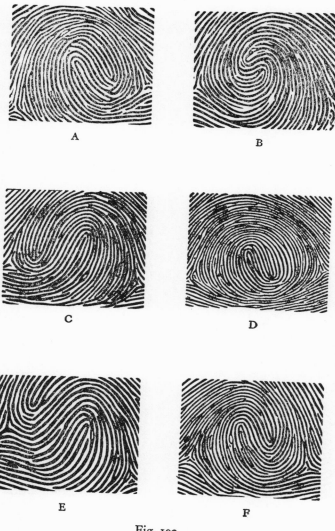

A

B

C

D

E

F

Fig. 102

Twin loops

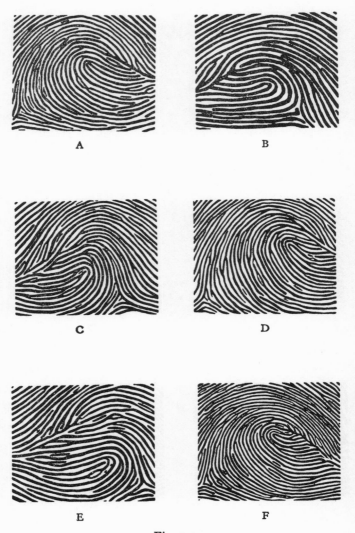

Fig. 103

Plain loops resembling twin loops

LATERAL POCKET LOOPS

Lateral pocket loops, like twin loops, are of the double-loop type, but in this case the core lines have their exits without being divided by either of the deltas. The pattern's basic factors are clearly shown in Fig. 104, and Fig. 105 illustrates

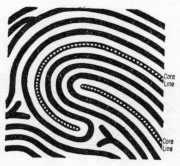

Fig. 104

various examples of the lateral-pocket-loop design. Although the lateral pocket resembles the twin loop in some respects, its general formation is distinctively original, irrespective of the tracing of the core lines. Twin loops and lateral pocket loops, being classified as double loops, as already stated, contain two distinct loops entirely free from each other; but should the side of one of the loops be connected with the side of the other, the pattern may still be considered as a double loop. Under the ten-finger method, as when dealing with plain whorls and central pockets, there is little need to consider the factors that distinguish twin loops from lateral pockets, since both fall in the same group, being considered as whorls; and both are assigned numerical values according to the especial finger where they are present.

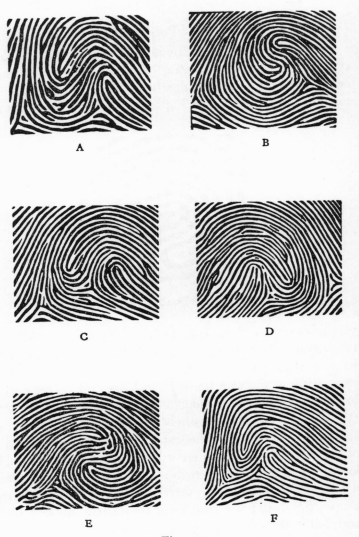

Fig. 105

Lateral pocket loops

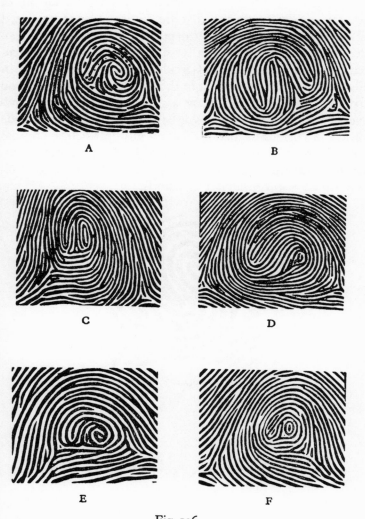

Fig. 106

Accidental designs

Fingerprint patterns that include the pictorial factors of several primary types, and that are too irregular to be placed in any of the conventional categories, are described as accidentals. Fig. 107 illustrates a formation of the accidental pattern, and actual examples of accidental designs are shown in Fig. 106, on page 83. Owing to their irregular appearance, no fixed or set description can be assigned to accidentals; however, the accidental group will be certain to include a wide variety of curious formations having multiple deltas, unusual recurvatures, and many other extraordinary appearances. In assigning numerical values for the primary classification, accidentals are also considered as whorls.

Fig. 107

IV

RIDGE COUNTING AND TRACING

A s ALREADY mentioned in the brief summary of the Henry system, a step that features importantly in the routine of fingerprint classification is that of ridge counting. With an understanding of type-lines, cores and deltas, and the various pattern forms, this phase of the treatment is clarified. It has been explained that loops are subdivided according to their included ridge counts, and are arbitrarily designated as being either "inner" or "outer," as the ridge count may indicate. The index finger having nine ridges or less, is considered as being inner, ten or more being an outer. The second finger is judged to be inner when ten or less ridges are present; eleven or more constitute an outer. The count for the little finger drops back to nine or less for an inner, and ten or more for an outer. These data, already given in the condensed version of the Henry system, are here repeated for the sake of clarity. Furthermore, though not included in the original Henry method, the ridge count of the ring finger has since been added, as explained elsewhere in the text, a count of thirteen or less being considered as inner, with fourteen or more ridges constituting an outer for that digit.

In counting the ridges in a loop pattern, it is first necessary to determine accurately the location of the delta and the core.

The core and delta are not included in the actual count, and only those ridges, or portions thereof, that lie exactly between the core and delta are considered. The count is made by establishing an imaginary straight line from the delta to the core, and all the ridges or ridge fragments touched by this line are enumerated. Should the "line of count," so called, cross a point where a ridge-forking occurs, both sides of the fork are counted, provided that the line of count falls at the point of bifurcation. Since this imaginary line is one having no diameter, and only one dimension, namely that of length, it is extremely important that its establishment be determined with exactitude, since a difference of even one ridge count may alter the classification formula and change the filing-place of a set of fingerprints.

The drawing presented in Fig. 108 shows a pattern of the loop type with a ridge count of fourteen. A line has been established between the core and delta, the "line of count." All ridge structure through which this line passes is counted. Each ridge included in this count will be discussed, and for that purpose the various ridges and portions thereof will be indicated by the letters A, B, C, D, E, etc., in the following itemized description:

Ridge A—1st count—a short ridge
  " B—2nd count—also a short ridge
  " C—3rd count—another short ridge
  " D—4th count—an ending ridge
  " E—5th count—a continuous ridge
  " F—6th count—a short ending ridge

(It will be observed that ridge F, the 6th count, is a short ridge that ends at the line of count, but since it touches the imaginary line between the delta and the core, it is included in the count of ridges between these two focal points.)

Ridge *G*—7th count—this count is only a dot

(All ridge structure, dots included, that falls in the line of count, should be included in the count of ridges.)

Fig. 108

Ridge *H*—8th count—the line of count here falls across a fork
      "   *I*—9th count—the other side of the same fork is counted

(As already explained, should the imaginary line of count fall across a point where a ridge forks, both sides of the fork are counted.)

Ridge *J*—10th count—this count is a continuous ridge
      "   *K*—no count at this point

(It will be noted that ridge *K* is interrupted at the line of count so that the imaginary line encounters no ridge structure at this point; consequently, there is no count given for the ridge marked *K*.)

Ridge *L*—11th count—this count is a short ridge
      "   *M*—12th count—this count is one side of an enclosure
      "   *N*—13th count—this count is the other side of the same enclosure

(This type of ridge structure, which is also known as an island, is the result of a ridge splitting, forking and rejoining once more to again form a single ridge. When the line of count passes across any such ridge formation of the "island" or "enclosure" type, both sides of the enclosure are counted as in counts 12 and 13, shown in this illustration.)

Ridge *O*—14th count—this 14th and last count is the left side of the loop or staple that surrounds the actual core of the pattern in this design

From the foregoing, it will be understood that the procedure of ridge counting is a task demanding care, in order to insure accuracy. It is advised in questionable patterns to check all ridge counts, since it sometimes happens that some short-ending ridge may have been excluded from the count when it should have been enumerated, or the opposite may have been the case.

RIDGE TRACING

As indicated in the outline of the Henry system, whorl patterns are subdivided by ridge tracing; and in this connection, certain rules must be observed (see Fig. 109), In the ridge counting of loops, it is necessary to establish two focal points: the delta and the core of the pattern; and in ridge tracing, two focal points also are determined. In this case, the focal points are the left and right deltas. When these focal points have been located, the ridge emanating from the lower side of the left delta is followed or traced from left to right toward the right-hand delta. When the traced ridge reaches a point opposite or nearest the right delta, the ridge formation at that point is carefully noted. If the traced ridge falls above, or "inside" the right-hand delta with three or more ridges intervening between the delta and the traced ridge, the pattern is judged to be an "inner," and indicated by a capital letter *I* (see Fig. 110). This situation is also illustrated in Figs. 111, 112, and 113. If the traced ridge falls above, or "inside" the right delta with but two ridges or less inter-

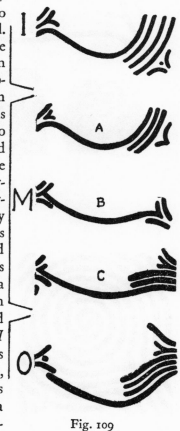

Fig. 109

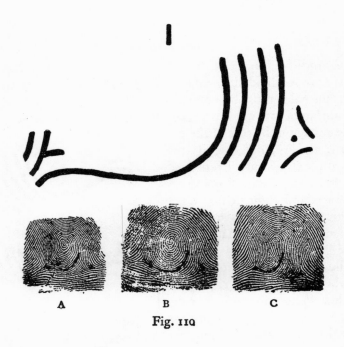

Fig. 110

Fig. 111   Fig. 112

vening between the right delta and the traced ridge at the point where the traced ridge is nearest the right-hand delta, the pattern is judged to be "meeting," and is indicated by the capital letter *M* (Figs. 114-*C* and 115). If the traced ridge falls below or "outside" the right-hand delta at the nearest point, with two or less ridges intervening between the traced ridge and the right-hand

Fig. 113

delta, the pattern is also judged as a "meet" (see Figs. 114-*A* and 117).

In some cases, the ridge that is traced from the left-hand

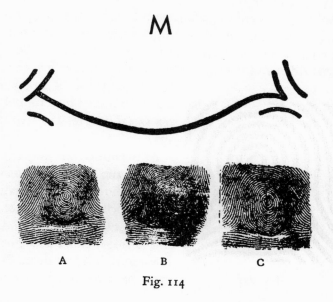

Fig. 114

Fig. 115

Fig. 116

delta will run directly to the right delta, actually "meeting" that focal point (see Figs. 114-*B* and 116). In such cases the pattern is considered as a "meet" pattern, and indicated by the capital letter *M*.

When the traced ridge falls outside or below the right-hand delta with three or more ridges intervening between the right-hand delta and the traced ridge at the point where the traced ridge and the right delta are nearest together, the pat-

Fig. 117

tern is judged to be an "outer," and is indicated by a capital letter *O* (Figs. 118, 119, 120, and 121).

At the outset, one may not appreciate the necessity of including in the "meet" subdivision such whorls as display two or less ridges between the delta and the traced ridge, either above or below the right-hand delta. However, the need for this measure is

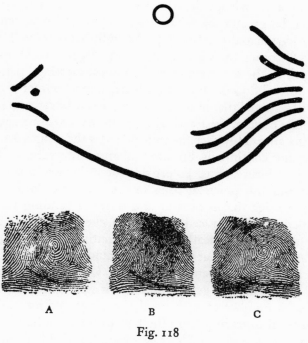

Fig. 118

Fig. 119   Fig. 120

seen with a knowledge that the percentage of inner and outer whorls is far greater than that of whorl patterns in which the traced ridge actually encounters the right-hand delta. Therefore, to distribute the whorl patterns equally in a collection of fingerprints, the inclusion of such "almost-meeting" patterns in the "meet" division provides a better apportionment.

It will be noted that in the preceding designs drawn to illustrate ridge tracing, the traced ridge is shown as continuous in every instance. However, in skin patterns the ridges are frequently not continuous, but are broken at intervals, or show forkings or bifurcations. To provide for such cases, it is necessary to establish practical rules in the tracing procedure. In tracing a ridge that is broken in a series of "ending ridges" (so called when the traced ridge ends), the method is to drop to the next ridge beneath and here continue the tracing. It must be understood that the tracing should be resumed on the lower ridge directly beneath the point where the previously traced ridge ends. In general practice it will frequently happen that a number of such breaks or ridge endings will be encountered in tracing from the left- to the right-hand delta. Figs. 122, 123, and 124 illustrate examples of this condition

Fig. 121   Fig. 122

Fig. 123   Fig. 124

in which one, two, and three breaks or ridge endings are
encountered respectively; Fig. 122 having one, Fig. 123, two,
and Fig. 124 displaying three endings.

Owing to temporarily damaged ridge structure, improper
inking, or particles of foreign matter becoming involved in
the inking process, skin patterns sometimes present an appearance of ridge interruption that is more or less common
throughout the entire design. In such cases it is necessary to
exercise extreme care when following a traced ridge, and to
ignore any semblance of a ridge ending that in reality is only
a passing appearance of the skin. This requirement will simplify with experience; however, some examples are offered
here. In Fig. 125, the traced ridge is shown as broken very
slightly in three places; this may be caused by enlarged pores,
worn ridges, or other temporary skin condition, and the interruption should be ignored, the ridge being traced as though
the breaks were not present. Fig. 126 illustrates a case in which
a great many small breaks are present throughout the entire
pattern area. This type of interruption may be caused by skin
wear or disease.

Interruptions such as these should be traversed as if the breaks were absent. Since such conditions are sure to vary with individual cases, their correct interpretation and treatment will be largely a matter of personal discretion.

In patterns where the traced ridge displays forks or bifurcations, the rule selects the lower fork and continues the tracing thereon at each point where a bifurcation is encountered. Fig. 127 shows an example of multiple forkings, and indicates the correct procedure, the design in this instance being traced as a "meet" whorl.

In tracing whorls, the tracing should begin at the exact point of the left delta in all cases, and under no circumstances should the tracing actually begin on a type-line. However, it often happens that the delta is only a dot, and in such cases it is necessary to drop at once to the lower type-line and proceed with the tracing. Such an example is illustrated in Fig. 128, in which the left delta is a fragmentary ridge, and it here becomes necessary to take the next lower ridge, which in this case is a type-line.

Sometimes a whorl pattern is found in which the technical delta is established on the first recurring ridge at a point nearest the type-lines' divergence. In such instances, tracing begins on this ridge, as shown by the letter *A* in Fig. 129, and not upon the next lower line as in Fig. 128. Tracing the design in this manner shows Fig. 129 to be an inner whorl, whereas if the next lower ridge were used, the design would become a meet, which obviously would be incorrect.

Since "accidental" patterns fall in the "whorl" category, having values assigned according to their location in the set of ten digital records, they too are subdivided by ridge tracing to indicate their being either "inner," "meeting," or "outer." Fig. 130 illustrates an example of the accidental pattern type. In this and in all similar cases, the tracing is made from the

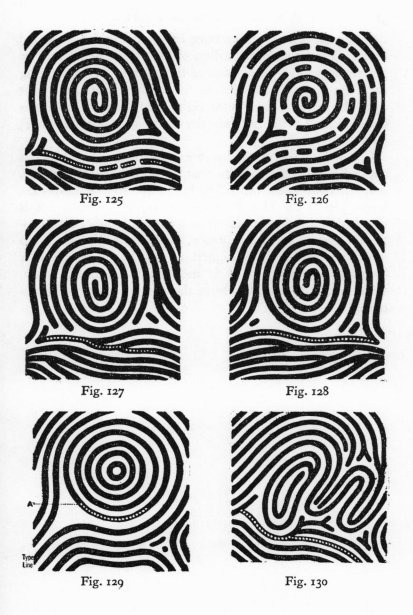

Fig. 125

Fig. 126

Fig. 127

Fig. 128

Fig. 129

Fig. 130

delta that appears at the extreme left to that which is located on the extreme right, regardless of how many deltas may be present in various other parts of the pattern. By considering the delta at the extreme left as the left-hand delta, and that upon the extreme right as the right-hand delta, the tracing is accomplished with no difficulty as in any normal whorl pattern.

It will be understood that the same tracing procedure is applied to all other patterns that fall in the whorl category, namely, twin loops, central-pocket loops, and lateral-pocket loops. Under the Henry system, no especial significance is attached to the circumstance that a pattern is either a central-pocket loop, an accidental, a twin loop, or any other design to which arbitrary value is assigned, all these being considered as "whorls," regardless of their more intimate configuration, which features so decisively in the various "singleprint systems."

V

FILING AND SEARCHING

WITH knowledge of the procedural steps in classifying fingerprints, the next requirement is a consideration of the methods of filing the classified fingerprint cards. It has been shown that the numerical description of a set of classified fingerprints is known as the formula, and consists of several factors, recorded in figures and letters.

The first item in this formula is the combined value of all the whorls, expressed in the form of a fraction written as 1 over 1 to 32 over 32, and known as the "primary" (see Fig. 17).

In filing and searching, according to the Henry method, the first part of the classification formula to be considered is the "denominator," or portion below the line, of this primary fraction. For example, a primary of 17 over 3, which indicates whorls in both of the index fingers, will require a search for the denominator first of all, which in this case is 3. When the files have been examined and the compartment located in which prints have been placed that bear the denominator 3, the next step is to find the subdivision of this group bearing the numerator 17, that is, 17 over 3. This means that, following the sequence beginning with 1 over 3, 2 over 3, and so on, the sought-for card will be found in the 17-over-3 division.

It must be understood that in the sequence of filing, the "primary" employs all possible combinations of 1 over 1 to 32 over 32; and that these combinations are considered in the order of their arrangement. All the numbers from 1 to 32 are first used as a numerator over a denominator of 1. Then the denominator changes to 2, and everything from 1 to 32 is again used over the new denominator. This is continued until every possibility of 1 over 1 to 32 over 32 has been exhausted, the denominator remaining constant throughout each series of numerator progression. Then, moving up one point, it is again used with the same progressive series in the numerator. The following illustrates this successive progression:

$$\frac{1}{1} \quad \frac{2}{1} \quad \frac{3}{1} \quad \frac{4}{1} \quad \frac{5}{1} \quad \frac{6}{1} \quad \frac{7}{1} \quad \frac{8}{1} \quad \frac{9}{1} \quad \frac{10}{1} \quad \frac{11}{1} \quad \frac{12}{1} \quad \frac{13}{1} \quad \frac{14}{1} \quad \frac{15}{1} \quad \frac{16}{1}$$

$$\frac{17}{1} \quad \frac{18}{1} \quad \frac{19}{1} \quad \frac{20}{1} \quad \frac{21}{1} \quad \frac{22}{1} \quad \frac{23}{1} \quad \frac{24}{1} \quad \frac{25}{1} \quad \frac{26}{1} \quad \frac{27}{1} \quad \frac{28}{1} \quad \frac{29}{1} \quad \frac{30}{1} \quad \frac{31}{1} \quad \frac{32}{1}$$

The next series would run thus:

$$\frac{1}{2} \quad \frac{2}{2} \quad \frac{3}{2} \quad \frac{4}{2} \quad \frac{5}{2} \quad \frac{6}{2} \quad \frac{7}{2} \quad \frac{8}{2} \quad \text{etc.}$$

Following this would come:

$$\frac{1}{3} \quad \frac{2}{3} \quad \frac{3}{3} \quad \frac{4}{3} \quad \frac{5}{3} \quad \frac{6}{3} \quad \frac{7}{3} \quad \frac{8}{3}$$

and so on until 32 over 32 has been reached, thus furnishing the already-mentioned 1024 variations in this division of the classification formula.

The next consideration in the formula is the "secondary," appearing in the classification line to the right of the fractional figures which represent the primary. This is shown in the formula by capital letters representing the basic types of patterns appearing in the index fingers of each hand. When arches appear in the index fingers they are indicated by the capital letter A, tented arches by T, radial loops by R, ulnar loops by U, and whorls by W. Here the capital letters are written one over the other in the relation of a fraction, with the letter representing the right index placed above the line, and that of the left index below. In the consideration of their filing sequence, the symbols in the secondary are utilized in the same manner as those in the primary, their order of progression being A, T, R, U, W, and their successive sequence being as follows:

$$\frac{A\ T\ R\ U\ W}{A\ A\ A\ A\ A} \quad \frac{A\ T\ R\ U\ W}{T\ T\ T\ T\ T} \quad \frac{A\ T\ R\ U\ W}{R\ R\ R\ R\ R} \quad \frac{A\ T\ R\ U\ W}{U\ U\ U\ U\ U} \quad \frac{A\ T\ R\ U\ W}{W\ W\ W\ W\ W}$$

It will be observed that all possibilities of numerator change are used over the first unit of a series as a denominator, this being followed by a second symbol as a denominator over which all the numerator possibilities are again utilized, and so on. Therefore, there are twenty-five possible combinations for the index fingers.

Prints with an arch or tented arch in any finger, or a radial loop in any except the index fingers, constitute the "small-letter" group of the secondary classification. Because of their vital importance to the classification system, the small-letter groups are described later in detail. They occur infrequently; hence, their very presence often enables the classifier to dispense with the usual sub-secondary classifications and the major divisions.

Ridge counting and ridge tracing are the basic methods employed to secure the second sub-classification. It appears in the formula at the right of the secondary classification, and is represented by a combination of letters I, M, and O. As in the previous cases, these symbols are also written above and below the line in the form of a fraction. Here too, as in the secondary, the symbols indicating the right hand are written above, and those of the left hand are placed below the line. Their progressive consideration is in the order given above, *I, M,* and *O,* and their successive sequence is as follows:

$\frac{II}{II}$	$\frac{IM}{II}$	$\frac{IO}{II}$	$\frac{MI}{II}$	$\frac{MM}{II}$	$\frac{MO}{II}$	$\frac{OI}{II}$	$\frac{OM}{II}$	$\frac{OO}{II}$
$\frac{II}{IM}$	$\frac{IM}{IM}$	$\frac{IO}{IM}$	$\frac{MI}{IM}$	$\frac{MM}{IM}$	$\frac{MO}{IM}$	$\frac{OI}{IM}$	$\frac{OM}{IM}$	$\frac{OO}{IM}$
$\frac{II}{IO}$	$\frac{IM}{IO}$	$\frac{IO}{IO}$	$\frac{MI}{IO}$	$\frac{MM}{IO}$	$\frac{MO}{IO}$	$\frac{OI}{IO}$	$\frac{OM}{IO}$	$\frac{OO}{IO}$
$\frac{II}{MI}$	$\frac{IM}{MI}$	$\frac{IO}{MI}$	$\frac{MI}{MI}$	$\frac{MM}{MI}$	$\frac{MO}{MI}$	$\frac{OI}{MI}$	$\frac{OM}{MI}$	$\frac{OO}{MI}$
$\frac{II}{MM}$	$\frac{IM}{MM}$	$\frac{IO}{MM}$	$\frac{MI}{MM}$	$\frac{MM}{MM}$	$\frac{MO}{MM}$	$\frac{OI}{MM}$	$\frac{OM}{MM}$	$\frac{OO}{MM}$
$\frac{II}{MO}$	$\frac{IM}{MO}$	$\frac{IO}{MO}$	$\frac{MI}{MO}$	$\frac{MM}{MO}$	$\frac{MO}{MO}$	$\frac{OI}{MO}$	$\frac{OM}{MO}$	$\frac{OO}{MO}$
$\frac{II}{OI}$	$\frac{IM}{OI}$	$\frac{IO}{OI}$	$\frac{MI}{OI}$	$\frac{MM}{OI}$	$\frac{MO}{OI}$	$\frac{OI}{OI}$	$\frac{OM}{OI}$	$\frac{OO}{OI}$
$\frac{II}{OM}$	$\frac{IM}{OM}$	$\frac{IO}{OM}$	$\frac{MI}{OM}$	$\frac{MM}{OM}$	$\frac{MO}{OM}$	$\frac{OI}{OM}$	$\frac{OM}{OM}$	$\frac{OO}{OM}$
$\frac{II}{OO}$	$\frac{IM}{OO}$	$\frac{IO}{OO}$	$\frac{MI}{OO}$	$\frac{MM}{OO}$	$\frac{MO}{OO}$	$\frac{OI}{OO}$	$\frac{OM}{OO}$	$\frac{OO}{OO}$

It will be noted that the symbols are selected to include both ridge counting for loops, and ridge tracing for whorls. The Henry system did not consider all the patterns in the index and second fingers, which comprise this portion of the formula, unless all the patterns were the same. However, as already stated, with the accumulation of records in modern bureaus, it was found that all available symbols are necessary to subdivide the patterns adequately for filing and searching. It is therefore advisable to include both ridge counting and ridge tracing in the sub-secondary of the classification formula.

In the sub-secondary, the first letter above the line refers to the right index, and the second letter describes the second finger of the right hand. The first letter below the line describes the index finger of the left hand, and the second symbol refers to the second finger of the left hand.

Additional division may be secured by the inclusion of the ring fingers of both hands. When these data are used and both loops and whorls are recognized in the classification, the progressive sequence runs from III over III to OOO over OOO, and utilizes all possibilities of I, M, and O, over III, then repeats the same progression over IIM, and so on, until all the available combinations have been used, thus:

$$\frac{III}{III} \quad \frac{IIM}{III} \quad \frac{IIO}{III} \quad \frac{IMI}{III} \quad \frac{IMM}{III} \quad \frac{IMO}{III} \quad \frac{IOI}{III} \quad \frac{IOM}{III} \quad \frac{IOO}{III}$$

$$\frac{MII}{III} \quad \frac{MIM}{III} \quad \frac{MIO}{III} \quad \frac{MMI}{III} \quad \frac{MMM}{III} \quad \frac{MMO}{III} \quad \frac{MOI}{III} \quad \frac{MOM}{III} \quad \frac{MOO}{III}$$

$$\frac{OII}{III} \quad \frac{OIM}{III} \quad \frac{OIO}{III} \quad \frac{OMI}{III} \quad \frac{OMM}{III} \quad \frac{OMO}{III} \quad \frac{OOI}{III} \quad \frac{OOM}{III} \quad \frac{OOO}{III}$$

Following this, as just explained, comes the progression

$$\frac{III}{IIM} \quad \frac{IIM}{IIM} \quad \frac{IIO}{IIM} \quad \frac{IMI}{IIM} \quad \frac{IMM}{IIM} \quad \frac{IMO}{IIM}$$ and so on, until reaching $\frac{OOO}{OOO}$.

When the little fingers are also included in the sub-secondary section of the formula, the sub-secondary is divided into two sections, the index and second fingers of both hands being written as one pair. These two pairs of symbols are considered through all the possibilities of I, M, and O, the index-and-second finger pair having first preference, that is, the ring-

and-little-finger pair runs through all the possible combinations with every progressive change in the index-and-middle-finger pair, thus:

$$\frac{II}{II} \quad \frac{II}{II} \qquad \frac{II}{II} \quad \frac{IM}{II} \qquad \frac{II}{II} \quad \frac{IO}{II} \qquad \frac{II}{II} \quad \frac{MI}{II} \qquad \frac{II}{II} \quad \frac{MM}{II} \qquad \frac{II}{II} \quad \frac{MO}{II}$$

$$\frac{II}{II} \quad \frac{OI}{II} \qquad \frac{II}{II} \quad \frac{OM}{II} \qquad \frac{II}{II} \quad \frac{OO}{II} \qquad \frac{II}{II} \quad \frac{II}{IM} \qquad \frac{II}{II} \quad \frac{IM}{IM} \qquad \frac{II}{II} \quad \frac{IO}{IM}$$

and so on to $\frac{II}{II} \frac{OO}{OO}$, after which the first changes to $\frac{IM}{II}$ and the second pair again runs through its entire possibility of variants. The first pair then changes to the next step, that of $\frac{IO}{II}$, and the second pair once more runs through all of its possibilities. This continues until both pairs are $\frac{OO}{OO} \frac{OO}{OO}$

It is advised that both little fingers be counted, and the count recorded in all cases, regardless of whether the patterns be loops or whorls. In the event of the little fingers' being whorls, they may be counted as if they were ulnar loops, from the left delta to the core in the right little finger, and from the right delta to the core in the left little finger. This pair of numbers may also be written like a fraction, with the right-hand figures above the line and the left below. In filing and searching, the right little finger is considered first; all left-little-finger counts being filed progressively under right-little-finger counts of 1. The same procedure is next observed under right-little-finger counts of 2, and so on.

SMALL-LETTER CLASSIFICATIONS

Since arches, tented arches, and radial loops appear less frequently in digits other than the index fingers, when any of the aforementioned patterns are found in any finger or fingers other than the index fingers, they are indicated by the letters *a, t,* or *r,* small letters being used. These small letters are placed after the primary and before or after the secondary, according to whether the pattern in question is present in the thumb or in some digit following the index finger. For example, a set of prints having a radial loop in the right thumb, ulnar loops in both index fingers, and another radial loop in some finger of the right hand other than the index, would be expressed thus: $\frac{rUr}{U}$. In a medium-sized collection, the small-letter group may not require any *I, M,* or *O* symbols, the small letters being ample data in conjunction with the primary, secondary, and little-finger counts; however, it is advisable to include these additional data as well. For convenience, the *I, M,* and *O* symbols may be enclosed in parentheses, thus:

$$5 \ Ua \ (I\text{---}) \ 12$$
$$17 \ R \ \ (IO) \ 17$$

The filing of small-letter classifications requires some especial mention. All small-letter fingerprint cards are filed behind the unlettered groups. For example, under the 5 over 17 division, the entire sequence of unlettered prints from *A* over *A,* and from *II* over *II* to *OO* over *OO,* will be filed in the customary manner. At the rear of the 5 over 17, *A* over *A* division, will be filed the small-letter cards beginning with *aA* over *A.* The filing sequence in the small-letter group is here shown in full for one progression. Just as in the other sections of the formula, all the possible combinations of symbols are used over the same symbols as denominators in all possibilities of variance. It will also be observed that the order of progression in the small-letter group is *a, t, r,* throughout all the possibilities of combination and placement (Fig. 131).

In Fig. 131 the index fingers, both right and left, are indicated in every instance as plain arches. It must be understood,

A	$tAra$	aA_2at	tA_2tr
aA	$tArt$	aA_2ar	$tAtra$
tA	tA_2r	$aAata$	$tAtrt$
rA	rA_2a	aAa_2t	tAt_2r
Aa	$rAat$	$aAatr$	tAr_2a
At	$rAar$	$aAara$	$tArat$
Ar	$rAta$	$aAart$	$tArar$
aAa	rA_2t	aAa_2r	$tArta$
aAt	$rAtr$	aAt_2a	tAr_2t
aAr	$rAra$	$aAtat$	$tArtr$
tAa	$rArt$	$aAtar$	tA_2ra
tAt	rA_2r	aA_2ta	tA_2rt
tAr	A_3a	aA_3t	tA_3r
rAa	A_2at	aA_2tr	rA_3a
rAt	A_2ar	$aAtra$	rA_2at
rAr	$Aata$	$aAtrt$	rA_2ar
A_2a	Aa_2t	aAt_2r	$rAata$
Aat	$Aatr$	aAr_2a	rAa_2t
Aar	$Aara$	$aArat$	$rAatr$
Ata	$Aart$	$aArar$	$rAara$
A_2t	Aa_2r	$aArta$	$rAart$
Atr	At_2a	aAr_2t	rAa_2r
Ara	$Atat$	$aArtr$	rAt_2a
Art	$Atar$	aA_2ra	$rAtat$
A_2r	A_2ta	aA_2rt	$rAtar$
aA_2a	A_3t	aA_3r	rA_2ta
$aAat$	A_2tr	tA_3a	rA_3t
$aAar$	$Atra$	tA_2at	rA_2tr
$aAta$	$Atrt$	tA_2ar	$rAtra$
aA_2t	At_2r	$tAata$	$rAtrt$
$aAtr$	Ar_2a	tAa_2t	rAt_2r
$aAra$	$Arat$	$tAatr$	rAr_2a
$aArt$	$Arar$	$tAara$	$rArat$
aA_2r	$Arta$	$tAart$	$rArar$
tA_2a	Ar_2t	tAa_2r	$rArta$
$tAat$	$Artr$	tAt_2a	rAr_2t
$tAar$	A_2ra	$tAtat$	$rArtr$
$tAta$	A_2rt	$tAtar$	rA_2ra
tA_2t	A_3r	tA_2ta	rA_2rt
$tAtr$	aA_3a	tA_3t	rA_3r

Fig. 131

however, that in the small-letter classification sequence, either index finger may display any of the various pattern types, arches, tented arches, radial loops, ulnar loops, or whorls. With this thought in mind, the possible variants to be obtained in the small-letter classification formulas become greatly increased; since with plain arches only in both index fingers, the progressive sequence of numerator change includes 160 variants, and as each of these may be used for the denominator in the same order as that shown for the numerator, 25,600 combinations are secured. Thus, when all the other possible variants of capital letter index-finger symbols are employed with each of the possible small-letter classification progressions, this subdivision of the formula is infinitely extended. It must also be remembered that a wide variety of variants is possible in the primary division of the classification formula, even though small-letter symbols occur in one or more of the ten digits.

MISSING FINGERS AND OTHER ABNORMALITIES

When classifying fingerprints, it will be remembered that a missing digit is given the same classification as the same finger on the other hand and referenced to every other possible classification. If more than two fingers are amputated no additional references are made. If both hands show the same finger missing, the absent ones are both given the classification of meet whorls. Thus, with all ten fingers missing, all the absent patterns would be described as meet whorls.

If a subject has more than ten fingers, as occasionally happens, the thumbs and the four fingers next to them should be printed, and any additional fingers should be printed on the other side of the card with a notation made to the effect that they are extra fingers. When a person with more than ten fingers has an intentional amputation performed, it is invariably the extra finger on the little-finger side that is removed.

It also happens, not infrequently, that a subject will have two or more fingers webbed together, making it impossible to roll the fingers on the inside. Such fingers should be rolled as completely as possible, and a notation made to the effect that they are joined.

Split thumbs, that is, thumbs having two nail joints, are classified as if the joint toward the outside of the hand were not present. In other words, the inner joint is used, and no consideration given the outer joint.

Utmost care is necessary in fingerprinting the aged, whose skin ridges are usually faint and ill-defined, because of wear; children, whose ridges are very fine and close together; those subjects whose occupations (bricklaying, stone and cement work, plastering, dishwashing, etc.), cause partial effacement or destruction of the ridges, and subjects with skin diseases that affect the hands. In the latter two cases, if possible, the prints should not be taken until a period of time after cessation of such labor has elapsed, sufficient to allow nature to reconstruct the ridges, or after a cure has been effected. If poor impressions are caused by excessive dryness of the skin, they may be improved by rubbing the fingers with olive oil.

It is imperative that all amputations, drawn or crippled fingers, those missing since birth, deformities, paralysis, fractures, burns, and cuts be noted on the fingerprint card. Should an injury be temporary, if possible, the prints should not be taken until after healing.

The science of fingerprint study recognizes a useful fact in the individuality found in skin patterns. However, the circumstance that each design is absolutely unique results in occasional complications that have been termed "questioned patterns." These prints are difficult to classify accurately because of accidental damage or natural irregularity.

In some instances, the formation in question may include characteristics of two or more standard types; and in other cases, it may resemble none of the conventional classes. It has already been explained how border-line fingerprints should be treated, namely, by giving one or more "reference" classifications in addition to the "first-choice" formula. Nevertheless, a more intimate consideration of some examples of questioned patterns will serve to illustrate what may be anticipated in the way of unusual ridge structure. (See Figs. 132 to 141 incl.)

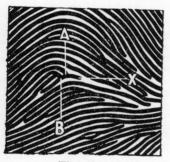

Fig. 132
Unusual pattern #1
PLAIN ARCH

Fig. 133
Unusual pattern #2
TENTED ARCH

Fig. 132. Here is an example which, for filing purposes, is given the preference of a plain arch. It will be noted that in the center of this fingerprint, ridge X bifurcates at points A and B. The formation of these points is caused by the bifurcation of ridge X and not by the meeting of two separate ridges. For this reason the pattern is given the preference of a plain arch.

Fig. 133. This impression is another example of design to be classified as a tented arch. Inspection of the print shows that while most of the ridges flow from one side of the impression to the other in an archlike formation, nevertheless ridge A tends to thrust upward and strikes into ridge B in such a manner as to form an angle. For this reason it is classified as a tented arch. However, a reference search should be conducted in the plain-arch group.

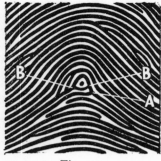 

Fig. 134
Unusual pattern #3
TENTED ARCH

Fig. 135
Unusual pattern #4
TENTED ARCH

Fig. 134. This illustration depicts an interesting design. It is believed that some might classify the pattern as a whorl; however, under the strict definition of a whorl, there should be two or more deltas, with recurving ridges in front of each delta. A complete circuit in the center of the pattern would, of course, meet the requirements of the two recurving ridges, but as all of the essentials are not represented in this pattern, it cannot be classified as a whorl. Furthermore it cannot be classified as a loop, as there is no recurve flowing in front of bifurcation A, which might otherwise serve as a delta. The design may be classified as a tented arch, consideration being given to the formation at points B, which removes the pattern from the plain arch type. It is judged to fall in the division of tented arches due to the presence of ridges which, either in changing their direction from upward to downward or in striking into an arching ridge, form an angle in the center of an arch-type pattern.

Fig. 135. The pattern shown in this illustration possesses some characteristics of the whorl, loop, and tented-arch types of pattern. However, it cannot be classified as a whorl, because all the recurves on both sides are involved with appendages connected with them. It cannot be classified as a loop, as there is no ridge that flows, or tends to flow, out of the pattern on the same side from which it entered. The design is classified as a tented arch because of the angular formation present. However, reference searches should be conducted both as to whorl and loop.

Fig. 136. The pattern here shown is deceiving, but not particularly difficult if closely examined. Though at first glance the design appears to be a whorl, it will be found that it does not conform to any of the definitions of the four whorl types. There is not the complete circuit required for a plain whorl, nor are there the two loops of the double-loop type. There is no recurve or obstruction at right angles to the line of flow, as required for a central pocket loop, nor is it a combination of two different types of pattern, as required for an accidental whorl. This pattern should be classified as a tented arch because of the angles and upthrust present. A reference search as an accidental whorl should be conducted.

Fig. 136
Unusual pattern #5
TENTED ARCH

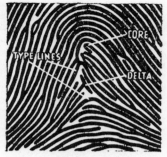

Fig. 137
Unusual pattern #6
LOOP

Fig. 137. In this illustration, the difficulty lies in locating the delta. The only ridges answering the definition of type-lines (ridges running parallel and then diverging to enclose the pattern area) have three ending ridges between them. The type-lines are marked, and the most central point between their divergence indicated as the delta. The pattern is classified as a six-count loop, the core being also indicated.

Fig. 138
Unusual pattern #7
LOOP

Fig. 139
Unusual pattern #8
LOOP

Fig. 138. The questionable pattern here offered for consideration consists of two well-formed looping ridges in juxtaposition upon the same common delta. Since it cannot be classified as a double-loop whorl, the two loops should be considered as one, with two rods in the center. The core is placed accordingly, upon the left shoulder of the far loop. The pattern is thus classifiable as a loop with four counts.

Fig. 139. The accompanying impression is one of the outstanding borderline types; transitional between a loop and a whorl pattern. In this case the fingerprint contains two deltas, one at A and the other at B, with ridges recurving in front of B. The ridges in front of A, however, are not free recurves in front of or above the upper delta. It appears that this formation is composed of ending and bifurcating lines with appendages appearing on the ends of the ridges in the center, so they do not constitute recurves. For this reason, the pattern is classified as a loop. Nevertheless, reference search should be conducted in the whorl division.

Fig. 140
Unusual pattern #9
WHORL

Fig. 141
Unusual pattern #10
ACCIDENTAL

Fig. 140. Finger impressions of the type illustrated in this example cause diversified opinions concerning their proper interpretation. It is readily seen that this pattern does not permit accurate classification into any of the standard groups of arches, tented arches, loops, or whorls. As already stated, an accidental is an impression which contains a combination of two or more different types of pattern within the same pattern area, or any pattern which cannot be classified into the standard groups because of unusual design. Under this interpretation, this design should be considered as an accidental whorl with an inner ridge tracing.

Fig. 141. The finger impression reproduced in this illustration is an unusual pattern containing four deltas; it is an accidental whorl of a very rare type. The only problem encountered in the classification of this print, is the one arising from ridge tracing. However, the rule governing the tracing of whorl formations having three or more deltas, is applicable in this case. Under such circumstances the two extreme outside deltas are located and the ridges then traced from left to right according to the methods pertaining to all whorl patterns. In this instance, deltas A and B are utilized and the pattern is judged to have an outer tracing.

VI

EXTENSION OF THE HENRY SYSTEM

WITH the march of time, which has seen fingerprint registration greatly extended, it has become necessary to provide additional subdivisions in the files of larger bureaus. Such a utility is currently used in the Federal Bureau at Washington and in many other sizable collections. Credit for the inception and development of this systemic advancement goes to the noteworthy California experts, Inspector Harry H. Caldwell and Captain Clarence D. Lee, now retired from the police departments of Oakland and Berkeley respectively. In no way conflicting with the pre-established Galton-Henry rules, this "extension" system furnishes a more intimate description of the patterns, thus greatly minimizing the work of filing and searching. Although some of the included definitions and descriptions may suggest a repetition of data appearing earlier in the text, for the sake of continuity it has been judged expedient to present the extension in its entirety.

MODIFICATION AND EXTENSION OF THE HENRY SYSTEM OF IDENTIFICA-
TION AS DEVISED FOR, AND APPLIED TO, THE FINGERPRINT FILES OF
THE FEDERAL BUREAU OF INVESTIGATION, UNITED STATES DEPART-
MENT OF JUSTICE, WASHINGTON, D. C.

The object of this modification and extension of the Henry
system is to subdivide the files by major divisions and sub-classifications, and by extending subdivisions, to create more practical and
less voluminous groups for the searcher to handle.

These extensions do not conflict with the fundamental principles of the Henry system, but are the natural developments of it,
the result of careful study and practical experience, the product of
meeting the problems that arise in the management of a large
fingerprint bureau.

These extensions were provided and thoroughly tested for use
in the fingerprint files of the Federal Bureau of Investigation,
before they were finally adopted. They are not to be applied to any
groups or subdivisions except where necessary. When they are
applied they are to be utilized only in so far as they may be necessary and practicable to afford proper subdivision to otherwise extensive or voluminous combinations.

Divisions of Classifications—The classification formula is divided
into seven possible divisions under the extension system:

> (*a*) Primary
> (*b*) Major Divisions
> (*c*) Secondary and Small Letter Groups
> (*d*) Sub-secondary
> (*e*) Secondary Sub-secondary
> (*f*) Final
> (*g*) Key

The positions in the classification line for these divisions when
completely applied are as illustrated:

Key	Major Divisions	Primary Classification	Secondary Classification	Second Sub-secondary Classification	
				Sub-secondary Classification	Final Classification
				S L M	
				M M S	
20	M	1	U	I O I	10
	L	1	U	I O I	

(*a*) *The Primary*—The Primary classification is the numerical value of the whorls in a set of prints. The arbitrary value assigned to the fingers for this purpose is as follows:

Fingers #1 and #2—16
Fingers #3 and #4— 8
Fingers #5 and #6— 4
Fingers #7 and #8— 2
Fingers #9 and #10— 1

The sum of the numerical value of whorls, if any, in fingers 1, 3, 5, 7 and 9, with one added, is the denominator of the primary classification. The sum of the numerical value of the whorls, if any, in 2, 4, 6, 8 and 10, with one added, is the numerator of the primary classification. Where no whorl appears in a set of impressions, the primary, therefore, would be $\frac{1.}{1.}$ It is noted that 1024 possible primaries may be attained from $\frac{1}{1}$ to $\frac{32,}{32,}$ which is the primary when whorls appear in every finger.

(*b*) *The Major Divisions* are created by counting and by tracing ridges of the left and right thumbs respectively. These divisions are to be used for the purpose of subdividing large collections of prints. They are explained in detail hereinafter.

(*c*) *The Secondary* represents the types of patterns that appear in the index fingers. When small letters appear they are used to subdivide the secondary and are brought into the classification line adjacent thereto, dependent upon which fingers these small letter patterns represent.

(*d*) *The Sub-secondary,* according to the Henry system, designates the ridge counts or tracings in the index and middle fingers of each hand, if in pairs. If not in pairs, only the index fingers are used. Under this extension system the *Sub-secondary* is extended to include the ridge counts or tracings appearing in the index, middle, and ring fingers of both hands, even though the patterns are not of the same type.

(*e*) *The Second Sub-secondary* is the extension of loops by the application of small, medium, and large divisions, and is an addition to the *Sub-secondary.*

(*f*) *The Final* is the ridge count of the loop in the little finger of the right hand, placed on the numerator line. If there is no loop in the right little finger, then the ridge count of the one appearing in the left little finger is used, in which case it is placed in the denominator of the classification line. If no loop appears in either little finger, the result of the ridge count of the whorl may be utilized by treating the whorl as an ulnar loop for counting purposes.

(*g*) *The Key* is the ridge count of the first loop in a set of prints, beginning with the right thumb, but not including either of the little fingers. If there is no such loop, the key is the result of the ridge count of the first whorl. The key is placed at the extreme left of the classification formula in line with the numerator, sufficient space being allowed for additional symbols.

Thus, the seven possible divisions of the classification, where all are necessary, are applied for sequence and filing purposes in the order given above.

MAJOR DIVISIONS OF LOOPS

In a large collection of prints where both thumbs are loops, they are divided into nine major divisions by counting the ridges of the thumbs. The ridge counts of the left thumb are represented in the denominator by the symbols *S, M,* and *L,* which are arrived at as follows: Ridge counts 1 to 11, inclusive, are *S* (Small); 12 to 16, inclusive, *M* (Medium); and 17 or over, *L* (Large).

The ridge counts of the right thumb are represented in the numerator by the same symbols, *S, M,* and *L.* The count in this instance for the Small, Medium and Large is the same, as just explained, for the denominator when an *S* or *M* appears as the denominator.

When there are 17 ridges or more making a "Large" (*L*) in the denominator, the combination changes in the numerator, thus: 1 to 17 inclusive *S*, 18 to 22 inclusive *M*, and 23 or more *L*.

TABLE OF MAJOR DIVISIONS OF LOOPS

Left Thumb Denominator	Right Thumb Numerator
1 to 11 inclusive, *S* (Small)	1 to 11 inclusive, *S* (Small) 12 to 16 inclusive, *M* (Medium) 17 or more ridges, *L* (Large)
12 to 16 inclusive, *M* (Medium)	1 to 11 inclusive, *S* (Small) 12 to 16 inclusive, *M* (Medium) 17 or more ridges, *L* (Large)
17 or more ridges, *L* (Large)	1 to 17 inclusive, *S* (Small) 18 to 22 inclusive, *M* (Medium) 23 or more ridges, *L* (Large)

The following symbols are used to illustrate the sequences of the nine combinations in this division.

$$\frac{S\;M\;L}{S\;S\;S} \qquad \frac{S\;M\;L}{M\;M\;M} \qquad \frac{S\;M\;L}{L\;L\;L}$$

MAJOR DIVISIONS OF WHORLS

In a large collection of prints when both thumbs are whorls, they are divided into nine major divisions by the result of the ridge tracing, Inner (*I*), Meet (*M*), and Outer (*O*) of both thumbs. The left thumb represents the denominator and the right thumb the numerator.

The following symbols are used to illustrate the sequences of the nine combinations in this division.

$$\frac{I\;M\;O}{I\;I\;I} \qquad \frac{I\;M\;O}{M\;M\;M} \qquad \frac{I\;M\;O}{O\;O\;O}$$

Major Divisions Combining the Loop and Whorl

In a large collection of prints where a whorl appears in one thumb and a loop in the other, they are divided by the same principle as just explained, using both ridge counting and ridge tracing.

If the ridge count in the right thumb does not produce a proper subdivision, then the rule governing the "Large" denominator in the major division of loops may be applied. Example:

```
16 M 17 W I  6          16 M 13 U 00 12
   M  1 R 00               I  1 R 00
25 L 29 W M  9
   O  4 W I
```

The following symbols are used to illustrate the sequence of the eighteen groups which may result from these combinations of loops and whorls:

(Loop on the right thumb, whorl on the left.)

```
S M L      S M L      S M L
I I I      M M M      0 0 0
```

(Whorl on the right thumb, loop on the left.)

```
I M 0      I M 0      I M 0
S S S      M M M      L L L
```

In counting the ridges of whorls, including composites, these types of patterns are to be treated as ulnar loops, and the count taken from the left delta to the core in the right hand, and from the right delta to the core in the left hand.

Secondary Classification

The secondary classification is shown by a capital letter for the patterns in the index fingers and the symbols are as follows:

(a) *A*, arch
(b) *T*, tented arch
(c) *R*, radial loop
(d) *U*, ulnar loop
(e) *W*, whorl
(f) *C*, central pocket
(g) *D*, double loop
(h) *X*, accidental

In the small-letter group the small letters are brought up on either side of the secondary, dependent upon the fingers in which the patterns appear.

Definitions of Patterns

(a) *Arches* (*A*): In an Arch, the ridges run from one side of the impression to the other, making no upward thrust, no backward turn, and there is no delta.

(b) *Tented Arches* (*T*): A Tented Arch is a pattern of the arch type primarily, but the ridges in the center must have a pronounced upward thrust, arranging themselves, as it were, on both sides of a spine or axis, toward which adjoining ridges converge or have an angular formation in at least one of the ridges at the point where that ridge changes from the upward to the downward flow, or lacking one of the requirements necessary for a loop type of pattern.

(c) *Radial Loop* (*R*): Any Loop is that type of fingerprint pattern in which one or more of the ridges enter on either side of the impression, recurve, touch or pass an imaginary line drawn from the core to the delta, and terminate on or toward the same side of the impression. In a radial loop the direction of the downward slope of the ridges is from the little finger toward the thumb. The recurve must be free of any appendage abutting it on the outside at a right angle.

(d) *Ulnar Loop* (*U*): An Ulnar Loop differs from a radial loop only in that the direction of the downward slope of the ridge or ridges is from the thumb toward the little finger.

(e) *Whorl* (*W*): A Whorl is a pattern in which the ridges about the core make at least one complete circuit. Whorls may be spiral, oval, circular or some other variant of a circle. (A Whorl has two deltas and may be single or double cored.)

(f) *Central Pocket Loops* (*C*): A Central Pocket Loop is a transitional pattern between the loop and whorl types, differing from the loop in that one or more of the simple recurves of the plain loop type has recurved again to make a complete circuit and to require a second delta. In distinguishing between the central pocket and plain whorl types, a straight line is placed so as to connect both deltas. In order to fulfill the requirements of the central pocket loop the line, when so placed, must not touch or cut through any one of the recurving ridges which lie between the core and the inner delta.

(g) *Double Loop* (D): A Double Loop is a pattern containing two distinct loops, one overlapping the other and in which both *shoulders* of one loop are *free* from the shoulders of the other. A ridge connecting the side of one loop with a side of the other does not prevent the pattern from becoming a double loop.

(h) *Accidental* (X): An Accidental is a pattern composed of two or more different types of patterns.

TABLE SHOWING SEQUENCE OF THE SYMBOLS OF THE SECONDARY CLASSIFICATION

$\frac{A}{A}$	$\frac{T}{A}$	$\frac{R}{A}$	$\frac{U}{A}$	$\frac{W}{A}$	$\frac{C}{A}$	$\frac{D}{A}$	$\frac{X}{A}$
$\frac{A}{T}$	$\frac{T}{T}$	$\frac{R}{T}$	$\frac{U}{T}$	$\frac{W}{T}$	$\frac{C}{T}$	$\frac{D}{T}$	$\frac{X}{T}$
$\frac{A}{R}$	$\frac{T}{R}$	$\frac{R}{R}$	$\frac{U}{R}$	$\frac{W}{R}$	$\frac{C}{R}$	$\frac{D}{R}$	$\frac{X}{R}$
$\frac{A}{U}$	$\frac{T}{U}$	$\frac{R}{U}$	$\frac{U}{U}$	$\frac{W}{U}$	$\frac{C}{U}$	$\frac{D}{U}$	$\frac{X}{U}$
$\frac{A}{W}$	$\frac{T}{W}$	$\frac{R}{W}$	$\frac{U}{W}$	$\frac{W}{W}$	$\frac{C}{W}$	$\frac{D}{W}$	$\frac{X}{W}$
$\frac{A}{C}$	$\frac{T}{C}$	$\frac{R}{C}$	$\frac{U}{C}$	$\frac{W}{C}$	$\frac{C}{C}$	$\frac{D}{C}$	$\frac{X}{C}$
$\frac{A}{D}$	$\frac{T}{D}$	$\frac{R}{D}$	$\frac{U}{D}$	$\frac{W}{D}$	$\frac{C}{D}$	$\frac{D}{D}$	$\frac{X}{D}$
$\frac{A}{X}$	$\frac{T}{X}$	$\frac{R}{X}$	$\frac{U}{X}$	$\frac{W}{X}$	$\frac{C}{X}$	$\frac{D}{X}$	$\frac{X}{X}$

Non-Numerical Group

The primary classification of the non-numerical group is $\frac{1.}{1.}$
That group may be comprised of all impressions other than whorls and composites.

The following is the secondary classification of this group:

$$\frac{A\ T\ R\ U}{A\ A\ A\ A} \qquad \frac{A\ T\ R\ U}{T\ T\ T\ T}$$

$$\frac{A\ T\ R\ U}{R\ R\ R\ R} \qquad \frac{A\ T\ R\ U}{U\ U\ U\ U}$$

The Secondary Classification
(Small-letter Group)

The following table represents the full sequence of the denominator of the small-letter group. The full sequence as listed may be used as a numerator in connection with each denominator as set out below.

A	tAar	A2rt	tA2ta
aA	tAta	A3r	tA3t
tA	tA2t		tA2tr
rA	tAtr	aA3a	tAtra
	tAra	aA2at	tAtrt
Aa	tArt	aA2ar	tAt2r
At	tA2r	aAata	tAr2a
Ar		aAa2t	tArat
	rA2a	aAatr	tArar
aAa	rAat	aAara	tArta
aAt	rAar	aAart	tAr2t
aAr	rAta	aAa2r	tArtr
	rA2t	aAt2a	tA2ra
tAa	rAtr	aAtat	tA2rt
tAt	rAra	aAtar	tA3r
tAr	rArt	aA2ta	
	rA2r	aA3t	rA3a

rAa		aA2tr	rA2at
rAt	A3a	aAtra	rA2ar
rAr	A2at	aAtrt	rAata
	A2ar	aAt2r	rAa2t
A2a	Aata	aAr2a	rAatr
Aat	Aa2t	aArat	rAara
Aar	Aatr	aArar	rAart
Ata	Aara	aArta	rAa2r
A2t	Aart	aAr2t	rAt2a
Atr	Aa2r	aArtr	rAtat
Ara	At2a	aA2ra	rAtar
Art	Atat	aA2rt	rA2ta
A2r	Atar	aA3r	rA3t
	A2ta		rA2tr
aA2a	A3t	tA3a	rAtra
aAat	A2tr	tA2at	rAtrt
aAar	Atra	tA2ar	rAt2r
aAta	Atrt	tAata	rAr2a
aA2t	At2r	tAa2t	rArat
aAtr	Ar2a	tAatr	rArar
aAra	Arat	tAara	rArta
aArt	Arar	tAart	rAr2t
aA2r	Arta	tAa2r	rArtr
	Ar2t	tAt2a	rA2ra
tA2a	Artr	tAtat	rA2rt
tAat	A2ra	tAtar	rA3r

In order to separate certain other combinations in the small-letter series and place them in their logical order for filing, whenever any small letter appears to the right of the index fingers, it is filed according to the position of the finger in which the small letter appears. A dash is used as an indication wherever a small letter does not appear.

1 A--a	1 Aa-a	1 A2a	1 A--a	1 A3a	1 A-a
1 A	1 Aaa	1 A-a	1 A-2a	1 A--a	1 Aa-a

Secondary and Sub-secondary Groups

Arches, tented arches, or radial loops which appear in other than the index fingers must be shown on the classification line in the order in which they appear, and they become the secondary classification of the lettered series, even though a whorl or a composite appears in either or both index fingers.

Whenever any of the following combinations of symbols appear in the index fingers *only,* the results of the ridge counts of the middle and ring fingers of both hands will be the sub-secondary classification:

$$\frac{A}{A} \quad \frac{T}{A} \quad \frac{A}{T} \quad \frac{T}{T}$$

Examples:

3 1 A II 5	3 1 T I0 5	13 5 A 00 5	3 5 A 00 5
1 A II 6	1 A I0 6	17 T 00 6	1 T 00 6

Whenever $\frac{R}{A} \quad \frac{U}{A} \quad \frac{R}{T} \quad \frac{U}{T}$ appear in the index fingers only, the result of the ridge counts of the right index, middle and ring and the left middle and ring fingers will be the sub-secondary classification. Examples:

3 5 R III 5	3 1 U II0 5	13 5 R 000 5	3 5 U I00 5
1 A II 6	17 A I0 6	17 T 00 6	1 T I0 6

Whenever $\frac{A}{R} \quad \frac{T}{R} \quad \frac{A}{U} \quad \frac{T}{U}$ appear in the index fingers only, the results of the ridge counts of the right middle and ring and the left index, middle and ring fingers will be the sub-secondary classification. Examples:

3 1 A II 5	3 1 T I0 5	3 5 A 0I 5	3 5 T 00 5
1 R III 6	17 R 000 6	1 U I00 6	1 U 000 6

The above examples illustrate the addition of the sub-secondary in the lettered groups; however, where both thumbs are loops they will be subdivided into major divisions as previously explained. Example:

$$
\begin{array}{cccccc}
3 & S & 1 & A & II & 5 \\
  & M & 1 & A & II & 6 \\
\end{array}
$$

In a large collection of prints, where both thumbs are whorls, they will be divided in the major divisions as previously explained. Example:

$$
\begin{array}{cccccc}
13 & I & 5 & A & 00 & 5 \\
   & M & 17 & T & 00 & 6 \\
\end{array}
$$

SUB-SECONDARY GROUPS

We shall now deal with prints which do not have an *a, t,* or *r* in other than the index fingers. To obtain the sub-secondary classification, Sir Edward Henry counted the ridges of loops appearing in the index and middle fingers of each hand, when such fingers were in pairs, that is, when they were both loops. A radial loop in the index finger and an ulnar in the middle finger, would be a pair, but this would not be so if one of the fingers were a loop and the other a whorl, or composite. In the same way, Henry resorted to ridge tracing in whorls and composites in the index and middle fingers if they were in pairs. The *I* and *O* (inner and outer) was the designation for loops, and the *I, M* and *O* was the designation for whorls and composites.

Under the Henry system the following sixteen combinations were used for loop pairs:

```
II IO OI 00 II IO OI 00 II IO OI 00 II IO OI 00
II II II II IO IO IO IO OI OI OI OI 00 00 00 00
```

As the above combinations required further subdividing, the ring fingers were included as an extension to the Henry system.

In counting the loops appearing in the ring fingers, it was found that there were as many loops in those fingers with a ridge count of thirteen or less, as there were with a ridge count of fourteen or more, therefore a ridge count of thirteen or less is an inner, *I,* and fourteen or more an outer, *O.*

Through the use of the ring fingers the sixteen combinations for loops were extended into sixty-four sub-secondary classifications.

CHART OF SIXTY-FOUR SUB-SECONDARY CLASSIFICATIONS

| III | IIO | IOI | IOO | OII | OIO | OOI | OOO |
| III | III | III | III | III | III | III | III |

| III | IIO | IOI | IOO | OII | OIO | OOI | OOO |
| IIO | IIO | IIO | IIO | IIO | IIO | IIO | IIO |

| III | IIO | IOI | IOO | OII | OIO | OOI | OOO |
| IOI | IOI | IOI | IOI | IOI | IOI | IOI | IOI |

| III | IIO | IOI | IOO | OII | OIO | OOI | OOO |
| IOO | IOO | IOO | IOO | IOO | IOO | IOO | IOO |

| III | IIO | IOI | IOO | OII | OIO | OOI | OOO |
| OII | OII | OII | OII | OII | OII | OII | OII |

| III | IIO | IOI | IOO | OII | OIO | OOI | OOO |
| OIO | OIO | OIO | OIO | OIO | OIO | OIO | OIO |

| III | IIO | IOI | IOO | OII | OIO | OOI | OOO |
| OOI | OOI | OOI | OOI | OOI | OOI | OOI | OOI |

| III | IIO | IOI | IOO | OII | OIO | OOI | OOO |
| OOO | OOO | OOO | OOO | OOO | OOO | OOO | OOO |

The following series of examples is given to show the advantage of the extension in the all-loops series:

```
Henry           1  U  II  6      partly  1  U  III  6
Classification: 1  U  II         extended: 1 U III

further  1  U  III  6      further  3  1  U  III  6
extended: 1  U  III  8     extended:    1  U  III  8
```

It will be observed that the count of the left little finger has been added below the final, and in filing it would be sequenced when necessary. It should be noted, however, that the FBI does not use the tenth finger in the final for its classifications.

In a collection of over two million prints further means of subdividing were found to be necessary.

The procedure employed is first to divide them into the "Major Divisions." Each of these divisions is then subdivided independently by the sixty-four combinations of the sub-secondary and within their respective secondary classifications. Examples:

```
10 S 1 R III 6      12 M 1 U IIO 7     17 L 1 R IOO 9
   S 1 R III 7         S 1 R III 6        S 1 U III 2

 9 S 1 U 000 3      13 M 1 R 000 9     18 L 1 U 000 12
   M 1 U III 4         M 1 R IIO 10       M 1 R IOO 13

 6 S 1 R 000 14     18 M 1 U III 15    23 L 1 R IIO 16
   L 1 U 000 12        L 1 U 000 12       L 1 R 000 13
```

SECOND SUB-SECONDARY

Whenever the all-loop series has been fully extended, it can be further subdivided by the 2nd sub-secondary classification in accordance with the following table, the symbols S, M, and L being shown above the sub-secondary and representing the ridge counts of the index, middle and ring fingers, as

Index		Middle		Ring	
1 to 5 (incl.)	S,	1 to 8 (incl.)	S,	1 to 10 (incl.)	S.
6 to 12 "	M,	9 to 14 "	M,	11 to 18 "	M.
13 and over	L,	15 and over	L,	19 and over	L.

CHART SHOWING SEQUENCE FOR FILING THE S M L IN THE SECOND SUB-SECONDARY

SSS	SSM	SSL	SMS	SMM	SML	SLS	SLM	SLL	MSS	MSM	MSL	MMS	MMM
SSS	SSS	SSS	SSS	SSS	SSS	SSS	SSS	SSS	SSS	SSS	SSS	SSS	SSS

MML	MLS	MLM	MLL	LSS	LSM	LSL	LMS	LMM	LML	LLS	LLM	LLL
SSS	SSS	SSS	SSS	SSS	SSS	SSS	SSS	SSS	SSS	SSS	SSS	SSS

SSS	SSM	SSL	SMS	SMM	SML	SLS	SLM	SLL	MSS	MSM	MSL	MMS	MMM
SSM	SSM	SSM	SSM	SSM	SSM	SSM	SSM	SSM	SSM	SSM	SSM	SSM	SSM

MML	MLS	MLM	MLL	LSS	LSM	LSL	LMS	LMM	LML	LLS	LLM	LLL
SSM	SSM	SSM	SSM	SSM	SSM	SSM	SSM	SSM	SSM	SSM	SSM	SSM

SSS	SSM	SSL	SMS	SMM	SML	SLS	SLM	SLL	MSS	MSM	MSL	MMS	MMM
SSL	SSL	SSL	SSL	SSL	SSL	SSL	SSL	SSL	SSL	SSL	SSL	SSL	SSL
MML	MLS	MLM	MLL	LSS	LSM	LSL	LMS	LMM	LML	LLS	LLM	LLL	
SSL	SSL	SSL	SSL	SSL	SSL	SSL	SSL	SSL	SSL	SSL	SSL	SSL	SSL
SSS	SSM	SSL	SMS	SMM	SML	SLS	SLM	SLL	MSS	MSM	MSL	MMS	MMM
SMS	SMS	SMS	SMS	SMS	SMS	SMS	SMS	SMS	SMS	SMS	SMS	SMS	SMS
MML	MLS	MLM	MLL	LSS	LSM	LSL	LMS	LMM	LML	LLS	LLM	LLL	
SMS	SMS	SMS	SMS	SMS	SMS	SMS	SMS	SMS	SMS	SMS	SMS	SMS	SMS
SSS	SSM	SSL	SMS	SMM	SML	SLS	SLM	SLL	MSS	MSM	MSL	MMS	MMM
SMM	SMM	SMM	SMM	SMM	SMM	SMM	SMM	SMM	SMM	SMM	SMM	SMM	SMM
MML	MLS	MLM	MLL	LSS	LSM	LSL	LMS	LMM	LML	LLS	LLM	LLL	
SMM	SMM	SMM	SMM	SMM	SMM	SMM	SMM	SMM	SMM	SMM	SMM	SMM	SMM
SSS	SSM	SSL	SMS	SMM	SML	SLS	SLM	SLL	MSS	MSM	MSL	MMS	MMM
SML	SML	SML	SML	SML	SML	SML	SML	SML	SML	SML	SML	SML	SML
MML	MLS	MLM	MLL	LSS	LSM	LSL	LMS	LMM	LML	LLS	LLM	LLL	
SML	SML	SML	SML	SML	SML	SML	SML	SML	SML	SML	SML	SML	SML
SSS	SSM	SSL	SMS	SMM	SML	SLS	SLM	SLL	MSS	MSM	MSL	MMS	MMM
SLS	SLS	SLS	SLS	SLS	SLS	SLS	SLS	SLS	SLS	SLS	SLS	SLS	SLS
MML	MLS	MLM	MLL	LSS	LSM	LSL	LMS	LMM	LML	LLS	LLM	LLL	
SLS	SLS	SLS	SLS	SLS	SLS	SLS	SLS	SLS	SLS	SLS	SLS	SLS	SLS
SSS	SSM	SSL	SMS	SMM	SML	SLS	SLM	SLL	MSS	MSM	MSL	MMS	MMM
SLM	SLM	SLM	SLM	SLM	SLM	SLM	SLM	SLM	SLM	SLM	SLM	SLM	SLM
MML	MLS	MLM	MLL	LSS	LSM	LSL	LMS	LMM	LML	LLS	LLM	LLL	
SLM	SLM	SLM	SLM	SLM	SLM	SLM	SLM	SLM	SLM	SLM	SLM	SLM	SLM
SSS	SSM	SSL	SMS	SMM	SML	SLS	SLM	SLL	MSS	MSM	MSL	MMS	MMM
SLL	SLL	SLL	SLL	SLL	SLL	SLL	SLL	SLL	SLL	SLL	SLL	SLL	SLL
MML	MLS	MLM	MLL	LSS	LSM	LSL	LMS	LMM	LML	LLS	LLM	LLL	
SLL	SLL	SLL	SLL	SLL	SLL	SLL	SLL	SLL	SLL	SLL	SLL	SLL	SLL
SSS	SSM	SSL	SMS	SMM	SML	SLS	SLM	SLL	MSS	MSM	MSL	MMS	MMM
MSS	MSS	MSS	MSS	MSS	MSS	MSS	MSS	MSS	MSS	MSS	MSS	MSS	MSS

```
    MML MLS MLM MLL LSS LSM LSL LMS LMM LML LLS LLM LLL
    MSS MSS MSS MSS MSS MSS MSS MSS MSS MSS MSS MSS MSS
SSS SSM SSL SMS SMM SML SLS SLM SLL MSS MSM MSL MMS MMM
MSM MSM MSM MSM MSM MSM MSM MSM MSM MSM MSM MSM MSM MSM
    MML MLS MLM MLL LSS LSM LSL LMS LMM LML LLS LLM LLL
    MSM MSM MSM MSM MSM MSM MSM MSM MSM MSM MSM MSM MSM
SSS SSM SSL SMS SMM SML SLS SLM SLL MSS MSM MSL MMS MMM
MSL MSL MSL MSL MSL MSL MSL MSL MSL MSL MSL MSL MSL MSL
    MML MLS MLM MLL LSS LSM LSL LMS LMM LML LLS LLM LLL
    MSL MSL MSL MSL MSL MSL MSL MSL MSL MSL MSL MSL MSL
SSS SSM SSL SMS SMM SML SLS SLM SLL MSS MSM MSL MMS MMM
MMS MMS MMS MMS MMS MMS MMS MMS MMS MMS MMS MMS MMS MMS
    MML MLS MLM MLL LSS LSM LSL LMS LMM LML LLS LLM LLL
    MMS MMS MMS MMS MMS MMS MMS MMS MMS MMS MMS MMS MMS
SSS SSM SSL SMS SMM SML SLS SLM SLL MSS MSM MSL MMS MMM
MMM MMM MMM MMM MMM MMM MMM MMM MMM MMM MMM MMM MMM MMM
    MML MLS MLM MLL LSS LSM LSL LMS LMM LML LLS LLM LLL
    MMM MMM MMM MMM MMM MMM MMM MMM MMM MMM MMM MMM MMM
SSS SSM SSL SMS SMM SML SLS SLM SLL MSS MSM MSL MMS MMM
MML MML MML MML MML MML MML MML MML MML MML MML MML MML
    MML MLS MLM MLL LSS LSM LSL LMS LMM LML LLS LLM LLL
    MML MML MML MML MML MML MML MML MML MML MML MML MML
SSS SSM SSL SMS SMM SML SLS SLM SLL MSS MSM MSL MMS MMM
MLS MLS MLS MLS MLS MLS MLS MLS MLS MLS MLS MLS MLS MLS
    MML MLS MLM MLL LSS LSM LSL LMS LMM LML LLS LLM LLL
    MLS MLS MLS MLS MLS MLS MLS MLS MLS MLS MLS MLS MLS
SSS SSM SSL SMS SMM SML SLS SLM SLL MSS MSM MSL MMS MMM
MLM MLM MLM MLM MLM MLM MLM MLM MLM MLM MLM MLM MLM MLM
    MML MLS MLM MLL LSS LSM LSL LMS LMM LML LLS LLM LLL
    MLM MLM MLM MLM MLM MLM MLM MLM MLM MLM MLM MLM MLM
```

```
SSS SSM SSL SMS SMM SML SLS SLM SLL MSS MSM MSL MMS MMM

MLL MLL MLL MLL MLL MLL MLL MLL MLL MLL MLL MLL MLL MLL

    MML MLS MLM MLL LSS LSM LSL LMS LMM LML LLS LLM LLL

    MLL MLL MLL MLL MLL MLL MLL MLL MLL MLL MLL MLL MLL

SSS SSM SSL SMS SMM SML SLS SLM SLL MSS MSM MSL MMS MMM

LSS LSS LSS LSS LSS LSS LSS LSS LSS LSS LSS LSS LSS LSS

    MML MLS MLM MLL LSS LSM LSL LMS LMM LML LLS LLM LLL

    LSS LSS LSS LSS LSS LSS LSS LSS LSS LSS LSS LSS LSS

SSS SSM SSL SMS SMM SML SLS SLM SLL MSS MSM MSL MMS MMM

LSM LSM LSM LSM LSM LSM LSM LSM LSM LSM LSM LSM LSM LSM

    MML MLS MLM MLL LSS LSM LSL LMS LMM LML LLS LLM LLL

    LSM LSM LSM LSM LSM LSM LSM LSM LSM LSM LSM LSM LSM

SSS SSM SSL SMS SMM SML SLS SLM SLL MSS MSM MSL MMS MMM

LSL LSL LSL LSL LSL LSL LSL LSL LSL LSL LSL LSL LSL LSL

    MML MLS MLM MLL LSS LSM LSL LMS LMM LML LLS LLM LLL

    LSL LSL LSL LSL LSL LSL LSL LSL LSL LSL LSL LSL LSL

SSS SSM SSL SMS SMM SML SLS SLM SLL MSS MSM MSL MMS MMM

LMS LMS LMS LMS LMS LMS LMS LMS LMS LMS LMS LMS LMS LMS

    MML MLS MLM MLL LSS LSM LSL LMS LMM LML LLS LLM LLL

    LMS LMS LMS LMS LMS LMS LMS LMS LMS LMS LMS LMS LMS

SSS SSM SSL SMS SMM SML SLS SLM SLL MSS MSM MSL MMS MMM

LMM LMM LMM LMM LMM LMM LMM LMM LMM LMM LMM LMM LMM LMM

    MML MLS MLM MLL LSS LSM LSL LMS LMM LML LLS LLM LLL

    LMM LMM LMM LMM LMM LMM LMM LMM LMM LMM LMM LMM LMM

SSS SSM SSL SMS SMM SML SLS SLM SLL MSS MSM MSL MMS MMM

LML LML LML LML LML LML LML LML LML LML LML LML LML LML

    MML MLS MLM MLL LSS LSM LSL LMS LMM LML LLS LLM LLL

    LML LML LML LML LML LML LML LML LML LML LML LML LML

SSS SSM SSL SMS SMM SML SLS SLM SLL MSS MSM MSL MMS MMM

LLS LLS LLS LLS LLS LLS LLS LLS LLS LLS LLS LLS LLS LLS
```

MML	MLS	MLM	MLL	LSS	LSM	LSL	LMS	LMM	LML	LLS	LLM	LLL
LLS	LLS	LLS	LLS	LLS	LLS	LLS	LLS	LLS	LLS	LLS	LLS	LLS
SSS	SSM	SSL	SMS	SMM	SML	SLS	SLM	SLL	MSS	MSM	MSL	MMS	MMM
LLM	LLM	LLM	LLM	LLM	LLM	LLM	LLM	LLM	LLM	LLM	LLM	LLM
MML	MLS	MLM	MLL	LSS	LSM	LSL	LMS	LMM	LML	LLS	LLM	LLL
LLM	LLM	LLM	LLM	LLM	LLM	LLM	LLM	LLM	LLM	LLM	LLM	LLM
SSS	SSM	SSL	SMS	SMM	SML	SLS	SLM	SLL	MSS	MSM	MSL	MMS	MMM
LLL	LLL	LLL	LLL	LLL	LLL	LLL	LLL	LLL	LLL	LLL	LLL	LLL
MML	MLS	MLM	MLL	LSS	LSM	LSL	LMS	LMM	LML	LLS	LLM	LLL
LLL	LLL	LLL	LLL	LLL	LLL	LLL	LLL	LLL	LLL	LLL	LLL	LLL

SPECIAL LOOP EXTENSION

The FBI uses an additional subdivision for the all Ulnar-Loop Group $\frac{1U}{1U}$. The ridge counts in fingers No. 2, 3, 4, 7, 8, 9, and if necessary, 10, are assigned values as follows:

Ridge Counts	Value	Ridge Counts	Value
1 through 4	1	17 through 20	5
5 through 8	2	21 through 24	6
9 through 12	3	25 and over	7
13 through 16	4		

These values are brought up into the classification formula directly above the sub-secondary in their respective positions, the right hand as numerator, the left as denominator. This extension includes a range of symbols from $\frac{111}{111}$ to $\frac{777}{777}$. The following is a partial filing sequence:

$$\frac{111}{111} \quad \frac{112}{111} \quad \frac{113}{111} \quad \frac{114}{111} \quad \frac{115}{111} \quad \frac{116}{111} \quad \frac{117}{111}$$

$$\frac{121}{111} \quad \frac{122}{111} \quad \frac{123}{111} \quad \frac{124}{111} \quad \frac{125}{111} \quad \frac{126}{111} \quad \frac{127}{111}$$

$$\frac{131}{111} \quad \frac{132}{111} \quad \frac{133}{111} \quad \frac{134}{111} \quad \frac{135}{111} \quad \frac{136}{111} \quad \frac{137}{111}$$

$$\frac{141}{111} \quad \frac{142}{111} \quad \frac{143}{111} \quad \frac{144}{111} \quad \frac{145}{111} \quad \frac{146}{111} \quad \frac{147}{111}$$

$$\frac{151}{111} \quad \frac{152}{111} \quad \frac{153}{111} \quad \frac{154}{111} \quad \frac{155}{111} \quad \frac{156}{111} \quad \frac{157}{111}$$

$$\frac{161}{111} \quad \frac{162}{111} \quad \frac{163}{111} \quad \frac{164}{111} \quad \frac{165}{111} \quad \frac{166}{111} \quad \frac{167}{111}$$

$$\frac{171}{111} \quad \frac{172}{111} \quad \frac{173}{111} \quad \frac{174}{111} \quad \frac{175}{111} \quad \frac{176}{111} \quad \frac{177}{111} \text{ etc., to } \frac{777}{777}.$$

However many of the divisions are used, the order remains the same, and each individual group is sequenced by the final and key.

THE WHORL AND COMPOSITE SERIES

In the classification of the principal or all-whorl groups, except where all the patterns are plain whorls, ridge tracing and the resultant attainment of the I, M, and O may be eliminated and the following substituted: Whenever a whorl (W), central pocket (C), double loop (D) or accidental (X) appears in the index fingers, the capital letter symbol is brought into the classification line. Whenever these patterns are to be considered in the extension of a classification, they are designated by a small letter (c, d, x) and must be shown in the classification formula in the order in which they appear, as in the small-letter groups of a, t and r, and they become the second subsecondary of a whorl series.

Table showing sequence of the secondary classification of whorls:

$$\frac{WCDX}{WWWW} \quad \frac{WCDX}{CCCC} \quad \frac{WCDX}{DDDD} \quad \frac{WCDX}{XXXX}$$

SMALL-LETTER GROUP (WHORLS AND COMPOSITES)

The following table represents the full sequence of the denominator of the small-letter group as applied to the whorl and composite group. The sequence as listed may be used as a numerator in connection with each denominator as set out on the following page:

cW	dWc	Wdc
dW	dWd	W2d
xW	dWx	Wdx
Wc	xWc	Wxc
Wd	xWd	Wxd
Wx	xWx	W2x
cWc	W2c	cW2c
cWd	Wcd	cWcd
cWx	Wcx	cWcx
cWdc	Wdxc	dW3c
cW2d	Wdxd	dW2cd
cWdx	Wd2x	dW2cx
cWxc	Wx2c	dWcdc
cWxd	Wxcd	dWc2d
cW2x	Wxcx	dWcdx
dW2c	Wxdc	dWcxc
dWcd	Wx2d	dWcxd
dWcx	Wxdx	dWc2x
dWdc	W2xc	dWd2c
dW2d	W2xd	dWdcd
dWdx	W3x	dWdcx
dWxc	cW3c	dW2dc
dWxd	cW2cd	dW3d
dW2x	cW2cx	dW2dx
xW2c	cWcdc	dWdxc
xWcd	cWc2d	dWdxd
xWcx	cWcdx	dWd2x
xWdc	cWcxc	dWx2c
xW2d	cWcxd	dWxcd
xWdx	cWc2x	dWxcx
xWxc	cWd2c	dWxdc
xWxd	cWdcd	dWx2d
xW2x	cWdcx	dWxdx

W3c	cW2dc	dW2xc
W2cd	cW3d	dW2xd
W2cx	cW2dx	dW3x
Wcdc	cWdxc	
Wc2d	cWdxd	xW3c
Wcdx	cWd2x	xW2cd
		xW2cx
Wcxc	cWx2c	
Wcxd	cWxcx	xWcdc
Wc2x	cWxcd	xWc2d
		xWcdx
Wd2c	cWxdc	
Wdcd	cWx2d	xWcxc
Wdcx	cWxdx	xWcxd
		xWc2x
W2dc	cW2xc	
W3d	cW2xd	xWd2c
W2dx	cW3x	xWdcd
		xWdcx
xW2dc	xWx2c	
xW3d	xWxcd	xW2xc
xW2dx	xWxcx	xW2xd
		xW3x
xWdxc	xWxdc	
xWdxd	xWx2d	
xWd2x	xWxdx	

Prints having all regular whorls (no composites), or those in which it becomes necessary to break up any particular group of the small-letter whorl series, may be again subdivided by ridge tracing as explained below:

THE WHORL AND COMPOSITE SERIES

The symbols for the patterns in the index fingers are *W*, *C*, *D*, and *X*, and will be the secondary classification.

For the sub-secondary classification of the all-whorl or composite prints, Sir E. R. Henry used the ridge tracing of the index and middle fingers, which he divided into *I* (inner), *M* (meet), and *O* (outer). It is evident that with all the impressions, whorls or composites, the index and middle fingers are always paired in the 32-over-32 group. From the combination of the index and middle fingers of both hands, there were eighty-one subdivisions.

The following was the sequence for filing:

II	IM	IO	MI	MM	MO	OI	OM	OO
II	II	II	II	II	II	II	II	II

II	IM	IO	MI	MM	MO	OI	OM	OO
IM	IM	IM	IM	IM	IM	IM	IM	IM

II	IM	IO	MI	MM	MO	OI	OM	OO
IO	IO	IO	IO	IO	IO	IO	IO	IO

II	IM	IO	MI	MM	MO	OI	OM	OO
MI	MI	MI	MI	MI	MI	MI	MI	MI

II	IM	IO	MI	MM	MO	OI	OM	OO
MM	MM	MM	MM	MM	MM	MM	MM	MM

II	IM	IO	MI	MM	MO	OI	OM	OO
MO	MO	MO	MO	MO	MO	MO	MO	MO

II	IM	IO	MI	MM	MO	OI	OM	OO
OI	OI	OI	OI	OI	OI	OI	OI	OI

II	IM	IO	MI	MM	MO	OI	OM	OO
OM	OM	OM	OM	OM	OM	OM	OM	OM

II	IM	IO	MI	MM	MO	OI	OM	OO
OO	OO	OO	OO	OO	OO	OO	OO	OO

To extend the eighty-one combinations of the Henry system the ring fingers are added, providing seven hundred and twenty-nine combinations.

In filing prints on the basis of the sub-secondary classification, they are first arranged according to the denominator—and then subdivided on the basis of the numerator.

CHART SHOWING SEQUENCE FOR FILING I M O

III	IIM	IIO	IMI	IMM	IMO	IOI	IOM	IOO	MII	MIM	MIO	MMI	MMM
III	III	III	III	III	III	III	III	III	III	III	III	III	III

MMO	MOI	MOM	MOO	OII	OIM	OIO	OMI	OMM	OMO	OOI	OOM	OOO
III	III	III	III	III	III	III	III	III	III	III	III	III

III	IIM	IIO	IMI	IMM	IMO	IOI	IOM	IOO	MII	MIM	MIO	MMI	MMM
IIM	IIM	IIM	IIM	IIM	IIM	IIM	IIM	IIM	IIM	IIM	IIM	IIM	IIM

MMO	MOI	MOM	MOO	OII	OIM	OIO	OMI	OMM	OMO	OOI	OOM	OOO
IIM	IIM	IIM	IIM	IIM	IIM	IIM	IIM	IIM	IIM	IIM	IIM	IIM

III	IIM	IIO	IMI	IMM	IMO	IOI	IOM	IOO	MII	MIM	MIO	MMI	MMM
IIO	IIO	IIO	IIO	IIO	IIO	IIO	IIO	IIO	IIO	IIO	IIO	IIO	IIO

MMO	MOI	MOM	MOO	OII	OIM	OIO	OMI	OMM	OMO	OOI	OOM	OOO
IIO	IIO	IIO	IIO	IIO	IIO	IIO	IIO	IIO	IIO	IIO	IIO	IIO

III	IIM	IIO	IMI	IMM	IMO	IOI	IOM	IOO	MII	MIM	MIO	MMI	MMM
IMI	IMI	IMI	IMI	IMI	IMI	IMI	IMI	IMI	IMI	IMI	IMI	IMI	IMI

MMO	MOI	MOM	MOO	OII	OIM	OIO	OMI	OMM	OMO	OOI	OOM	OOO
IMI	IMI	IMI	IMI	IMI	IMI	IMI	IMI	IMI	IMI	IMI	IMI	IMI

III	IIM	IIO	IMI	IMM	IMO	IOI	IOM	IOO	MII	MIM	MIO	MMI	MMM
IMM	IMM	IMM	IMM	IMM	IMM	IMM	IMM	IMM	IMM	IMM	IMM	IMM	IMM

MMO	MOI	MOM	MOO	OII	OIM	OIO	OMI	OMM	OMO	OOI	OOM	OOO
IMM	IMM	IMM	IMM	IMM	IMM	IMM	IMM	IMM	IMM	IMM	IMM	IMM

III	IIM	IIO	IMI	IMM	IMO	IOI	IOM	IOO	MII	MIM	MIO	MMI	MMM
IMO	IMO	IMO	IMO	IMO	IMO	IMO	IMO	IMO	IMO	IMO	IMO	IMO	IMO

MMO	MOI	MOM	MOO	OII	OIM	OIO	OMI	OMM	OMO	OOI	OOM	OOO
IMO	IMO	IMO	IMO	IMO	IMO	IMO	IMO	IMO	IMO	IMO	IMO	IMO

III	IIM	IIO	IMI	IMM	IMO	IOI	IOM	IOO	MII	MIM	MIO	MMI	MMM
IOI	IOI	IOI	IOI	IOI	IOI	IOI	IOI	IOI	IOI	IOI	IOI	IOI	IOI

MMO	MOI	MOM	MOO	OII	OIM	OIO	OMI	OMM	OMO	OOI	OOM	OOO
IOI	IOI	IOI	IOI	IOI	IOI	IOI	IOI	IOI	IOI	IOI	IOI	IOI

III IIM IIO IMI IMM IMO IOI IOM IOO MII MIM MIO MMI MMM
IOM IOM IOM IOM IOM IOM IOM IOM IOM IOM IOM IOM IOM IOM
   MMO MOI MOM MOO OII OIM OIO OMI OMM OMO OOI OOM OOO
IOM IOM IOM IOM IOM IOM IOM IOM IOM IOM IOM IOM IOM IOM

III IIM IIO IMI IMM IMO IOI IOM IOO MII MIM MIO MMI MMM
IOO IOO IOO IOO IOO IOO IOO IOO IOO IOO IOO IOO IOO IOO
   MMO MOI MOM MOO OII OIM OIO OMI OMM OMO OOI OOM OOO
IOO IOO IOO IOO IOO IOO IOO IOO IOO IOO IOO IOO IOO IOO

III IIM IIO IMI IMM IMO IOI IOM IOO MII MIM MIO MMI MMM
MII MII MII MII MII MII MII MII MII MII MII MII MII MII
   MMO MOI MOM MOO OII OIM OIO OMI OMM OMO OOI OOM OOO
MII MII MII MII MII MII MII MII MII MII MII MII MII MII

III IIM IIO IMI IMM IMO IOI IOM IOO MII MIM MIO MMI MMM
MIM MIM MIM MIM MIM MIM MIM MIM MIM MIM MIM MIM MIM MIM
   MMO MOI MOM MOO OII OIM OIO OMI OMM OMO OOI OOM OOO
MIM MIM MIM MIM MIM MIM MIM MIM MIM MIM MIM MIM MIM MIM

III IIM IIO IMI IMM IMO IOI IOM IOO MII MIM MIO MMI MMM
MIO MIO MIO MIO MIO MIO MIO MIO MIO MIO MIO MIO MIO MIO
   MMO MOI MOM MOO OII OIM OIO OMI OMM OMO OOI OOM OOO
MIO MIO MIO MIO MIO MIO MIO MIO MIO MIO MIO MIO MIO MIO

III IIM IIO IMI IMM IMO IOI IOM IOO MII MIM MIO MMI MMM
MMI MMI MMI MMI MMI MMI MMI MMI MMI MMI MMI MMI MMI MMI
   MMO MOI MOM MOO OII OIM OIO OMI OMM OMO OOI OOM OOO
MMI MMI MMI MMI MMI MMI MMI MMI MMI MMI MMI MMI MMI MMI

III IIM IIO IMI IMM IMO IOI IOM IOO MII MIM MIO MMI MMM
MMM MMM MMM MMM MMM MMM MMM MMM MMM MMM MMM MMM MMM MMM
   MMO MOI MOM MOO OII OIM OIO OMI OMM OMO OOI OOM OOO
MMM MMM MMM MMM MMM MMM MMM MMM MMM MMM MMM MMM MMM MMM

III IIM IIO IMI IMM IMO IOI IOM IOO MII MIM MIO MMI MMM
MMO MMO MMO MMO MMO MMO MMO MMO MMO MMO MMO MMO MMO MMO

MMO	MOI	MOM	MOO	OII	OIM	OIO	OMI	OMM	OMO	OOI	OOM	OOO
MMO	MMO	MMO	MMO	MMO	MMO	MMO	MMO	MMO	MMO	MMO	MMO	MMO

III	IIM	IIO	IMI	IMM	IMO	IOI	IOM	IOO	MII	MIM	MIO	MMI	MMM
MOI	MOI	MOI	MOI	MOI	MOI	MOI	MOI	MOI	MOI	MOI	MOI	MOI	MOI

MMO	MOI	MOM	MOO	OII	OIM	OIO	OMI	OMM	OMO	OOI	OOM	OOO
MOI	MOI	MOI	MOI	MOI	MOI	MOI	MOI	MOI	MOI	MOI	MOI	MOI

III	IIM	IIO	IMI	IMM	IMO	IOI	IOM	IOO	MII	MIM	MIO	MMI	MMM
MOM	MOM	MOM	MOM	MOM	MOM	MOM	MOM	MOM	MOM	MOM	MOM	MOM	MOM

MMO	MOI	MOM	MOO	OII	OIM	OIO	OMI	OMM	OMO	OOI	OOM	OOO
MOM	MOM	MOM	MOM	MOM	MOM	MOM	MOM	MOM	MOM	MOM	MOM	MOM

III	IIM	IIO	IMI	IMM	IMO	IOI	IOM	IOO	MII	MIM	MIO	MMI	MMM
MOO	MOO	MOO	MOO	MOO	MOO	MOO	MOO	MOO	MOO	MOO	MOO	MOO	MOO

MMO	MOI	MOM	MOO	OII	OIM	OIO	OMI	OMM	OMO	OOI	OOM	OOO
MOO	MOO	MOO	MOO	MOO	MOO	MOO	MOO	MOO	MOO	MOO	MOO	MOO

III	IIM	IIO	IMI	IMM	IMO	IOI	IOM	IOO	MII	MIM	MIO	MMI	MMM
OII	OII	OII	OII	OII	OII	OII	OII	OII	OII	OII	OII	OII	OII

MMO	MOI	MOM	MOO	OII	OIM	OIO	OMI	OMM	OMO	OOI	OOM	OOO
OII	OII	OII	OII	OII	OII	OII	OII	OII	OII	OII	OII	OII

III	IIM	IIO	IMI	IMM	IMO	IOI	IOM	IOO	MII	MIM	MIO	MMI	MMM
OIM	OIM	OIM	OIM	OIM	OIM	OIM	OIM	OIM	OIM	OIM	OIM	OIM	OIM

MMO	MOI	MOM	MOO	OII	OIM	OIO	OMI	OMM	OMO	OOI	OOM	OOO
OIM	OIM	OIM	OIM	OIM	OIM	OIM	OIM	OIM	OIM	OIM	OIM	OIM

III	IIM	IIO	IMI	IMM	IMO	IOI	IOM	IOO	MII	MIM	MIO	MMI	MMM
OIO	OIO	OIO	OIO	OIO	OIO	OIO	OIO	OIO	OIO	OIO	OIO	OIO	OIO

MMO	MOI	MOM	MOO	OII	OIM	OIO	OMI	OMM	OMO	OOI	OOM	OOO
OIO	OIO	OIO	OIO	OIO	OIO	OIO	OIO	OIO	OIO	OIO	OIO	OIO

III	IIM	IIO	IMI	IMM	IMO	IOI	IOM	IOO	MII	MIM	MIO	MMI	MMM
OMI	OMI	OMI	OMI	OMI	OMI	OMI	OMI	OMI	OMI	OMI	OMI	OMI	OMI

MMO	MOI	MOM	MOO	OII	OIM	OIO	OMI	OMM	OMO	OOI	OOM	OOO
OMI	OMI	OMI	OMI	OMI	OMI	OMI	OMI	OMI	OMI	OMI	OMI	OMI

```
III IIM IIO IMI IMM IMO IOI IOM IOO MII MIM MIO MMI MMM
─── ─── ─── ─── ─── ─── ─── ─── ─── ─── ─── ─── ─── ───
OMM OMM OMM OMM OMM OMM OMM OMM OMM OMM OMM OMM OMM OMM

    MMO MOI MOM MOO OII OIM OIO OMI OMM OMO OOI OOM OOO
    ─── ─── ─── ─── ─── ─── ─── ─── ─── ─── ─── ─── ───
OMM OMM OMM OMM OMM OMM OMM OMM OMM OMM OMM OMM OMM OMM

III IIM IIO IMI IMM IMO IOI IOM IOO MII MIM MIO MMI MMM
─── ─── ─── ─── ─── ─── ─── ─── ─── ─── ─── ─── ─── ───
OMO OMO OMO OMO OMO OMO OMO OMO OMO OMO OMO OMO OMO OMO

    MMO MOI MOM MOO OII OIM OIO OMI OMM OMO OOI OOM OOO
    ─── ─── ─── ─── ─── ─── ─── ─── ─── ─── ─── ─── ───
OMO OMO OMO OMO OMO OMO OMO OMO OMO OMO OMO OMO OMO OMO

III IIM IIO IMI IMM IMO IOI IOM IOO MII MIM MIO MMI MMM
─── ─── ─── ─── ─── ─── ─── ─── ─── ─── ─── ─── ─── ───
OOI OOI OOI OOI OOI OOI OOI OOI OOI OOI OOI OOI OOI OOI

    MMO MOI MOM MOO OII OIM OIO OMI OMM OMO OOI OOM OOO
    ─── ─── ─── ─── ─── ─── ─── ─── ─── ─── ─── ─── ───
OOI OOI OOI OOI OOI OOI OOI OOI OOI OOI OOI OOI OOI OOI

III IIM IIO IMI IMM IMO IOI IOM IOO MII MIM MIO MMI MMM
─── ─── ─── ─── ─── ─── ─── ─── ─── ─── ─── ─── ─── ───
OOM OOM OOM OOM OOM OOM OOM OOM OOM OOM OOM OOM OOM OOM

    MMO MOI MOM MOO OII OIM OIO OMI OMM OMO OOI OOM OOO
    ─── ─── ─── ─── ─── ─── ─── ─── ─── ─── ─── ─── ───
OOM OOM OOM OOM OOM OOM OOM OOM OOM OOM OOM OOM OOM OOM

III IIM IIO IMI IMM IMO IOI IOM IOO MII MIM MIO MMI MMM
─── ─── ─── ─── ─── ─── ─── ─── ─── ─── ─── ─── ─── ───
OOO OOO OOO OOO OOO OOO OOO OOO OOO OOO OOO OOO OOO OOO

    MMO MOI MOM MOO OII OIM OIO OMI OMM OMO OOI OOM OOO
    ─── ─── ─── ─── ─── ─── ─── ─── ─── ─── ─── ─── ───
OOO OOO OOO OOO OOO OOO OOO OOO OOO OOO OOO OOO OOO OOO
```

In order to further subdivide the various combinations of the sub-secondary classification the results of ridge tracing of both thumbs are added to the formula. Example:

$$\text{I} \quad 32 \quad \text{D} \quad \text{IOI}$$
$$\text{I} \quad 32 \quad \text{X} \quad \text{OII}$$

Owing to the fact that the ridge tracing of the right and left little fingers would result mostly in O over I, ridge counting was necessarily resorted to. Example:

$$\text{I} \quad 32 \quad \text{D} \quad \text{IOI} \quad 16$$
$$\text{I} \quad 32 \quad \text{X} \quad \text{OII}$$

As noted, the key is the result of the ridge count of the whorl in the right thumb. Fully extended:

```
20   I  32  D  IOI  16
     I  32  X  OII
```

Examples:

```
18 I 32 W IOO 19   28 O 32 X OOO 18   16 M 32 D III 17
   M 32 C IOO          I 32 D OOI        M 32 X III
```

EXAMPLES OF MODIFICATION AND EXTENSION

The modification and extension is best explained by examples. First, we shall deal with the classifications where arches, tented arches or radial loops appear in other than the index fingers. The figures which precede some of the loops in the following examples, are the ridge counts of loops and are thus shown (only when needed) to illustrate the classification. The formula according to Henry and the extension is as follows:

Example 1

```
                4        3
Right hand: u T u a u         Henry:        1 Ta 3
                         4                   1 A
Left hand:  u A u u u
                              Extension:  4 1 Ta 3
                                           1 A  4
```

It will be noted in Example 1, above, that the ridge count of the right thumb is 4, which is made the key.

Example 2

```
              7
Right hand: u U u a a          Henry:        1 U2a
                       2                      1 U
Left hand:  u U u u u
                              Extension:  7 1 U2a
                                           1 U  2
```

It will also be noted in Example 2, above, that the ridge count of the left little finger is 2, which is made the final.

Example 3

	7		
Right:	u U u a a	Henry:	1 U2a
	2		1 Ua

Left hand:	u U a u u		
		Extension:	7 1 U2a
			1 Ua 2

In small-letter groups, after they have been separated into major divisions, *S, M,* and *L,* and by the numerical value as previously explained, the result of the ridge counts will be used and known as the sub-secondary.

Example 1

```
                                                           (0)
                                                           (8)
5   4 3 6   Henry: 1 A    6 Extension: 5 S 1 A   (II) 6
u A u u u          1 A a                 S 1 Aa  ( I) 2

u A a u u
7     9 2
```

Example 2

```
                                                           (0)
                                                           (9)
6   4 3 6   Henry: 1 A    6 Extension: 6 S 1 A   (II) 6
u A u u u          1 A a                 S 1 A a(0 ) 2

u A u a u
7  11   2
```

Example 3

```
                                                           (0)
                                                           (8)
7  12 3 6   Henry: 1 A    6 Extension: 7 S 1 A   (0I) 6
U A u u u          1 A a                 S 1 A a( I) 2

u A a u u
7    12 2
```

Example 4

```
                                                           (3)
                                                           (0)
5      3 6  Henry: 1 A a 6 Extension: 5 S 1 A a( I) 6
u A a u u          1 A                 S 1 A   (0I) 2

u A u u u
7  11 9 2
```

Example 5

```
                                                              (4)
                                                              (0)
6    3   6   Henry: 1 A a 6   Extension: 6 S 1 A a(I ) 6
u A u a u           1 A                    S 1 A (OI) 2

u A u u u
7  11 9 2
```

Example 6

```
                                                              (5)
                                                              (0)
7   8 3     Henry: 1 A a     Extension: 7 S 1 A a(II)
u A u u a           1 A                    S 1 A (OI) 2

u A u u u
7  11 9 2
```

Example 7

```
                                                              (3)
                                                              (8)
5    14 3   Henry: 1 A a 3   Extension: 5 S 1 A  a(0) 3
u A a u u           1 A a                  S 1 A  a(I) 2

u A a u u
7     9 2
```

Example 8

```
                                                              (4)
                                                              (9)
6   8   3   Henry: 1 A a 3   Extension: 6 S 1 A  a(I) 3
u A u a u           1 A a                  S 1 A  a(0) 2

u A u a u
7  12    2
```

Example 9

```
                                                              ( 5)
                                                              (10)
7   8 8     Henry: I A a     Extension: 7 S 1 A  a(II)
u A u u a           I A a                  S 1 A  a(OI)

u A u u a
7  12 9
```

EXAMPLES OF EXTENSIONS

The following examples show the Henry classification formulae and also illustrate the extensions:

```
Henry:  3 U IO 14   Extension: 10 S 3 U IO     (I) 14
        1 U I                      M 1 U I     (MI)  3
Henry:  1 U I  12   Extension: 10 S 1 U I      (MO) 12
        9 R IO                     L 9 R IO    ( 0)  4
        1 T         Extension: 18 M 5 U        (IIO) 9
Henry:  5 U     9                  I 1 T       ( OI) 6
```

```
Henry:  5 T     12    Extension:  5 S 5 T       (IO) 12
        1 R                         M 1 R      (OII)  6

Henry:  5 R II  5     Extension:  9 S 5 R IIO        5
        1 R II                      M 1 R III         6

Henry:  1 U OI  4     Extension: 10 I  1 U OII        4
       17 R IO                     L 17 R IOO        10

Henry:  9 U 00  10    Extension: 21 M 9 U 00    (M) 10
        1 U OI                     L 1 U OI     (O)  7

Henry:  1 R OI  7     Extension: 15 M 1 R OI    (O)  7
        2 R 00                     M 2 R 00     (M)  7

Henry: 17    M  20    Extension: 15 M 17 W M   (IO) 20
        1    IO                    M 1 U IO    ( I)  5

Henry:  1    IO 20    Extension: 15 M 1 U IO   ( I) 20
        3    M                     M 3 W M     (IO)  5

Henry:  9 U IO 9      Extension: 16 M 9 U IO    (M)  9
        2 U OI                     M 2 U OI     (I)  3

Henry: 25   I  10     Extension: 18 L 25 W I   (IM) 10
        1   OI                     M 1 U OI    ( I)  5

Henry: 25   I  12     Extension: 13 M 25 W I   (IM) 12
        2   IO                     S 2 U IO    ( M)  8

Henry:  9   00 4      Extension: 11 S 9 U 00   ( I)  4
        3   I                      M 3 C I     (II)  2

Henry: 17   M  14     Extension: 15 M 17 D M   (IO) 14
        3   M                      M 3 W M     (00)  7

Henry: 27   M  13     Extension: 20 M 27 D M   (II) 13
        3   MM                     L 3 W MM    ( 0) 12

Henry: 11   00 10     Extension: 16 M 11 U 00   (I) 10
        4   II                     S 4 W II     (0) 10

Henry: 25   I  21     Extension:  9 S 25 C I   (OM) 21
        4   0                      S 4 D 0     (OM) 14

Henry: 27   I  11     Extension: 14 M 27 D I   (OM) 11
        4   OI                     M 4 C OI    ( M)  7

Henry: 27   IM 14     Extension: 23 L 27 D IMO       14
       12   OI                     L 12 X OIO        12

Henry: 25   IO 16     Extension: 22 M 25 W IO  ( M) 16
       12   0                      L 12 W 0     (IM) 17

Henry: 25   0  14     Extension: 17 0 25 W 0   (OM) 14
       17   00                     L 17 R 00   ( 0) 14
```

```
Henry: 29   M  17        Extension: 16 O 29 W M  (OM) 17
       17   00                       I 17 U 00 ( O)   9

Henry: 31   IO 18        Extension: 19 O 31 W IO  (M) 18
       27   OI                       O 27 W OI  (O) 17

Henry: 27   II 15        Extension: 17 M 27 X II  (M) 15
       28   II                       L 28 X II  (M) 13
```

When both little fingers are whorls, the ridge count of the right little finger may be used as the final.

```
Henry: 30   0           Extension: 20 I 30 W 0  (OM) 16
       22   00                       I 22 R 00 ( M)

Henry: 14 U 00          Extension: 14 O 14 U 00  (I) 10
       22 U 00                       O 22 U 00  (M)
```

When one or both index fingers are whorls and an *a, t,* or *r* appears in any of the other fingers, under the extensions, the classifications are shown thus:

```
Henry: 25 I 8           Extension: 17 25   I  8
       10 0                          10   Ua 5

Henry:  9 A 11          Extension: 17  9   A 11
       20 M 15                       20   M 15

Henry: 17 M  4          Extension:  9 17   Ma 4
        3 I                           3   aI 2

Henry: 17   I  3        Extension:  5 17   Iat 3
        3   M                         3   M   4

Henry: 17   I  3        Extension:  6 17   I2r 3
       17   II                       17   U   3

Henry: 18   I  5        Extension: 10 18   I2r 5
       17   00                       17   R   4
```

When an *A,* or *T,* appears in either index finger, over or under a whorl or a composite, and an *a, t,* or *r* appears in any other finger, it is shown thus:

```
Henry: 10   A  4        Extension:  7 10   A   4
       19   M                         19  aM

Henry: 17   I 18        Extension: 10 17   I  18
       25   T                         25  Tt 19
```

ADDITIONAL SUBDIVISIONS

Fingerprint groups may be further subdivided by sex (male and female) and by age (either by year or by setting an age limit beyond which a print would be filed separately in a "Reference" or a "Presumptive Dead" file).

For example, the FBI filing system places all prints bearing an age of 55 to 74 inclusive in the "Reference" group. Prints bearing an age of 75 or older are placed in the "Presumptive Dead" file, since serious criminal activity is not anticipated in a person of advanced years. Thus, cards with this age are systematically removed from the files, whether or not a notice of death is received. A separate file is maintained on deceased persons for possible future reference.

Prints bearing amputations and clearly labeled as such by the contributor should be placed in a separate file.

Permanent scars may yield an additional set of three groupings, determined by whether the permanent scars appearing on the prints are on the right hand, the left hand, or both hands. A separate file is suggested for mutilated prints whether or not the permanent scar subdivision is used. The prints in this file will appear damaged in a manner suggesting deliberate mutilation to prevent identification.

VII

THE BATTLEY SINGLE-FINGERPRINT SYSTEM

THIS SYSTEM of registration was devised by Harry Battley, former Chief Inspector in charge of the Fingerprint Bureau at Scotland Yard. It is a very simple method employing the use of a special magnifying glass (Fig. 142) for examining the prints. This glass has a fixed focus and a plain glass window at the base inscribed with seven concentric circles of 3 mm., 5 mm., 7 mm., 9 mm., 11 mm., 13 mm., and 15 mm. radii respectively (Fig. 143). The center of the innermost circle is marked with a dot. The area within the smallest circle is denoted by the letter A, and the areas between the successive circles by B, C, D, E, F, and G; the area outside circle G is denoted by the letter H, and everything that does not fall in A, B, C, D, E, F, or G, is regarded as falling in H. When using the glass, all minutiae that may fall under the line of any circle are considered as falling in the next outer circle, or the larger of the two zones that the involved glass line divides.

The system establishes ten files, one for each of the fingers, in the order in which they are considered in the Henry system. For example, the right thumb is #1, the right index is #2, and so on, until finally the left little finger is reached, which will be #10. The print to be classified and filed is first given a number to correspond with the finger, or file, to which it refers. Secondly, the print is classified according to the pattern it displays (Arch, Exceptional Arch, Tented Arch, Radial Loop, Ulnar Loop, Whorl, Central Pocket Loop, Twinned Loop, Lateral Pocket Loop, Accidentals, and Scars). In this outline of the Battley system, it has been deemed advisable to include certain slight modifications and additions which have proven of utility with practical experience in current usage. These addenda are not offered by the writer as an alteration of the original method, but only as an additional facility and convenience. In this connection, it has been considered appropriate to include a division at the rear of each of the ten files in which are placed "questioned" patterns. It sometimes happens that a set of submitted fingerprints will include certain impressions that are not legibly recorded, and consequently are not readily identifiable as to pattern, but may still include some useful areas of ridge structure. Such prints may be placed in the proper file behind the tab marked "Questioned Patterns."

The following is an itemized listing of the main and subdivisional tabs in one file, with some slight modifications, as arranged under the Battley system. It will be understood that this is but one of the ten similar files, there being just such a file provided for each finger, as already explained:

Arches—Plain
Exceptional arches—Radial, Ulnar
Tented arches—*A B C D E F G H*
Loops
    Radial loops—*A B C D E F G H*
    Ulnar loops—*A B C D E F G H*
Whorls—*A B C D E F G H*
Central pocket loops—*A B C D E F G H*
Twinned loops—*A B C D E F G H*
Lateral pocket loops—Radial, Ulnar

Fig. 142

Special Magnifying Glass Used in the Battley Method

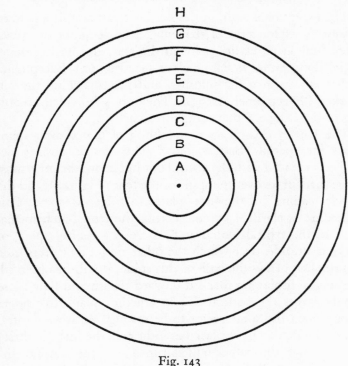

Fig. 143

Enlarged view of Battley glass concentric circles

Accidentals—No subdivision
Scars—As to probable pattern type
Questioned patterns—As to probable pattern type

Under the Battley system, patterns are considered as plain arches only when the design shows no especial ridge involvement, and consists of plain ridge structure that flows from side to side without recurvature (see Fig. 58). Such patterns, after being allotted their file number, are filed behind the tab marked "Plain Arches," and are given no further subdivision.

The exceptional arch, in the Battley treatment, is a pattern possessing characteristics that suggest a loop, as described more fully at an earlier point in the text, and having directional slope, either radial or ulnar (see Fig. 62). Exceptional arches are given a file number, and placed behind the tab marked "Exceptional Arches." They are subdivided according to their slope, either radial or ulnar.

The Battley classification and filing of tented arches employs the special "Battley glass." This device, already described, is placed with the central dot just above the innermost ridge that curves over the spine of the tent (Fig. 144), and the "circle reading" of the first "platform ridge" is noted. This procedure is clarified by considering the tented-arch formation. In the typical tented arch, there is a central spine, of varying altitude, over which the other ridges flow from side to side. Just below the base of this spine, it will be observed, the ridges display no marked upward thrust, and flow more evenly across the pattern. These are the "platform" ridges upon which the spine seems to be resting. With the central dot of the Battley glass placed as indicated, the first (highest) of these platform ridges will fall in one of the zones of the glass, either *A, B, C, D, E, F, G,* or *H*. Should the ridge lie directly beneath one of the lines forming the circles, the reading is given as the outer circle. This circle reading is used as the subdivision for tented arches. In the event of a large accumulation of singleprint records, tented arches may be fur-

Fig. 144

Correct position of Battley glass when classifying a tented arch. In this example, the first platform ridge is in the E circle

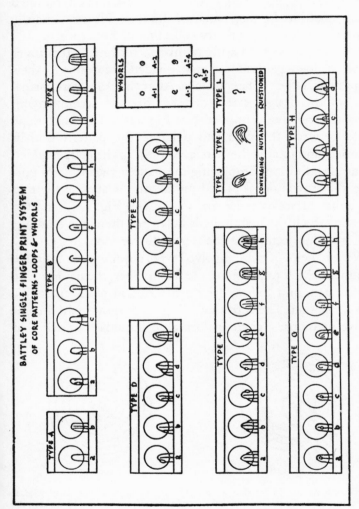

Fig. 145

ther subdivided according to their core formation, as outlined in the procedure for loop patterns, although this would hardly be necessary for any ordinary collection of fingerprints.

After being assigned a file number according to the finger involved, loop patterns are first divided according to their ridge slope, either radial or ulnar. After this, the "core formation" of the design is recorded. In this, the accompanying chart of core types is utilized (see Fig. 145). The exact ridge count between the core and delta of the pattern is then recorded, and finally, the "circle reading" of the delta is added to the classification. Employing the Battley glass for this purpose, the central dot is placed just above the apex of the first ridge that curves over the core design (see Fig. 146), and the zone in which the delta falls is taken for the circle reading; this procedure completes the treatment for loops.

Whorls, being a more involved type, require more intimate treatment. After establishing the file number, the pattern type is indicated, and followed by a description of the pattern's core formation. The core chart (Fig. 145) shows whorl cores in five divisions: a circle inclosing no minutiae, a circle that

Fig. 146

Correct position of the Battley glass when classifying a loop. In this example, the delta falls in the E circle

Fig. 147

Correct position of the Battley glass when classifying a whorl. In this case, the first recurving ridge falls inside the A circle. As a result of this circumstance, note how the ridge counts are made

encloses some fragment or other ridge structure, a spiral to the left, a spiral to the right, and finally, types of core formation that are too irregular to classify. Here also the Battley glass is used, the central dot being placed just above the apex of the first recurving ridge that forms the core (Fig. 147). The concentric zone that encloses this first recurving ridge will indicate the pattern's circle reading for its core formation, and will be indicated by either *A, B, C, D, E, F, G,* or *H*, depending on which zone of the glass encloses all (top and bottom) of the first recurving ridge. The second item of the core's description will be the core's type, either *1, 2, 3, 4,* or *5,* as the case may be. Therefore, the whorl core will be *A-1, A-2, A-3, A-4,* or *A-5; B-1, B-2, B-3, B-4,* or *B-5;* or *C-1, C-2, C-3, C-4,* or *C-5;* etc. Following the core formation, the circle reading of the left delta is recorded, the reading secured with the glass placed as indicated in Fig. 147. The pattern is next traced to show it as being either Inner, Meeting, or Outer (indicated on the Battley card as *I, M,* or *O*). This is succeeded by the circle reading of the right delta. Next is recorded the exact ridge count from the left delta to the core of the pattern, which is followed by the ridge count from the right delta to the core. In this connection, the ridge counts are made to the apex of the core (as indicated in Fig. 147) if the first recurving ridge falls inside the *A* circle or central zone of the glass. Should the first recurving ridge fall *outside* the *A* circle, the count is made from both deltas to the *bottom* of the first recurving ridge, as indicated in Fig. 148. This ridge count completes the treatment of whorls.

Central pocket loops are classified exactly the same as whorls.

Twinned loops are given slightly different treatment. Following the file number and pattern type, twinned loops are

Fig. 148

Correct position of the Battley glass when classifying a whorl. In this case, the first recurring ridge falls in the C circle. As a result, the ridge counts are made to the *bottom* of the first recurring ridge as herein indicated

Fig. 149

Correct position of the Battley glass when classifying a twinned loop. Note how the ridge counts are made in this instance, as indicated

next subdivided according to the "core slope" of the "descending loop," either radial or ulnar, as indicated in Fig. 149. This is followed by the circle reading of the core of the descending loop, the same being read with the central dot of the glass placed just above the innermost recurring ridge of the "ascending loop," as indicated. This step is followed by the exact ridge count between the cores of the two loops (see Fig. 149). Next is recorded the ridge count between the core and delta of the "descending loop" (as indicated). The circle reading of the left delta is recorded, and the pattern is traced for *I, M,* or *O;* and finally, the circle reading of the right delta is given. This completes the classification for twinned loops.

Lateral pocket loops, being a more uncommon pattern, require less subdivision. After the file number and the pattern type, the slope (radial or ulnar) of the majority of the ridges is noted. Finally, the ridge count between the core and delta of the innermost loop is taken, completing the classification of this pattern type.

In dealing with lateral pockets, it must be remembered that the chief characteristic which distinguishes them from twinned loops, is the fact that their core lines are not divided by either of the deltas as in twin loops (see Figs. 101 and 104). In this connection, it should be remembered also that the object of a singleprint file is to learn the identity of an unknown person from a single fingerprint. Since latent prints seldom include as much area as do "rolled" impressions, in many cases it will be impossible to distinguish lateral pockets from twin loops by tracing the core lines, since both deltas may not show in the latent. For this reason, it is advisable to classify as lateral pockets only such patterns as resemble those shown in Fig. 105, *a, c, d,* and *f,* and to give more consideration to the central portion of the design and the relationship of the loops, than to tracing their respective core lines.

As explained, Accidentals are unusual pattern designs that are too irregular to fall in any of the conventional type divisions. Owing to their comparative rarity, they need little subdivision under the Battley method. After being given a file number and pattern symbol, they are placed behind the tab marked "Accidentals," with no further subdivision.

In the "Scar" division will be filed patterns that display permanent damage or disfigurement likely to be recognized in a latent fingerprint, temporary scars being disregarded.

The subject of "questioned" patterns has been discussed, and such prints are given their correct file number, marked according to their probable pattern type, or else marked "unidentifiable," and filed behind the tab marked "Questioned Patterns."

Since the creation and maintenance of a Battley file entails considerable time and effort, it is well to eliminate as much unnecessary work as possible. Of course the data on all persons in the file should be accessible, that is, the name, offense, place of arrest, "Henry" or ten-finger formula, etc. Including all of this information on each of the ten Battley cards is not necessary. The data may be made available through a simple cross-index filing system that includes an alphabetical file in which each person is recorded according to name, and a number file wherein the subjects are assigned numbers, and listed numerically. The file cards and their accompanying index cards for one set of prints, are illustrated in Fig. 150. It will be noted that the cards bearing the actual fingerprints have no description of the person, aside from the file number and singleprint formula; however, each card bears a number which refers to the "number file." In this file the cards (filed numerically) include the subject's name in each instance, while in the alphabetical file, the corresponding names will be found on cards that include all the necessary descriptive information.

With the use of a singleprint system, certain significant factors will be recognized. As cited, the purpose of such a file is to identify a previously unknown person from one fingerprint or fragment thereof. Consequently, it is important to remember that fingerprints left by lawbreakers are seldom likely to be as legible as those rolled in an identification bureau. This circumstance should modify the treatment of patterns that are placed in the singleprint file. Latent impressions include little more than a central area of their pattern. Furthermore, they are certain to be more or less modified by the surface upon which they are impressed, the degree of pressure exerted in their registration, the condition of the subject's hands, etc., to say nothing of the many factors resulting from powdering, fuming, "lifting," or other methods employed for the development and preservation of the evidence.

Therefore, the operator will find it prudent when classifying and filing prints in the singleprint file, to consider how any special design may look if found at the scene of a crime, and to govern the classification accordingly. For example, a pattern *technically* may fall in a certain standard-type divi-

(MASTER CARD)

DOE, John Thomas
(Subject's Name)

Larceny   (Offense)
5-17-34   (Date of Arrest)
6 mos.   (Disposition)
6795   (Photo Number)
1761   (Singleprint Number)

15 O)13 Aa (--O) 8   (Complete Formula)
   I)18 Ta (--I) 9

1761   (Singleprint Number)

John Thomas Doe   (Subject's Name)

No. 1   SCAR   C.P.   A-3   E O C   15   5
1761

No. 6   W   A-4   D I E   12   13
1761

No. 2   A   Plain
1761

No. 7   Ex A   Ulnar
1761

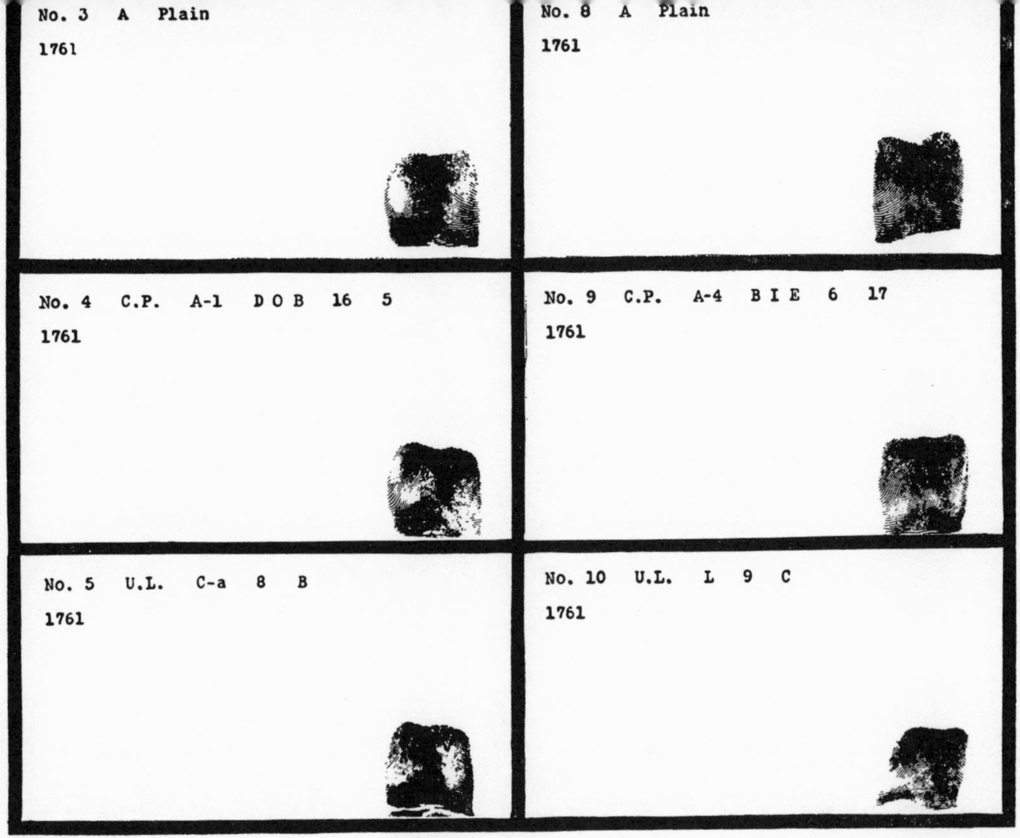

No. 3   A   Plain
1761

No. 4   C.P.   A-1   D O B   16   5
1761

No. 5   U.L.   C-a   8   B
1761

No. 8   A   Plain
1761

No. 9   C.P.   A-4   B I E   6   17
1761

No. 10   U.L.   L   9   C
1761

Fig. 150

sion, but only through some minor or obscure ridge formation that could easily show quite differently, were the same
fingerprint recorded under less favorable circumstances.
When possible, a good practice will be that of filing "reference" cards in the singleprint file; that is, a "first-choice"
formula on one card, and the "second-choice" singleprint
classification on a second. Even more "references" may be filed
if extra "ten-finger" cards are available. This precaution will
increase the probability of making an identification when
confronted with some illegible latent that would not be
"matched" under ordinary circumstances.

With any sizable accumulation of records, it will be noted
that the singleprint filing methods bring together those patterns which resemble one another. Therefore, should the
formula assigned to some evidence impression agree exactly
with none in the file, a further search among neighboring
prints may disclose the sought-for design, filed under some
similar classification.

It should be noted, however, that the Battley System entails considerable labor and care in its maintenance and in
searching. The Federal Bureau of Investigation has adopted
a different and simpler system which is better suited to the
Bureau's operations. This is the so-called "Five-Finger System." The five fingerprints of each hand are recorded on a
single horizontal strip, which is attached to one-half of an
8 x 8-inch file card. The file is maintained for a few special
crimes—bank robbery, kidnapping and certain other serious
crimes within Federal jurisdiction.

With the wider use of electronic data processing equipment, it is expected that the Battley System will enjoy an
increased popularity, since its complexity offers a number of
features suited to these methods.

VIII

OTHER SYSTEMS IN USE

MORE than fifty methods are used throughout the world for classifying and filing fingerprints; the majority of these, however, are based upon either the Henry system or that of Juan Vucetich. Since the latter procedure is employed in most Latin countries, it would seem appropriate to include its description here.

Under the Vucetich method, the "primary" classification is composed of letters and numbers, the letters being *A, I, E,* and *V,* and the numbers *1, 2, 3,* and *4.* Their arbitrary significance in this connection is indicated in the following chart:

A—indicates Arches of all types.
I—indicates Loops having an "Internal Inclination," or inclination to the left, with the delta to the right of the observer (the terms "radial" and "ulnar" are not used in the Vucetich system).
E—indicates Loops having an "External Inclination," or inclination to the right, with the delta to the left of the observer.
V—indicates Whorls, all Composites, and Accidentals.

The above symbols are used to describe the patterns in the thumbs only; when the other fingers are considered, the same designs are indicated numerically, as follows:

156

1—indicates Arches.

2—indicates Loops having Internal Inclination.

3—indicates Loops having External Inclination.

4—indicates Whorls, all Composites, and Accidentals.

With the thumbs indicated by capital letters, and the following digits described by numbers, a set of ten prints consisting entirely of Arches would be recorded as follows: $\frac{A\ 1111}{A\ 1111}$, while the formula $\frac{E\ 3333}{I\ 2222}$ would describe ten prints that were all "ulnar" loops (Henry system). A set of patterns showing a whorl in the right thumb, an external loop in the left thumb, arches in both index fingers, internal loop in right middle finger, external loop in the left middle finger, and arches in all other digits, would be classified thus: $\frac{V\ 1211}{E\ 1311}$; the same set of patterns would be classified under the Henry system in this manner: $\frac{1\ \ Ar2a}{17\ rAr2a}$

Following the primary, the Vucetich method furnishes a more intimate description of all ten digits by a secondary set of figures, ten in number, those describing the right hand being written above the line, and those referring to the left hand below. It will be noted that in the Vucetich treatment, all symbols for the right hand are above, and those for the left hand below the line. The following table shows the significance of the numbers used in the sub-secondary classification:

Arches:

5—indicates a "natural" or plain arch.

6—indicates an "internal" arch, or one having a slope toward the left.

7—indicates an "external" arch, or one having a slope toward the right.

8—indicates a tented arch.

9—indicates an "irregular" arch, or one that does not fall in any of the preceding type formations.

Loops:

5—indicates a "natural" loop, or a plain pattern having no unusual ridge-structural involvement.

6—Indicates a loop with "adhering" ridges, or something of the *J* core type in the Battley system.

7—indicates an "internal" loop approximating a central pocket.

8—indicates an "external" loop approximating a central pocket.

9—indicates all "irregular" loops, or those that do not fall in any of the aforementioned types.

Whorls:

5—indicates all "natural" whorls, or those that present no unusual ridge-structure characteristics.

6—indicates twin loops or lateral-pocket loops.

7—indicates all whorls having an ovoid shape.

8—indicates central pockets.

9—indicates accidentals, and all whorls that can not be classified in any of the above-mentioned type divisions.

Under the Vucetich method, ridge counting is also employed. However, the actual counts are not recorded as in the Henry system, but the approximate numbers of ridges are indicated by the group numbers 5, 10, 15, 20, and 25, their significance being shown in the following table:

5 indicates loops having 1 to 5 ridges between core and delta.
10 indicates loops having 6 to 10 ridges between core and delta.
15 indicates loops having 11 to 15 ridges between core and delta.
20 indicates loops having 16 to 20 ridges between core and delta.
25 indicates loops having 21 or more ridges between core and delta.

These symbols are employed to describe the index and little fingers, should they be loops, and are placed in two groups following the sub-secondary section of the classification formula.

Under the Vucetich method, all amputations and illegible patterns are filed separately.

A consideration of the following sample registration formulae, and chart of fingerprint patterns that it is designed to describe, will serve to clarify the system:

RIGHT HAND

R. Thumb	R. Index	R. Middle	R. Ring	R. Little
Tented Arch	Internal Loop Natural with 4 ridges	Arch Inclined to the Left	Whorl of the Central Pocket Type	Internal Loop approximating a Central Pocket with 14 ridges

LEFT HAND

L. Thumb	L. Index	L. Middle	L. Ring	L. Little
Whorl with an ovoid formation	External Loop with adhering ridges and ridge count of 21	Whorl of the Twinned Loop Type	Arch with Right Inclination	External Loop approximating Central Pocket with ridge count of 25

Under the Henry system, this pattern arrangement would be expressed as $\frac{15 \text{ tRa } 14}{1 \text{ Ra } 25}$.

Under the Vucetich method, the above set of fingerprints would be described in the following formula:

A 2142 85687 (5) (15)
V 3413 76678 (25) (25)

Primary Classification	Sub-Classification	Approximate Ridge Counts Index	Little
A 2142	85687	(5)	(15)
V 3413	76678	(25)	(25)

By referring to the included tables describing the significance of the symbols utilized, it will be recognized that the capital A in the upper line refers to the right thumb, and indicates it as an arch, while the capital V underneath shows the left thumb is a whorl. The 2, and 3, the upper and lower figures in the first number group, refer to the right and left index fingers respectively, and describe them as shown in the chart above, namely, the right index as an internal loop, and the left as an external loop.

The next pair of figures in the first number group, the 1 above the 4, indicates the right second finger as an arch, and the left second finger as a whorl. The following pair, namely, the 4 over the 1, designates the right ring finger as a whorl, and the left ring finger as an arch. The final pair, that of 2 over 3, describes both little fingers as internal and external loops respectively.

As already indicated, the second group of numbers constitutes a sub-classification, and furnishes a more intimate description of the involved patterns in all ten digits.

It will be noted that the "primary" includes but four number pairs, the thumbs being represented by capital letters, and the fingers by numbers, whereas in the sub-classification group, all digits (both thumbs and fingers) are described by numbers.

The first pair in the sub-classification consists of 8 over 7, and by referring to the foregoing table it will be noted that the subdivision of arches, which is the pattern in the right thumb, shows tented arches represented by the number 8. The pattern in the right thumb, already shown to be an arch, as indicated in the primary, is further described in the sub-classification as a tented arch. The left thumb, already expressed in the primary as a whorl, is further described by the figure 7 in the sub-classification as being of ovoid formation.

Itemized description of the succeeding sets of numbers in

the sub-classification is hardly necessary, since reference to the tables of sub-classifications will show the significance of each of the number pairs. However, it should be pointed out that the figures in brackets following the sub-classification group describe the approximate ridge counts in both index fingers and little fingers as well. The figure 5 refers to the right index, and shows it to contain between one and five ridges, four to be exact. These approximating figures that describe the ridge count inclusions are shown in a separate table already recorded. The bracketed figure 25 under the 5 refers to the left index finger, and shows its ridge count to be over 21. The second pair of figures surrounded by brackets, namely 15 over 25, refers to the little fingers, with a determination of between 11 and 15 ridges in the right, and over 21 ridges in the left.

From the foregoing, the simplicity of the Vucetich method is readily apparent. As already stated, the considerable popularity it has attained is attested by its extensive adoption. Nonetheless, there are many more classification and filing systems in use throughout the world. Following are outlines of some of these systems. The student will find them useful for comparative study and in the "translation" of unfamiliar systems that may be encountered from time to time.

The devisers of these methods displayed some originality; however, despite the considerable number of systems included, the influence of the Galton-Henry and the Vucetich methods will be observed in nearly every instance.

The basic problem for which each of these systems purports to give a solution is the same—namely, to represent the ridge formations of the ten fingers by a set of symbols providing a widely dispersed set of classifications which can be readily labeled in an ordered manner and rapidly located in a filing arrangement.

The Galton-Henry system approached the problem of classification by defining a set of pattern types in terms of the recurving of specified ridges. In the whorl these ridges recurve through a complete revolution; in loops only a half-circuit is made; plain arches constitute a null set in which there is no recurve.

To aid recognition, characteristic ridge formations were used to define the elements of a pattern type, namely, pattern area, type lines, cores and deltas. The scope of classification was extended by introducing a quantitative aspect. With the elements as reference points, rules were devised to make reproducible ridge counts in loop and whorl patterns. Again, the arches were a null set, lacking core or delta, and hence without ridge count.

To pattern type and ridge count, the Galton-Henry system added other elements such as loop direction, and specified numerical values for each finger of each hand. Symbols were then selected for the identifying features and set in a form to constitute the "classification."

The logic in the selection of identifying features is one of convenience and practicality. Similarly, the choice of letters and numbers is also a matter of convention guided by utility and subject primarily to the rule of self-consistency. By choosing other sets and subsets of ridge features and symbols, other fingerprint systems have been devised. On reflection, however, the student will see their basis in the Galton-Henry system, and will be able to relate the terms of a new system to those of the parent system.

THE BUDAPEST OR HUNGARIAN SYSTEM

The Budapest system follows the Galton-Henry system except for slight modifications, especially in the terminology. The terminology is a mere shifting of letters; that is, Hungarian letters, peculiar to the language, have been substituted for the letters used in the Galton-Henry system of classification. The Hungarian Terminology is as follows: *I* for *A*, *O* for *R*, *Z* for *W*, *T* is *T*, and *S* is *U*.

Ridge Counting:

A for *I* (The *A* is taken from the Hungarian *also* meaning "under." Thus *A* indicates an "inner" in ridge counting.)

F for *O* (The *F* is derived from the Hungarian *folso*, meaning "above." Thus *F* indicates an "outer" in ridge counting.)

Ridge Tracing in Sub-Classification:

B for *I* (The *B* is from the Hungarian *belso*, meaning "inside." Thus *B* indicates an "inner" in ridge tracing.)

E for *M* (The *E* is from the Hungarian *egyesulo*, meaning "meeting." Thus *E* indicates a "meeting" in ridge tracing.)

K for *O* (The *K* is from the Hungarian *kulso*, meaning "outside." Thus *K* indicates an "outer" in ridge tracing.)

THE VALLADARES SYSTEM

This system was introduced in Portugal, and is based entirely upon the Henry system of classification.

THE BERTILLON SYSTEM

This represents Bertillon's modification of the Vucetich system.

Patterns:

Loops: Terminating to the right (symbol *e*).

Loops: Terminating to the left (symbol *i*).

Loops must have at least *two* recurring ridges.

Whorls: (symbol *o*): Must have at least *four* complete circuits, otherwise is classified as an *e* or an *i*.

Sub-Classification:

oc: ellipses, circles and spirals.

ov: volutes.

Arches: (symbol *u*): All patterns less than two recurring ridges, and all patterns which cannot be classified under *e*, *i* or *o*.

Registration Formula: Patterns indicated by lower-case letters according to position in the hand.

First letter refers to the thumbs, for example: $\dfrac{o\ i\ e\ e\ e}{e\ e\ i\ e}$

THE DAAE SYSTEM

This system was introduced in Norway and represents a modification and combination of the Vucetich and Henry systems.

Loops: Ridge Counting (no differentiation is made between fingers):

   1 to 9 lines: *a.*
   10 to 13 lines: *b.*
   14 to 16 lines: *c.*
   17 or more lines: *d.*

Whorls: Same as Henry system for ridge tracing.

The index finger is used at the head of the series and section. The ridge count of one finger is noted on the card. The left index is used and not the little finger as in the Henry system.

Registration Formula: Series number is the right hand. Section number is the left hand. Ridge counts are made only for the four fingers of the left hand and are written above the section numbers: The index finger is indicated numerically by the exact number of ridges, others by alphabetical symbols. Missing fingers are filed in a separate file.

THE PROTIVENSKI SYSTEM

This system was introduced in Prague, and combines with it some of the features of the Vucetich and Henry systems. The primary classification is the same as in the Vucetich. Differentiation is made between ulnar and radial loops in thumb and fingers. In the sub-classification the ridge counting and tracing is the same as that used in the Henry system except that the actual count of ridges is used for filing.

THE BRUSSELS SYSTEM

Primary Classification: Same as the Vucetich system except that the thumb is also numbered. Missing fingers are expressed through the type or number of the corresponding finger, except "2" in the right hand becomes "3" in the left hand and vice versa.

Sub-Classification:

Index Fingers: Loops	Middle Fingers: Loops
1: 1 to 9 ridges	1: 1 to 10 ridges
2: 10 and more ridges	2: 11 and more ridges

Whorls: Same as the Henry system except for the substitution of symbols: "*i*" becomes "1"; "*m*" becomes "2"; and "*o*" becomes "3." The ridge count of the right ring finger is added, and is the final classification.

THE KLATT SYSTEM

This system was used in Berlin in 1909, and represents some of the features of the Bertillon and Vucetich systems. However, it proved inadequate, and later on elements of the Henry system were introduced.

Four classes:

E: Loops terminating to the right.
I: Loops terminating to the left.
O: Whorls, spirals and double spirals.
W: Lateral, twinned and pocket.
U: Arches and patterns not falling in the foregoing classes.

Primary classification is the same as that used in the Henry system.
First Sub-Group: According to type of the two index fingers.
Second Sub-Group: According to type of two middle fingers.
Third Sub-Group: Based on the year of birth of the person.
Fourth Sub-Group: Ridge count of the little finger.

Missing and distorted fingers classified according to the corresponding finger of the other hand. If both are missing the *O* form is assumed. If the right little finger is missing the left is counted, and if both are missing a dash is placed in the formula.

THE WEHN SYSTEM

The Klatt system proved to be unsuccessful, and by 1915 further elements of the Henry system were introduced. The following is the Wehn system as used in Berlin.

Determination of Type:

E Loops having two overlapping recurving ridges with recurvature to the right. The inner may consist of two rods which are treated as if connected at their tops. These rods must not meet below, but may touch the outer loop with their lower ends. Outer loop may be formed through a hook if downward thrust of hook indicates the direction conclusively. Two parallel loops are also included.

I Same as *E* except with recurvature to the *left*.

O Whorls as in Henry.

U Arches.

First Sub-Group:

Expressed in letters in accordance with the ridge patterns of the index and middle fingers of both hands. The two fingers of the right hand appear in the numerator, those of the left hand in the denominator. Pattern of the index fingers is designated by capitals, and that of the middle fingers in lower case type.

Second Sub-Group: Ridge Counting:

Index Fingers: Loop patterns *E* or *I*.

   a: 1 to 9 ridges.

   b: 10 or more ridges.

Middle Fingers: Loop patterns *E-I*.

   a: 1 to 10 ridges.

   b: 11 or more ridges.

Whorls in the index and middle fingers of both hands: Ridge tracing for *I, M,* and *O* (as in Henry system) but with following symbols:

   a: If above the right delta.

   b: If below the right delta.

   c: If traced ridge meets the lowest line of the right delta.

Note: If traced ridge should terminate or end abruptly, the course of the next ridge *above* is pursued.

U patterns in the index and middle fingers are designated as *a*. If *U* pattern occurs in the index and middle fingers, then the thumbs and ring finger are added. Missing and badly injured fingers are classified according to the type of the corresponding finger of the other hand. If both are missing the "O" type is assumed.

Third Sub-Group:

Ridge counting of the right little finger same as Henry system. If right little finger is missing, left one is used. *U* patterns are not counted, but are designated as "————". The count in double and twinned loops is to the middle pair of loops lying nearest the delta. If the ridge count is uncertain the symbol "?" is placed after the assumed numerical figure.

Fourth Sub-Group:

Age of the subject or estimation of the correct age.

THE ROSCHER SYSTEM

The Roscher system used by the Hamburg Police represents a goodly part of the Henry system with some elements of the Vucetich and Daae systems. The Henry system of the division of patterns is followed (*A, R, U* and *W*) as well as the method of ridge counting and tracing. However, the Roscher system divides the *U* patterns into four groups, as in the Daae system (1 to 9, 10 to 13, 14 to 16, and 17 or more). The use of letters in the registration formula has been rejected and all types are designated with numbers as follows:

A	*R*	*U* with ridges				*W*			Missing prints
		1-9	10-13	14-16	17-x	i	m	o	
1	2	3	4	5	6	7	8	9	0 or ⊙

O indicates finger is missing. ⊙ indicates finger is present, but an orderly print is impossible. Both are counted as *O*.

Like Vucetich, the Roscher system uses numbers as symbols for each finger. However, unlike the Vucetich system, numbers are also used as symbols for the thumbs. The symbol for the index finger is placed at the head. The left hand is the numerator and the right the denominator.

In taking prints a different procedure is used than that employed in the Henry system. In the Roscher system prints are taken first of the left hand and then of the right hand in the following order: Index, middle, ring, little finger and thumb. Roscher states that the index fingers show the greatest number of basic patterns, and that the pattern *U* occurs more frequently in prints. Therefore, more sub-groups may be had. The left hand is used as numerator because, according to Roscher, it is less subject to loss of fingers or deformation than the right hand.

The pattern-number is placed in the middle beneath each impression, and in the right-hand corner is written the exact ridge count of the *U* type. The registration-formula is placed in the upper right-hand corner of the sheet. The ridge count of the left middle finger is the final classification. If no loop is present the count is given an *O*.

If further extension is necessary, or desired, ridge counting of the right middle finger, left ring finger, and right ring finger is recommended. Each count is separated by a period. The final count is placed in line with the line dividing the numerator and the denominator. Two separate prints are made of doubtful cases with cross references to each other.

THE JAPANESE NATIONAL SYSTEM

Same as Roscher system except: Ulnar with ridges

1-7	8-11	12-14	15-x
3	4	5	6

THE LEBEDEFF SYSTEM

This system, introduced in Russia by Lebedeff, is a combination of the Roscher system and the Henry primary classification. The Henry primary classification appears first in the registration formula and is followed by the Roscher formula.

THE GASTI SYSTEM

This is an Italian system and includes certain of the elements in the Vucetich, Henry, and Roscher systems. The Henry method of ridge counting and tracing is followed. The types are designated as shown in the following chart (the numbers indicating the type):

A	R	U			W			Composites, and such as do not come under 1 to 8
		1-10	11-15	16-x	i	m	o	
1	2	3	4	5	6	7	8	9

Primary Classification:
 Left hand: Index, thumb, and ring fingers form the series: Right hand: Index, thumb, and ring fingers form the section.
Sub-Classification:
 Middle finger and little finger of the left hand, and middle finger and the little finger of the right hand. Examples: 601—412—4975.

THE PORTILLO SYSTEM

This system was introduced in Barcelona, and follows the Gasti system.

THE SMALLEGANGE SYSTEM

This system was introduced in Holland in 1912, and represents a modification of the Roscher system with a strong Henry influence.

Primary Classification:

O: Arches and tented arches	1: Thumb, 16 lines or less
1: Loops to the right	2: " 17 lines or more
4: Loops to the left	1: Index, 9 lines or less
7: Whorls, etc.	2: " 10 lines or more
	1: Middle, 10 lines or less
Whorls:	2: " 11 lines or more
1: If traced lines goes above right delta	1: Ring, 13 lines or less
	2: " 14 lines or more
2: If traced line goes below right delta	1: Little, 11 lines or less
	2: " 12 lines or more

When the fractions 1/4 or 7/7 occur four times or more, all fingers are sub-classified if possible. In all other cases only the middle, ring and little fingers are sub-classified.

Missing fingers: If the pattern O or 7 appears in the corresponding finger in the other hand, it is assumed that the missing finger has the same pattern. In case of loops, it is assumed that the missing finger has the *opposite* pattern of the corresponding finger of the other hand. If the same fingers are missing in both hands, it is assumed that they were whorls and that the ridge tracing resulted in l.

The registration formula consists of two fractions. The first fraction contains the thumbs and indexes; the second, those of the remaining fingers. Sub-classification figures (1 and 2) are added to the primary classification. Any further sub-classification by ridge counting is independent of the formula. Assuming that the main or primary classification of a fingerprint set results in the

following formula: $\dfrac{4\ 1\ 0\ 7\ 1}{1\ 4\ 4\ 7\ 4}$

the sub-classification is then added to this formula as follows:

$$\frac{4\ 1 \quad\quad 0 \quad\quad 7+2 \quad\quad 1+2}{1\ 4 \quad\quad 4+2 \quad\quad 7+1 \quad\quad 4+1}$$

resulting in the following formula: $\dfrac{41\quad 093}{14\quad 685}$

There was no need for further sub-classification, as the fraction 1/4 or 7/7 did not occur four times or more in the formula.

THE PATEER SYSTEM

This system, introduced in Amsterdam in 1913, has combined with it certain characteristics of the Henry system.

1: Arches
2: Tented arches
3: Loops to the right
4: Loops to the left
5: Twinned and double loops
6: Central pocket loops to right

7: Central pocket loops to the left
8: Whorls
9: Accidentals
0: Missing fingers
⊙: Illegible prints

Main or Primary Classification:

The five fingers of each hand form the main classification thus: Index, Middle, Ring, Little, and Thumb.

Sub-Classification:

Ridge counting in loops: Limits in counting are: 9/10 lines in the index, 10/11 in the middle, and 13/14 lines in the ring finger.

THE POTTECHER SYSTEM

Introduced in Indo-China in 1902, this system shows no resemblance to the Henry system but is slightly influenced by the Vucetich:

Sd: Arches with inclination to the right.
Si: Arches with no inclination.
Sg: Arches with inclination to the left.
Td: Loops terminating to the right.
Tg: Loops terminating to the left.
C: Whorls concentric.
Vd: Whorls to the right.
Vg: Whorls to the left.

Primary Classification: Right Index Finger.
Sub-Group Classification: The Thumbs.
Subdivision Classification: Middle, Ring, and Little Finger.

The pattern is determined by the use of a measuring instrument called the "Gabarit." This is used only for prints of adults. Red ink is used to mark the auxiliary lines in determining the pattern. The registration formula of minors is filed separately from that of adults. In doubtful or borderline cases a double formula is filed.

THE OLORIZ SYSTEM

This system, as used by the Madrid Police in 1910, consists of most of the Vucetich system combined with the ridge-tracing and counting of the Henry system. However, the main feature of the Oloriz system is the registration book which was furnished to all Madrid policemen. It contained information regarding the known criminals of Madrid. It is divided into three sections: (1) Personal description, (2) Fingerprints, and (3) Alphabetic description; that is, name, aliases, name of parents, place of birth, occupation, record, etc. This manual is for the purpose of aiding the police to identify the criminal on the street, at the scene of a crime, in hang-outs for known criminals, etc. However, we are here only concerned with the registration formula under the Oloriz system. The formula is much in accordance with the Vucetich system (letters for the thumbs and numbers 1 to 4 for the remaining fingers). The letters used by Oloriz to designate the pattern types are as follows:

A: Arch or pattern without delta.
D: Patterns containing a right delta.
S: Patterns containing a left delta.
V: Double deltas or Whorl types.
O: Missing or distorted patterns.

The formula made up from the foregoing pattern types is the primary classification. Below this formula is then added the sub-formula, or sub-classification, as follows: Ridge count for loops as in the Henry system. Ridge tracing for whorls with letters *i, m* and *e,* corresponding to the Henry letters *I, M,* and *O*.

Final or sub-type classification: *p*: Tented Arch pattern (pseudo delta).

MARTINEZ SYSTEM

This method of determining the registration-formula was introduced in Mexico and represents the Vucetich system, but in addition it employs the Henry ridge count. The Vucetich system is the primary classification; and the Henry ridge count is the sub-classification.

Sub-Classification:

I: From 1 to 6 ridges III: From 11 to 14 ridges
II: From 7 to 10 ridges IV: 15 or more ridges

WINDT-KODICEK SYSTEM

This system, as used in Germany, is essentially the Henry system, and the registration formula is that used under the Henry method.

BORGERHOFF SYSTEM

This system, as used in Belgium in 1910, represents the primary classification of the Vucetich system; the sub-classification of the Henry system, with certain modifications, and an entirely original sub-classification.

Primary Classification:

From the Vucetich system: However, letters are not used for the thumbs. When a print is undecipherable the type of the corresponding finger of the other hand is substituted. If corresponding fingers in both hands are missing, they are classified as whorls (4).

In missing or undecipherable prints a right loop in the right hand corresponds to a left loop in the left hand.

First Subdivision:

The ridge-counting and tracing of Henry is used for the right index and the right middle finger, and then for the left index and left middle.

Loops: I: Index 1 to 9 ridges.   II: Index 10 or more.
        I: Middle 1 to 10 ridges. II: Middle 11 or more ridges.
Whorls: Uses Henry's $I, M,$ and $O.$

Second Subdivision:

If the right little finger is an external loop, the primary formula and the sub-formula are arranged according to the ridge count. If the whorl types predominate, ridge tracing is applied to the right ring finger.

Third Subdivision:

If ulnar loops predominate in the card, the formula contains the ridge count of the right little finger and the right thumb. If the index and middle finger of the same hand are of different types, the pattern of the middle finger is excluded. However, if both fingers of the same hand contain identical patterns—for example, if the whorl type appears in both fingers in the right hand, and loops in both fingers in the left hand—the first subdivision will contain the four prints. Missing and distorted fingers are classified according to the corresponding finger of the other hand. When two corresponding fingers are missing or distorted, they are classified as type 4, sub-type 2.

If the whorl pattern predominates and the little finger of the right hand is a right loop, then the subdivision is continued by the numeration of the ridges of this little finger.

THE SPIRLET SYSTEM

This system, as introduced at The Hague in 1910, has combined with it certain features of the Henry system.

Primary Classification:

1. Group L (loops)
   A 1: Arches
   B 2: Tented arches
   C 3: Loops opening to the right
   D 4: Loops opening to the left

2. Group (whorls)
   E 5: Central pocket
   F 6: Whorls (spiral)
   G 7: Twinned loop
   H 8: Indefinable

The prints are classed as follows:

Numerator: Right Hand: Index, Middle, Ring, Little, and Thumb.

Denominator: Left Hand: Same as above.

The patterns of the indexes are lettered, all other fingers numbered.

Numerical value of patterns: As in Henry system, only the whorls are considered. Member is added to member, but without transposing or adding 1.

16: value of Index.
8:    "   " Middle Finger.
4:    "   " Ring Finger.
2:    "   " Little Finger.
1:    "   " Thumb.

Subdivision: Ridge counting for Loops:

i 1 to 7 ridges in index finger.

i 1 to 9 ridges in other fingers.

O 8 or more ridges in index finger

O 10 or more ridges in other fingers.

Ridge Tracing for Whorls (type F): i: meeting; o: Outer and Inner Whorls. Capital letters are used for the index fingers and small letters for the other fingers.

Final Subdivision: In the case of i or o loops, the figure, indicating the exact number of lines, is inscribed above the letter.

Incomplete Formulas: Missing fingers or distorted fingers are marked X. If the print is badly blurred, the files are searched to see if there is an identical card filed; if not, the pattern is definitely marked X.

THE STEEGERS SYSTEM

This system was introduced in Cuba by Juan Steegers, and is a modification of the Henry system. Steegers replaces the Henry symbols with others peculiar to his own language. Under the Steegers system, the impressions are not made on cards or ordinary paper, but on a transparent photographic paper from which may be obtained as many reproductions as desired. Steegers' Terminology:

Henry Steegers

A:	*A,*	(Arch)
T:	*A*	(Sharp arch)
L:	*P*	(Loop)
W:	*E*	(Spiral)
C:	*Cp*	(Composite)
LP:	*C,C,*	(Lateral pocket)
CP:	*CC*	(Central pocket)

Henry Steegers

TL:	*C.C.*	(Twinned fork)
Ac:	*Ac*	(Accidental)
U:	*C*	(Right hand ulnar)
R:	*R*	(Right hand radial)
U:	*C*	(Left hand ulnar)
R:	*R*	(Left hand radial)

Primary Classification: Formula established same as in Henry.

THE HARVEY-PACHA SYSTEM

This system was introduced in Egypt, and bears a close resemblance to the Vucetich and Henry systems.

Types: Same as the types in the Vucetich system.

Symbols: Whorls: O   Outside Loop: \
          Inside Loop: /   Arch: ∧

Sub-Classes: Whorls (indicated by the numbers)

1: Spiral to the left
2: Spiral to the right
3: Ellipse
4: Right lateral pocket
5: Left lateral pocket

6: Twinned loop (left superior)
7: Twinned loop (right superior)
8: High circle
9: Circle, depressed vertically
10: Miscellaneous

If there is a majority of whorls, the type numbers of the right in· dexes, middle, and ring fingers are inscribed in the sub-formula.

Loops: Ridge Counting: The left index and ring fingers are used, and sometimes the right middle finger. Symbols are not used. The number of the cut lines is inscribed, placing the first two fingers as a fraction.

THE CABEZAS SYSTEM

This system was introduced in Valparaiso in 1927, and includes the Vucetich system of classification with certain features of the Henry system (ridge tracing and counting). There are two keys, that is, two ways of classing the prints. Key for small col· lections (including less than 50,000 cards):

1: Arch
2: Internal loop, 1 to 5 ridges
3: External loop, 1 to 5 ridges
4: Internal loop, 6 to 11 ridges
5: External loop, 6 to 11 ridges
6: Internal loop, 11 or more ridges
7: External loop, 11 or more ridges
8: Spiral whorl
9: Sinuous whorl
10: Oval whorl
O: Amputated finger
X: Deficient or doubtful patterns

Complete key for large collection:

					Whorls:	
o:	Arch				r:	Inside Spiral
1:	Internal loop with		1 line		R:	Meet Spiral
2:	"	"	"	2 lines	rr:	Outside Spiral
3:	"	"	"	3 "	s:	Sinuous Internal
4:	"	"	"	4 "	S:	Sinuous Meet
5:	"	"	"	5 "	ss:	Sinuous Outside
6:	"	"	"	6 "	v:	Oval Inside
7:	"	"	"	7 "	V:	Oval Meet
8:	"	"	"	8 "	vv:	Oval Outside
9:	"	"	"	9 "	X:	Doubtful or defective
a:	"	"	"	10 "		prints
I:	"	"	"	11 "	Z:	Amputated fingers
1:	"	"	"	12 "		
E:	External loop with		5 lines or less			
o:	"	"	"	6 to 10 lines		
m:	"	"	"	11 to 15 lines		
n:	"	"	"	more than 15		
p:	Internal loop with		13 lines			
q:	"	"	"	more than 13		

THE LYONNESE SYSTEM

This system, used in Lyons, France, shows elements of many finger-print systems.

Primary Classification: Essentially the Vucetich-Daae system: However, instead of classifying loops as either external or internal, the Lyonnese system designates right loops as those which are to the right of the operator, and left loops as those which are to the left of the operator. The index finger comes at the head of the formula for the series and for the section, and it is indicated by the alphabetical symbol. The rest of the fingers are indicated by numerals.

Four Groups: *A* *1*: Arch   *D* *3*: Right loop
                 G *2*: Left loop   *V* *4*: Whorl

Sub-Classification:

This division is based upon the form of the core of the pattern. Ridge counting and ridge tracing have been rejected.

Arches: *A* or *1* Simple arch and/or Tented arch.

Loops:

a: Single rod or ridge with free end.

b: Single rod reaching the curve of the loop.

c: Two or more rods. Also, the types in which the center is composed of a loop and a rod with free end terminating on the same level.

d: A loop (two rods joined at the top).

e: Varied figures, notably a racket, a ring or spire; Henry's central pocket loop.

Whorls:

Type *a*: A circle or an ellipse.

"   *c*: A spiral turning toward the right or left.

"   *y*: A double spiral.

"   *s*: Varied figures (hooks, crooks, etc.).

The registration formula contains the core pattern type of the middle, ring, and little finger of the right hand. If necessary, the subdivision may be extended to the other hand or fingers.

Sub-Classification by measurement of the Galton-Henry Line: This consists of measurement in millimeters of the distance which separates the summit of the loop from the center of the triangle, that is, the Galton line. Measurements are made with a compass placed on a millimetric ruler. In Lyons this sub-classification is applied to: Right Index and Right Middle Finger, Left Index and Left Middle Finger.

1 to 5.9 mm. : *p*   6 to 7.9 mm. : *m*   8 mm. and over : *g*

THE PESSOA SYSTEM

The primary classification is that of Vucetich. However, letters are not used to designate the thumbs; only numerals are used. The right hand is the numerator and the left the denominator. The cards are filed in numerical order, and all similar thumbs placed in one division. The right thumb is the guide.

Arches:
1: Simple arch
2: Tented arch

Loops:
1: A free rod
2: Rod touching loop
3: Two rods or more
4: Staple

Whorls:
1: Circle or ellipse
2: Spiral
3: Twinned loops
4: Other bidelta figures

THE MIRANDA PINTO SYSTEM

This system was devised by Miranda Pinto, an assistant in the police laboratory at Lyons, and planned for use in Chile. It uses some of the fundamentals of Vucetich.

Basic Types:

A or 1: Arch—simple form.

I or 2: Loop (Presilla Interna) determined by a delta with intersection to the right.

E or 3: Loop (Presilla Externa) determined by a delta with intersection to the left.

V or 4: Whorl (verticilo) two deltas with intersection between which are concentric circles, spirals or volutes.

The capital letters are used for the index fingers, and all other fingers are designated by a numeral.

Fingerprint Types:

A or 1: Arch

L or 2: Left loop, delta to right

R or 3: Right loop, delta to left

W or 4: Whorl with two deltas

S or 5: Whorl with S form

Z or 6: Whorl; reversed S form

L or 7: Central pocket loops and whorls with noose to the left

R or 8: Central pocket loops and whorls with noose to the right

Amputated fingers and distorted prints classified as *X* or *O*. Sub-classification by measurements as in the Lyonnese system. The cards are filed in two sections, one beginning with the right hand, the other with the left hand.

THE LERICH METHOD

Primary Division:

1: Left loops
2: Right loops
3: Arches or assimilated figures (loops with delto-central zone cutting fewer than 5 ridges)
4: Whorls

First Subdivision:

Loops: By ridge counting: 5 to 15 lines. More than 15 lines.
Arches: By number of lines between the articulation and the rectilinear base of the pattern: 0 to 5 lines: More than 5 lines.
Whorls: By ridge tracing.

Second Subdivision: By pattern of the core.

Loops: Right or left.
1: A free rod
2: 1 adhering rod
3: Several rods
4: Varied

Arches:
1: No central figure (pure arch)
2: One delta
3: A right loop
4: A left loop

Whorls:
1: Spiral from right to *L*
2: Spiral from left to *R*
3: Circles or ovals
4: Twinned loops and central pockets
5: Varied figures

Third Subdivision—description of the peripheral zone:

i: Isle
f: Fork
c: Curl or hook

b: Point or dot
c: Cicatrice
d: Delta
o: No peculiarities

THE JOUENNE METHOD

This system was adopted by the Colonial Service in Western French Africa.

Primary Classification:

1: Left loop	4: Double volute
2: Right loop	5: Arch
3: Volutes or spirals	

Sub-Classification: The Lyonnese method, by the measurement of the Galton line in millimeters.

THE CONLAY SYSTEM

This system was introduced by the Federated Malay States Police. It follows the Henry system rather closely, except for important modifications. Only these modifications of the Henry system will be dealt with here. Types of impressions:

Loops: Same as in the Henry system: R and U loops are determined as in the Henry system. However, the ulnars are divided into two groups: If the ridge count between the delta and the core is 10 or less, it is classed as U; if the ridge count exceeds 10, it is known as X. Radials are known as R.

Whorls: Same as in the Henry system: Composites are also included in this group. If an impression has two deltas it is a whorl. Ridge tracing follows the Henry method; however, only inners and outers are regarded. It is an inner (I) if the ridge traced goes above the right delta; if it goes below, it is an outer (O).

Arches: Same as in the Henry system; must be no recurvature and no ridge count.

Main Classification:

	Thumb	Index	Middle	Ring	Little	
Right Hand:	1	2	4	8	16	Numerator
Left Hand:	1	2	4	8	16	Denominator

Value is only given to whorls: 1/1 is not added to the fraction as in the Henry system; therefore, the groups are arranged numerically from 0/0 to 31/31. In filing and searching the files, the right hand is dealt with first, and only when the classification of two right hands is the same does one refer to the left hand.

Sub-Classification of the 31/31 Group: To decrease the congestion in this group it has been divided into three sub-groups: Small (S), Medium (M), and Large (L). The division is based on the left little finger count, as follows: S: Ridge count of 7 or less; M: count of 8, 9 or 10; L: 11 or more. This count is made from the delta to the lowest point in the core.

Ridge counting in loops: Same as the Henry method. Ridge counting in whorls: The count is taken from the left delta. If the whorl is composed of two loops, the count is made to each loop and the combined total is halved.

Sub-Classification of the o/o file (all loop or arch file): This concerns only those prints in which all the digits are ulnars, or there is a radial in either or both of the index fingers. This sub-classification is for the purpose of filing and to enable a better and more adequate search of the files.

Missing Digits: If completely amputated, they will be classified as A, unless more than two digits are missing, when they will be the classification of the corresponding digits in the other hand. If more than two digits are missing (two of them being found to be corresponding fingers), then both will be classified as O.

THE O'NEILL EXTENSION OF THE HENRY SYSTEM

All loops are ridge counted, and whorls are treated as ulnar loops. A ridge count is made, first of the fingers of the right hand, and then of the left hand. The ridge counts of the right hand are added and become the numerator. Those of the left hand, when added, become the denominator. This then becomes the final classification.

COLLINS SINGLE FINGERPRINT SYSTEM

Charles Collins, many years in charge of New Scotland Yard, devised this system in 1921. It is essentially the Henry system. The registration formula provided for a telegraphic code divided into two main parts. One part dealt with types of patterns, ridge counts, and ridge tracing, while the other concerned the location of ridge characteristics. Prints considered in their standard sequence: Right thumb, index, middle, ring and little, left thumb, etc.

Pattern Types:

A: Arch

B: Tented arch

C: Loop—radial

D: Loop—ulnar

E: Central pocket (inner)

F: Central pocket (outer)

G: Whorl (inner)

H: Whorl (meeting)

J: Whorl (outer)

K: Lateral pocket (inner)

L: Lateral pocket (meeting)

M: Lateral pocket (outer)

N: Twinned loop (inner)

O: Twinned loop (meeting)

P: Twinned loop (outer)

Q: Compound pattern (inner)

R: Compound pattern (meeting)

S: Compound pattern (outer)

T: Accidental

U: Finger amputated

V: Finger damaged; scarred; bad print

W: Finger under medical treatment

When coding loops, the standard ridge count between core and delta should be inserted after the code letter, as for example: $D9$ (Ulnar loop with a ridge count of nine). In coding whorls or central pockets which classify inner or outer, the number of ridges intervening between the extended ridge of the right delta and that of the left delta should be added to the code letter; i.e., $G4$ (Whorl, inner, with ridge count of 4). The count is determined in the same manner as when determining whether a whorl is an inner or outer under the Henry system of classification. The following fingerprint card would be coded as follows:

$$D7D12D19C8C9E9G6E8J8L9.$$

Right thumb .... Ulnar loop with ridge count of 7

Right index .... Ulnar loop with count of 12

Right middle .... Ulnar loop with count of 19

Right ring .... Radial loop with count of 8

Right little .... Radial loop with ridge count of 9

Left thumb .... Central pocket (inner) with count of 9

Left index .... Whorl (inner) ridge count of 6

Left middle .... Central pocket (inner) with count of 8

Left ring .... Whorl (outer) with count of 8

Left little .... Lateral pocket (meeting) count of 9

For the purpose of coding peculiarities of ridge detail, he has adopted a plan for sectoring the print. Across the glass and near the center, two very fine, horizontal, parallel lines were drawn, six millimeters apart, joined by a third line in the center perpendicular to both. Numerals were used in the coding of ridge characteristics, and only four characteristic peculiarities of fingerprint ridge formation were considered: the pure ridge, terminating ridge, the bifurcation, and the eye.

Code Symbols were as follows:

1: A pure ridge cutting both lines of the glass and possessing neither of the other three characteristics.

2: A descending ridge cutting the top line, but which terminates before reaching the lower line, and possessing no other characteristics.

3: An ascending ridge cutting the lower line, but which terminates before reaching the top line, and possessing no other characteristics.

4: A short independent ridge cutting neither of the two parallel lines between which it falls, and possessing no other characteristics.

5: A ridge bifurcating downward, the point of bifurcation appearing between the two parallel lines.

6: A ridge bifurcating upwards, the point of bifurcation appearing between the two parallel lines.

7: A ridge enclosure or eyelet formation appearing within the two parallel lines.

8: A ridge which is partly scarred or damaged.

9: Code number for the delta.

It is not necessary to telegraph the ridge characteristics of the entire ten fingers. The coding of about fifteen characteristics is more than sufficient. Usually the selection of only one of the ten individual prints proves more than adequate for the necessary information. The coding of ridge detail should be always preceded by the code letter of the digit selected, the symbols being: *RT*, Right Thumb; *RF*, Right Forefinger; *RM*, Right Middle; *RR*, Right Ring; *RL*, Right Little; *LT*, Left Thumb; *LF*, Left Forefinger; *LM*, Left Middle; *LR*, Left Ring; and *LL*, Left Little Finger.

Coding Ridge Characteristics and Loops: The top parallel line of the glass should be placed in such a position that it is in direct line from the point of the delta to, and passing immediately over, the summit of the first or innermost recurving ridge or staple of the core. Only those ridge characteristics appearing within the parallel lines and between the core and delta are considered for coding purposes. The sequence of coding is from left to right, beginning with the ridge next to that of the innermost recurving ridge or staple of the core on the delta side, provided this recurving ridge or staple cuts the lower parallel line. If it does not cut the lower line, then, without moving the glass, pass on toward the delta until the first ridge is struck which cuts both lines, and commence coding with the next ridge nearer the delta. Should the ridge selected, which cuts both lines, bifurcate within the area scrutinized, the bifurcating limb nearer the delta is examined, and should it be found to possess an eye or further bifurcation, it is selected as the point from which to begin coding. Should it possess neither an eye nor bifurcation, coding begins with the next ridge nearer the delta. The ridge nearer the delta from bifurcation or ridge would still be ignored in passing, if it did not disclose another bifurcation or eyelet. Each ridge is then coded in turn until the delta is reached. Ridges containing bifurcations or eyes which terminate within the parallel lines are coded. Any *O* is inserted after coding each ridge for the purpose of eliminating punctuation marks.

Coding should never be extended beyond the delta. It is not generally necessary to proceed as far as the delta, but when this is reached, the figure 9 should be inserted as the delta symbol. In the event that characteristic data between the delta and core are considered insufficient, coding may be continued by considering the ridges on the opposite side of the core. Occasionally two or more characteristics appear in one ridge and within the area set off by the parallel lines, and additional rules are necessary for coding:

a. All characteristics in a ridge are coded in sequence commencing from the top.
b. When a ridge bifurcates, the lower limb nearer the core is considered one separate ridge, and the limb nearer the delta another separate ridge, if it possesses characteristic data.

c. When an additional ridge appears between the prongs of a fork or bifurcation, the coding of this is done immediately after coding the bifurcation, and any characteristics appearing in the limb from bifurcation which is nearer the core.

Coding the Twinned Loop: It is judged necessary to consider only one of the loops. The ascending loop is selected, and the delta used is the one reached from the core of loop without traversing ridges forming the core of the other loop. The glass and parallel lines are placed the same as for loops. The coding sequence and method is similar to that for loops with the following addition: Should a ridge be considered to recurve before reaching the lower parallel line of the glass, it is deemed to cut this line if it cuts the perpendicular line, and is coded accordingly.

Coding Lateral Pockets: The same procedure is followed as for Twinned Loops.

Coding Tented Arches: The top parallel line is placed across the summit of the first recurving ridge or staple, enveloping the core in horizontal position; the perpendicular line should cut the center of this ridge. The pattern is coded in much the same manner as an ulnar loop of the right hand. However, the sequence of coding arches is always from left to right on the right-hand side of the core.

Coding Central Pocket Loops: When the result of ridge tracing from the two deltas of this type of pattern shows it to be inner, the right delta is used; when outer, the left delta is employed. The top parallel line of the glass is placed in a direct line from the delta used to the summit of the first recurving ridge over the core. The first ridge coded is that next to the first ridge from the core which cuts both parallel lines. Then follow coding procedure for loops.

Coding Whorls: Either one of the parallel lines of the glass is placed in a direct line from the right delta, cutting the lower edge of the innermost recurving ridge below the core and continuing. The sector considered for coding is that below the parallel line, and it does not extend beyond either delta. It is not necessary to code all the ridges within the area, but if a delta is reached, this fact should be designated by the figure 9. Coding of whorls begins with the ridge which is next to the recurring ridge immediately below the core, and which is cut by the parallel line. Coding is done by following its course clockwise, recording the code symbols in sequence of all the ridge characteristics discovered. It is assumed that with a terminating ridge the same procedure would be followed as in tracing the branch of a delta.

Collins states that compound patterns and accidentals are very rare, and it is therefore unnecessary to code the characteristics of these. But they are capable of being coded by the same system outlined above. No satisfactory method was developed for coding plain arches.

THE LARSON SINGLEPRINT SYSTEM

The types used in this work are similar to those used in the Henry system, viz.—Arches, Loops, S types, or the Henry Twin Loop and Lateral Pocket, Whorls, Central Pockets, and Combinations or Accidentals.

Arches: The patterns of the arch type have the ridges running across the pattern and there is usually no delta, but if there is a delta, no ridge must intervene between the delta and the core, unless this ridge be part of the delta. There must not be a single recurving ridge. There must be no ridge count. Of all the patterns the arch, because of its often extreme simplicity, gives the most trouble in the attempt to devise a satisfactory and yet simple system of classification. The problem is, given the simplest form of the arch, to classify it independently of all other arches. The only safe method is to deal with the individual ridges and to classify them according to their particular characteristics. In the identification of the simple arch by ridge characteristics, obviously the problem is to find a starting point. It was finally decided to use the first bifurcation at the bottom of the print. If two investigators should vary as to this point, they will come together by the ridge sequence, which is ultimately the same.

A. Primary Classification:
    I—Natural arch: Simplest form of arch.
    II—Dotted arch: Many dots and very short ridges.
    III—Tented arch: Defined according to the Henry system.

IV—Arch approximating a loop: In this type there is a core present, an apparent delta or a delta fused with the core.

V—Transitional arch: Intermediate between the natural and the tented arch.

VI—Staircase arch: In this form of pattern there is a characteristic appearance due to a series of long and short ridges.

VII—Irregular arch: This group is a combination group.

B. Sub-Classification:

I—According to Inclination:
1. Non-inclination
2. Inclination to the right
3. Inclination to the left

II—According to the core, if present. In natural arches there is no core, but there may be one in the tented arches, and arches which approximate the central pockets are in the following divisions.

1. Junction
2. Spiral-like origin
3. One rod
4. Dots
5. One-eyed rod
6. Enclosure
7. Compound form, which consists of a dot in the apparent delta and a rod for the core
8. Enclosure combined with a staple
9. Archipelago, which consists of an irregular formation such as might result from a scar
10. Forks or bifurcations
11. Two forks with inclination in the opposite direction
12. Enclosures; staple and dot
13. Tented ridges
14. More than one rod

In the case of tented arches the core may consist of one intricate series of ridges. This network can be handled by a series of simple formulae: Forks: F R or L—i.e. the fork opens to the right or left. Junctions: J R, T or L, i.e. the junction may be at the right, top, or left side. These may be plain or parted.

III—According to the ridge characteristics. Whenever there is a core present, the first ridge above the core forms the starting point for the enumeration of the ridges. If no core is present the first fork is used. If ever necessary, a subsidiary set of ridges has been devised. Here there are several hundred divisions, but the chief point of differentiation from the first set is that there is an exact orientation. That is, if there happen to be five forks and four enclosures, it is possible to know where each characteristic is in respect to the other. The chief objection to this set is that it is not as practical for use with latents. Therefore, the former set is used in the bureau. All types of ridge characteristics may be resolved into a few groups. To label a ridge it is essential that its entire course be followed, unless otherwise indicated. The shape assumed will depend upon the pattern, but the character remains the same. The main divisions are as follows:

I. Simple forks:
  1. Right-angle bifurcations, single
  2. Simple forks, single
  3. Two bifurcations, the two forks being on the same side
  4. Two bifurcations, the two forks being on opposite sides

II. Composites, consisting of junctions, closed formations, and spurlike configurations.
  1. Consists of bifurcations, enclosures and ridges. Here is about as complex an arrangement as may exist, for there may be single or complex ridge systems intervening among the branches of the bifurcations. There are three subdivisions, and these comprise 1 to 30 divisions in each. (a) Bifurcations 1 to 30. (b) Enclosures 1 to 30. (c) Ridges 1 to 30. Recurring ridges. Combinations of recurring ridges with forks, enclosures and ridges. Combinations of enclosures and bifurcations. Combinations of bifurcations alone, and more than two. Bifurcations with included ridges.
  2. All natural ridges
  3. Interrupted ridges
  4. Dots
  5. Enclosures
  6. Recurring ridges
  7. Archipelago, such as left by a scar.
  8. Adhering ridges
  9. Abrupt or fractional ridges
  10. Combination of two recurving ridges, which envelope the pattern

Loops: Loops as to type are defined according to Henry, modified as follows: When a ridge passes between the core and the delta of a simple bifurcation which forms both the core and the delta, the pattern is classified as an arch.

A. Primary Classification:

I. Natural loop
II. Indented loop
III. Approximating S type
IV. Approximating central pocket
V. Approximating the arch
VI. Approximating the tented arch
VII. Irregulur loop
VIII. Adhering ridges
IX. Converging ridges
X. Bifurcation or the invaded loop

B. Sub-Classification:

I. Inclination of the pattern: 1. Inclination to the right. 2. Inclination to the left.

II. Core. There are approximately 1,000 cores. Every main division is left open so that new ones may be added, if found. The subdivisions are as follows:

1. Combinations
2. Composite cores
3. Enclosures
4. Junctions
5. Rods
6. Double rods
7. Eyed rods
8. Multiple rods
9. Forks
10. Forks and rods
11. Staples
12. Double staples
13. Double staples and rods
14. Eyed staples
15. Forked staples
16. Triple staples

All the foregoing are filed alphabetically.

III. Envelopes. Every ridge characteristic given off the first ridge about the core is identified and labeled. The main divisions are as follows:

1. Plain envelopes or staples
2. Envelopes with one or more bifurcations
3. Junction or connection between two staples
   a. One or more enclosures on inside staple
   b. One or more forks on inside staple
   c. Both enclosures and forks on inside staple
4. Horseshoe enclosure which extends either partly or wholly over the top:
   a. With enclosure
   b. With bifurcations
   c. With enclosures and bifurcations

    5. Recurring bifurcation
      a. With enclosure
      b. With bifurcations
      c. With both enclosures and bifurcations
    6. Two recurring ridges

IV. Delta. The delta defined as in the Henry system and further classified as follows:
    1. Open form:
      a. Combination of forks and enclosures
      b. Dot being the closure
      c. Enclosure on one of the diverging ridges
      d. Fork on one of the diverging ridges
      e. Plain
      f. Rod being the closure
    2. Closed form:
      a. Combination of forks and closures
      b. Enclosures on one of the diverging ridges
      c. Fork on one of the diverging ridges
      d. Plain

Rule: When there are dots or rods forming the closure, the number of each is indicated. In addition to indicating the form of closure, the two diverging ridges which constitute the type-lines are classified. These type-lines are followed from the origin as far as a line drawn through the center of the core. When forks or enclosures are given from the type lines, the lines are classified as R, L or M, meaning that the forks are on the right or left side and go in that direction, or that the two diverging lines come together as in the closed form. Here the letter M (meeting) is used, and this followed by R or L (fork on the right or left side). If one type-line is plain and the other has a fork or enclosure, the letters T and L are prefixed to the respective sides. Only the forks and enclosures which come directly from the type-lines are considered. $O\ D\ R\ P\ L\ F$ means that the delta is of open formation with a dot for the enclosure. The right type-line is plain while the left one has a fork.

V. First ridge in from the delta. This is the first ridge directly in front of the delta or point of divergence of the type-lines. It is classified according to the divisions of ridge characteristics previously enumerated. If the course of the ridge is long, its course is never followed further than the point of recurvature at the top. It may be considered limited by a line drawn through the center of the core and is never followed beyond this point of recurve.

S Type: The Henry twinned loop and lateral pocket fall into this division. This pattern is treated as though composed of two distinct loops. There must be two deltas and two sets of recurving, not converging, ridges present.

A. Primary Classification:

  I—The patterns here have an ovoid configuration. There are two distinct cores and two separate envelopes.

  II—Same as I, only there is but one envelope which is common to both cores.

  III—All patterns not in the first two classes which have two envelopes.

  IV—All patterns not in the other classes which have a common envelope.

B. Sub-Classification:

  I—Inclination: 1. None; 2. To the right; 3. To the left.

  II—According to the inclination of each core. From here on the formula for the loop which is the uppermost, is placed in the numerator of a fraction and that for the lower loop in the denominator.

  III—According to the core of each loop. The formula for the upper loop is placed in the numerator and that for the lower one in the denominator. The ridges are only followed to the place of the recurvature. The same cores are used as in the core of loops.

  IV—According to envelope of each loop. If there are two envelopes, the formula for the upper loop is placed in the numerator and that of the lower one in the denominator. The same envelopes are used as in loops.

  V—According to the type of delta. The formula for the right-hand delta is placed in the numerator and that of the left in the denominator.

  VI—According to the first ridge in front of the delta. That in front of the right delta is placed in the numerator and that in front of the left delta in the denominator.

VII—According to the exit of the ridges in reference to the deltas. Here there are 30 subdivisions.

VIII—According to the ridge count. The count for the upper loop is placed in the numerator and that for the lower loop in the denominator. The envelopes are excluded from the count.

Whorls: In patterns of the whorl type there are two deltas and the ridges make at least more than two complete circuits around the core.

Primary Division:

I—Circular enclosures. In this division there are one or more enclosures in the center of the pattern. The contour is circular.

II—Ovoid enclosures. Here there are one or more enclosures, but the pattern as a whole has an ovoid configuration.

III—Spiral or open origin. The pattern as a whole has a circular contour.

IV—Spiral open origin. The pattern as a whole has a distinct ovoidal or elliptical appearance.

V—Adhering or bifurcation ridge type. It is characterized by a series of ridges which are joined to each other either by ridges of the junctional or recurving type, or many ridges seem to adhere to one or both sides of the pattern.

Sub-Classification:

I—Inclination. 1. None. 2. To the right. 3. To the left.

II—Cores:

1. Simple core formation within a circle.
2. Same as 1 except that some of the central core unites with the enveloping enclosure.
3. Composite enclosures.
4. Combinations of two enclosures with minutiae.
5. Combination of three enclosures with minutiae.
6. Combination of four enclosures with minutiae.
7. Combination of more than four enclosures with minutiae.
8. Junctional enclosures with adhering ridge form, without enclosure.
9. Junctional adhering ridge form, without enclosure.
10. Spirallar origin.
11. Open cores cut off from the pattern.

12. Transitional groups, intermediate between the whorl and the S types. There are over 500 of these cores, but each division is left open so that new ones may be added.

III—Envelopes of Whorls:

1. Spurs and bifurcations from a central enclosure.
2. Recurring ridge united with the central enclosure.
3. Combinations of recurring ridges with spurs, bifurcations and the central enclosure.
4. Adhering ridges combined with the central enclosure.
5. Simple spirals.
6. Spirals with bifurcations.
7. Spirallar recurring ridges.
8. Spirallar recurring ridge with bifurcation.
9. Spirallar formation with adhering ridges.
10. Junctional and combinations.

IV—According to ridge tracing. Here there are three divisions as in the Henry system. These are Inner, Meeting, and Outer (Henry rule).

V—According to the type of delta. The same formula is used as before. Here there is this difference, however: the formula for the right delta is placed in the numerator and that of the left in the denominator.

VI—According to the first ridge in front of the delta. The formula for the ridge in front of the right delta is placed in the numerator and that for the left in the denominator of the fraction.

Central Pockets:

This type represents a group which is intermediate between the loop and the whorl. It may possess the characteristics of both the whorl and the loop. It is defined as in the Henry system, with this important difference: there may be at least *two* complete circuits of ridges forming the core, and the pattern is still a central pocket. However, if there are more than two, the pattern is a whorl.

A. Primary Classes:

I—Open formation with adhering ridges

II—Open formation without adhering ridges

III—Closed formation with adhering ridges

IV—Closed formation without adhering ridges

B. Sub-Classification:

I—Inclination
  a. To the right
  b. To the left
II—Core formation the same
  as whorls
III—Envelope formation
  same as in whorls

IV—Delta only the external—
  same as in loops
V—First ridge in front of the
  delta, or external the same
  as in loops

Combination Group:

This group comprises all of those forms not covered in the other types. The chief combinations are:

A. Arch and loop
B. Arch and whorl
C. Arch and central pocket
D. Loop and whorl

E. Loop and central pocket
F. More than two loops
G. Any other combinations

The above are primary divisions, and the subdivisions depend upon the specific forms. As these are compound, the formulae are expressed in fractions. The order of sequence is arch, loop, whorl, S type, and central pocket. Thus in classifying the arch and loop group combination, the classification of the arch is placed in the numerator and that of the loop is the denominator.

THE OLORIZ SINGLE-FINGERPRINT SYSTEM

The primary classification is the same as in the Oloriz system for the ten fingers.

Subdivisions:

I—Centers of cores of the fingers:

  r: A straight line
  b: Two straight lines
  t: Three straight lines
  h: A staple
  p: A central pocket loop
    inclined to the right

  i: A central pocket loop left
  c: A circle
  e: An ellipse
  d: Whorl to the right
  l: Whorl to the left
  k: Two curves
  s: An S (sinuous)

II—Marginal limiting lines: The varied placement of the limiting lines starting from the left delta, with relation to the lines starting from the right delta.

(a) The two left limiting lines end between the two right lines.

(b) The upper left comes under the upper right line; the inferior ones meet.

(c) The superior left passes above, the inferior left ends between the two right lines.

(d) The upper left line comes between the two right lines.

(e) The superior and inferior lines meet.

(f) The superior left comes above the right; the inferior lines meet.

(g) The left lines come under the respective right lines.

(h) The superior left meets, the interior left comes under the right.

(i) The left and right lines merge.

Abbreviations are used for each type in the formula.

III—Types of deltas: There are two kinds of deltas, hollow and prominent.

Hollow (hundidos) deltas:

Ha: Triangle open at its three angles
Has: Triangle open only at the top
Hai: Triangle open only on inner side
Hae: Triangle open only on outer
Hcs: Triangle closed only at the top
Hc: Triangle closed at its three angles
Hci: Triangle closed on inner side
Hce: Triangle closed on outer side

Tripod forms:

Tc: Three short branches
Tcs: Only the upper branch short
Tci: Only the inner branch short
Tce: Only the outer branch short
Tl: Three long branches
Tls: Only upper branch long
Tli: Only inner branch long
Tle: Only the outer branch long

IV—Central basal angle: The angle has for its apex the apex of the center of the figure and for sides: (1) the axis of the center of the figure, (2) the Galton line.

(a) Proximal, when it has more than 60 degrees
(b) Intermedio, when it has 60 degrees
(c) Distal, when it has less than 60 degrees

V—Special or peculiar marks:

(a) Abrupt lines. (b) The bifurcations. (c) Convergences.

Oloriz has used here the characteristic points of Vucetich. These points are brought out by marking squares on the pattern, or by numbering the ridges beginning with some natural point on the pattern.

THE BORGERHOFF SINGLE-FINGERPRINT SYSTEM

The following methods were diversely combined by the various identification services in Belgium:

1. The classing of prints under a certain number of types (types of Galton-Henry, Vucetich, Balthazard, etc.).
2. Counting of ridges between the core and delta, as in the Henry system.
3. Tracing of ridges (Galton-Henry).

The combination of these methods permitted rapid search in a collection of some hundreds of thousands of patterns. However, certain patterns increase very rapidly, and it was found necessary to invent a means of classifying these particular patterns, especially ulnar loops (external in the right hand, internal in the left hand). The ulnar loops are ridge-counted to the third ridge beyond the center (inner terminus or point of core—Henry system). A segment is formed which presents the following characteristics:

Type:

1: The segment encloses three arcs of circle, or three tops of loops, without peculiarities.
2: One or several ridges start in the segment, go out toward the delta.
3: One or several ridges starting in the segment go out in the opposite direction.
4: Ridges starting in the segment and leaving it in two directions.
5: One or several ridges start and end in the segment, nothing more.

6: The segment comprises one or several ridges more or less short of type 3 and one or more departing from type 4.

To these six types two others are added:

1: The traced ridge passes above the delta.

2: The traced ridge meets the upper arm of the delta.

Second Subdivision:

Borgerhoff replaces the Henry ridge counting for loops by substituting for it the Henry ridge tracing, and applies this to loops as follows:

s: The ridge traced goes out from the core.

r: The ridge traced meets the delta, within one, two, or three ridges.

i: The traced ridge remains within the core.

THE STOCKIS SINGLE-FINGERPRINT SYSTEM

This method was introduced in the medico-legal laboratory at Liège, by Eugene Stockis. The prints were first classified according to the Vucetich method in four classes: arches, internal loops, external loops and whorls, with subdivisions as follows:

Type Arch:

Distinction between simple arch, pyramidal arch (Henry's tented arch), arches with centers (with a single loop to the right or left). One further subdivision secured by counting the ridges between the rectilinear base of the pattern and the flexion fold of the phalanx (from 2 to 24).

Type Loop:

1. Ridge counting.
2. Centrobasilar angle of Oloriz. However, the figure limit separating the three classes is 70 degrees and not 60 degrees.
3. Type of the center of the figure (core).
4. Type of the delta (with sixteen varieties of Oloriz).
5. Counting the infra-delta lines between the delta and the flexion fold of the phalanx.

Type Whorl:

1. Ridge tracing.
2. Type of center of figure (core) with division in four types.

3. Angle formed by the two centro-deltic lines of Galton.
4. Ridge counting on each of the Galton lines.
5. Types of deltas, with 16 varieties of Oloriz for each.
6. Number of infra-delta lines to the fold of the joint.

In doubtful cases two or three cards are filed.

THE GASTI SINGLE-FINGERPRINT REGISTER

Gasti's register consists of an album with a hundred columns, ten for each type of classification, one by type and one by fingers. Upon each are inscribed the complete fingerprint formulas, the primary formula, the letters and figures representing the type of delta, and the number of ridges between the delta and the core (ridge counting).

THE MORAN CODE

This code was designed by Deputy Sheriff Boyd B. Moran of San Diego County, California, and consists of an engraved transparent design of one hundred squares, each of 2 mm. dimensions. Indicia A to K, excluding I, are used to indicate particular squares across the top of the design. Similarly, digits from 1 to 0 indicate squares along the side. In use this device is fitted to a fingerprint magnifier, and determines the definite points at which identifying characteristics are present in a finger impression.

THE BORN SINGLE-FINGERPRINT SYSTEM

This system was introduced in the Police Department in Berne, Switzerland. It is original, but shows a close analogy with Jorgensen's method. Born bases his method upon the description of the para-central zones. For this purpose he has invented a magnifying glass provided with a zone scheme, which limits the zone to be described. This arrangement consists of two parallel lines cut by a perpendicular. This method implies two conditions: (1) the designation in figures of the minutiae in the zone described; (2) the manner in which the zone scheme is to be placed on the print so that the zone to be considered will be determined.

Description of Minutiae:

0: Line without minutiae
1: Islet or eye
2: Lower bifurcation
3: Upper bifurcation
4: A dotted line, or one of dashes, or a faintly marked inter-line
5: Fragment—small line cut at top or below
6: Starting line (cut at top)
7: Ending line (cut at bottom)
8: Loop
9: Delta

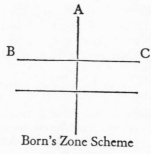

Born's Zone Scheme

Determination of the zone to be described:

The middle of the zone should correspond to the center of the figure, and one describes the minutiae of the nine lines which are to the right and the nine lines which are to left of the center between the parallels of the apparatus. The intersection of the vertical line with the upper parallel line *BC* is called *A*. The two parallel lines are 4 millimeters apart.

Detail following the types of impression:

1. Loops and twinned loops: The point *A* at the summit of the loop; the vertical line in the axis of the figure.
2. Whorls, Spirals, and Central Pockets: The point *A* at the summit of the internal spiral of the inner circle; the vertical line on the axis of the figure.
3. Tented arches of more than 4 mm. in height, as for loops.
4. Tented arches of less than 4 mm. in height: Here the position is inverted. The point *A* is at the summit of the tent, but the parallel *BC* follows the axis of the figure. The zone scheme is then perpendicular to the fold of flexion of the phalanx. Only the ridges to the right of *A,* going toward the farther extremity of the print, are described.
5. Arches: As in the preceding cases, line *BC* follows the axis of the figure and the description is made only to the right of *A* going toward the farther extremity of the print.

Fingerprint Cards:

For each individual, a large notched sheet is used. It is cut into ten cards; each one carries a rolled impression with the complete name, date of birth, fingerprint formula, and the name of the finger. At the top is the registration formula bearing the indication of class, and on 20 little attached squares are the numbers corresponding to the ten lines to the left and the ten lines to the right seen in the zone scheme.

THE SAGREDO SINGLE-FINGERPRINT SYSTEM

Sagredo states that latent impressions of the little fingers are almost always too poor to be used, and he deliberately refrains from filing this finger. However, he further states that good latent prints are to be found on glasses, bottles, windowpanes, etc., and they are usually placed in such a manner that one can readily tell from which fingers they come.

Primary Classification:

As with Oloriz, there are four types: without a delta, left delta, right delta, and double or bi-delta, according to whether the lacking delta is to the right or to the left, or whether there are two deltas.

Sub-Classification without Delta:

Those without deltas or arches, are first grouped by fingers: T: thumb; M: middle; I: index, R: ring. The left-hand fingers are placed with the corresponding right-hand fingers. They are indicated by the exponent 2; thus $T2$ means left thumb. Each kind of finger is divided into 7 classes:

1. Plain or simple arch
2. Arch, point of confluence to the left
3. Arch with point of confluence to the right
4. Arch with central point
5. Piniform, or tented arch
6. Arch with right core
7. Arch with left core

Sub-Classification of One-Deltas:

The loops are one-deltas and are first grouped into right and left, and then are regrouped by the finger: T, M, I, R. Then each group is divided according to type of the center figure (Oloriz).

1. Straight line
2. Two or three straight lines
3. Staples
4. Central pockets
5. Interrogation point
6. Indefinite

Each of these six classes is subdivided by ridge counting (Galton line). In the case of a loop the following formula: $M2H/14$, will mean: Right loop on left middle finger, center of figure a hairpin, with 14 ridges in the ridge count.

Sub-Classification of Bi-Deltas:

The whorls or double deltas are first grouped according to fingers (T, I, M, R), and are then divided according to type of center (as by Oloriz).

1. Circular
2. Spiral
3. Two enlaced staples

4. Sinuous
5. Indefinite

Each of these classes is subdivided by ridge tracing (Henry). Finally a sub-class is made by type of delta (tripod, hollow, etc.) as with Oloriz.

THE DRESDEN SINGLE-FINGERPRINT SYSTEM

This system consists of 220 compartments containing 11,000 single fingerprint files. The classification is made in the following order: Arch to the right. Arch to the left. Tented arch, middle. Middle arch. Tented arch to the right. Tented arch, left.

Right loop, left delta,   1 to 5 ridges
   "   "   "   "   6 to 10 ridges
   "   "   "   "   11 to 15 ridges
   "   "   "   "   16 to 20 ridges
   "   "   with single rod in the center and 1 to 5 ridges
   "   "   "   "   "   "   "   "   "   6 to 10 ridges
   "   "   "   "   "   "   "   "   "   11 to 15 ridges
   "   "   "   "   "   "   "   "   "   16 to 20 ridges
   "   "   "   "   "   "   "   "   "   21 or more ridges
   "   "   "   two or several rods in center
   "   "   in form Z
   "   "   in form V (broken loop)
Left loop, right delta (same sequence as with Right Loop)
Whorl, circle to right
   "   "   in the middle
   "   "   to the left
Simple spiral to right, middle, and left
Double spiral to right, middle, and left

Ellipse to the right, middle, and left
Central pocket to the right, middle, and left

Abnormal types: Other forms of arches, right loops, left loops, whorls. The classification is made with the aid of a small magnifying glass mounted on a tripod, and provided on the lower side with a circle and cross. When searching, characteristic points are studied.

THE NEBEN REGISTER OF ROSCHER

The ten-finger classification system of Roscher provides for a single fingerprint method, with a counter-register and a series of annexed registers. There are six of the latter, classifying the left middle fingers, left little fingers. These fingers are grouped in sub-classes, using nine types as in the ten-finger classification.

THE LYONNESE SINGLE-FINGERPRINT SYSTEM

This system coincides to a large extent with those of Oloriz and Stokis. The prints are divided into four classes: arch, left loop, right loop, whorl. Then follow the subdivisions.

Arches—Subdivided into four classes (Stokis): a. Simple arch; b. Pyramidal arch; c. Arch containing a single right loop; d. Arch containing a single left loop. These four sub-classes are then subdivided by counting the lines between the rectilinear base and the fold at the flexion of the phalanx.

Loops, right or left, are first divided by the type of the center (core) of the figure (Oloriz). Sub-Type division of loops: a. A single rod with free extremity; b. A single rod ending at the curve of the loop; c. Two or more rods; d. A loop (two rods joined at the top); e. Varied figures: staples, circles, spirals, two loops. Each sub-type may be divided by the centro-basal angle of Oloriz. They may be subdivided by ridge counting or by measurement in millimeters (Heilmann).

Whorls: Subdivided into 5 sub-types by the center (core) of the figure (Oloriz). Sub-Type: *a*: Circle or ellipse. *c*: Spiral turning to left. *y*: Spiral turning to right. *s*: Twinned loops. *e*: Varied figures (hooks, hairpins, etc.).

Each type is then divided by ridge tracing (Henry).

THE GIRAUD AND HENQUEL SYSTEM

This system was devised by Professor Giraud of the Laboratory of Police Science in Algiers, and represents a classification method which is intermediate to the general collection and the single-fingerprint method. The left and right hands are classed separately. The index finger comes first, and is represented by a letter. The other fingers then come in the following order: thumb, middle, ring, and little finger. Each is represented by a fraction, the numerator being the class, and the denominator the subdivision. The classes, represented by letters for the index and by numerators of the fraction for the other fingers, are as follows:

1. Arches
2. Loops with staples to the left
3. Loops with staples to the right

4. Spirals
5. Circles, ovals, and rackets
6. Whorls
7. Not classifiable

Subdivision: Represented by letters for the index and by the denominators of the fractions for the other fingers as follows:

A 1/1: Pure arch
T 1/2: Tented arch or arch with single loop
V 1/3: Other forms of arches
E 2/1: Simple loop or containing one line
F 2/2: Loop circumscribing several lines
G 2/3: Composite loop and racket with at least four spirals
H 3/1: Simple loop or with one line
I 3/2: Loop circumscribing several lines
J 3/3: Small composite loop and racket with less than 4 spirals
C 4/1: Four spirals at least in form of C
CR 4/2: At least four spirals in form of reversed C
CS 4/3: At least three spirals surrounding a circle
O 5/1: Two isolated circles surrounded by at least three other ovals or spirals
OV 5/2: An oval surrounded by at least three other ovals or spirals
Q 5/3: Racket with at least four spirals
D 6/1: Knapsacks or joined central pockets

S 6/2: Double volute in S form
Z 6/3: Double volute in form of reversed S
Y 7/1: Permanent scars
K 7/2: Amputations or stiff joints
X 7/3: Unreadable prints

THE BARLOW SINGLE-FINGERPRINT SYSTEM

This system is used in the Los Angeles Police Department, and was devised by Captain H. L. Barlow, Superintendent of the Record and Identification Division. There is a separate file or compartment for each finger. The next segregation is according to pattern: Loop, whorl, central pocket, lateral pocket, twin loop, accidental, arch, and tented arch. The segregation within the pattern groups is as follows:

Loops:

LL: Common loop with exit of ridges flowing to the left (ulnar if in the left hand)

LR: Common loop with ridges to the right

LCP: Loops approximating central pocket (left and right slopes are taken into consideration when classifying loops)

LS: Loop approximating S type. Twin loops and lateral pockets

Lind: Loop indented, with ridges at core, turning abruptly at an angle to the exit of ridges

Ridge count between core and delta

Core formation:

A: An abrupt ridge or dot forms the core

B: Blurred at point of core

C: Complex—does not fall into other divisions

D: Scarred (any part of pattern)

E: Enclosure at point of core

F: Fork at point of core

R1: One rod at point of core

R2: Two rods at point of core

R3: Three rods at point of core

S: Staple at point of core

S½: Staple one-half parted at point of core

SDP: Staple double parted at point of core

Subdivision of $R1$, S, and $S\frac{1}{2}$—according to core formation:

A: An abrupt ending of rod or staple

EL: Enclosure to left of core

EM: Enclosure to middle

ER: Enclosure to right of core

FU: Fork up on rod or staple

FD: Fork down on rod or staple

Whorls:

1. Circular enclosure
2. Ovoid enclosure
3. Circular spiral to right
4. Circular spiral to left
5. Ovoid spiral to right
6. Ovoid spiral to left
7. Irregular—does not fall in any other divisions
8. Approximating S type
9. Circular enclosure with dot or abrupt ridge inside
10. Interlocked core pattern
11. Ovoid enclosure with dot or abrupt ridge inside
12. Close in delta, core difficult to decipher, count the ridges to the nearest delta

The foregoing twelve whorl classifications are then subdivided by counting the ridges intervening between the core and the nearest delta. Inclination of core: A, straight up, L, left, and R, right.

Subdivision of Twin Loops and Lateral Pockets (S type):

$S1A$: Left loop pointed downward; inclination of loops straight up and down.

$S1L$: Left loop pointed downward; inclination of loops to left.

$S1R$: Left loop pointed downward; inclination of loops to right.

$S2A$: Left loop pointed upward; inclination of loops straight up and down.

$S2L$: Left loop pointed upward; inclination of loops to the left.

$S2R$: Left loop pointed upward; inclination of loops to right.

SA: Inclination of loops lies straight across the finger in a horizontal position.

Subdivision of Twin Loop and Lateral Pocket by counting the ridges intervening between the extreme end of one of the loops forming the S type, and the nearest delta. Scarred patterns are filed under Scar.

Arches:

Inclination of the pattern: A, if no general slope or inclination; L, if inclination is to left; R, if inclination is to right.

Common arches are subdivided according to characteristics of the center of the pattern (enclosure present, a ridge forks to left or right, or a dot or an abrupt ridge appears).

Arches approximating loops are subdivided: Appearance of a delta with no recurring ridge whereby ridge counting is possible, or recurring ridge and no delta. Inclination of pattern—exit of ridges, provided the pattern was a loop.

Tented Arches: Inclination—same as under Arches. Preponderance of the ridges to the left or right of the central ridges, determines the inclination. If the ridges approximate a loop formation with ridge or ridges indicating such approximate formation flowing to left or right, the inclination would be left or right (*L* or *R*) accordingly.

IX

FILE AND SEARCH FACILITIES

From an administrative point of view, a large police headquarters is simply a large business office, whose management is subject to the same general rules and criteria by which efficiency is fostered and measured in more prosaic businesses. A casual reading of the typical manual of police regulations will reveal its character to be that of a manual of office procedures. With regard to field operations, the manual instructs the patrolman in his actions prior and subsequent to an actual police incident with special emphasis on communications, reports, and availability. The manual does not purport to guide the patrolman in his performance during the actual police incident except negatively, in the form of prohibitions and caveats with implied sanctions. Nor should we expect positive instruction and inflexible rules of action on matters so dependent on individual circumstances, on the interactions of the personalities involved, and on the police officer's capacity for judgment—and, in the final analysis, judgment in dealing with persons in conflict situations is the one quality that should preeminently distinguish the policeman from his fellow citizens.

The manual of regulation is, in effect, a manual of office procedure. Too often it is an outdated manual in the sense that it reflects few of the major improvements developed within the last few decades. Limitations of budget and personnel all too frequently have hobbled police departments in their efforts to convert to modern office practices.

FILING FACILITIES

Happily, the identification bureaus of large police departments have been in the forefront of those who recognize and act on the need for a more efficient and more effective set of office procedures. The urgency is obvious in the case of the identification bureau since this unit contains the largest set of office files in the police department and is effective only when it can perform file searches systematically, thoroughly, reliably, and rapidly. Fingerprints and criminal records are simply office files of a special nature which require sorting and setting up along lines which will insure a quick and effective search. A number of police departments, appreciating the excessive labor load of their identification bureaus, have availed themselves of modern machine methods to facilitate filing and shorten file-search time without sacrifice of reliability.

The identification bureau of the St. Louis Police Department is a good example of modern machine methods applied to identification work. Most of the desiderata of an efficient filing system have been achieved: reduced floor space requirements; lower personnel operating costs; faster reference to records; simplified guiding system to shorten filing and finding time; and suitable provision for future expansion. Before the installation of mechanized filing units, the records division of the St. Louis Police Department maintained about nine million cards housed in vertical filing cabinets. Arrayed in rows these cabinets extended a distance of 80 feet. In the current system the cards are divided into work stations, responsibility is fixed, and personnel reduced by 20 per cent.

Two aspects of a modern identification bureau must be considered; one is concerned with the convenient and efficient maintenance of the records while the other is related to the method of searching (including filing) employed. This latter should be an electronic data processing method chosen with a view to the size and complexity of the files.

The maintenance of the records refers to the orderly housing of the four or more major classifications. In the New York Police Department these are:

1. The Master Criminal File, containing the criminal records and fingerprints in serial number sequence.

2. The Fingerprint File:
   a. Criminal record sheets.
   b. Card-size fingerprint records 8" x 8".

3. The Index File, consisting of 3" x 3" cards filed alphabetically and by fingerprint classification.

4. The "Mug" Shot File.

ELECTRONIC DATA PROCESSING

Thus far, fingerprint files have been discussed primarily in terms of the efficiency resulting from mechanization, a word which implies for the most part a capability of using electrical motors and other aids to bring a filing area quickly within the reach of the operator.

More significant, perhaps, is the application of methods of electronic data processing to fingerprint file searches. Punched-card systems such as the IBM are currently favored. A punched-hole pattern is imposed on the card to correspond to selected fingerprint data and other identifying facts associated with the subject. An electronic data processing system for fingerprints is currently in use in the New York State Department of Identification.

Used for a fingerprint search alone, the punched-card system is adapted to a suitable code for fingerprint classifications. Each finger is considered in the search and all ten fingers are searched simultaneously. Technical sequence is not considered; that is, a 32/32 may well be filed in front of a 2/1 or other combination. A tolerance for human error in ridge counting is considered. Thus, in a count of 16, the machine may be set to search with a tolerance of ± 3, that is, 13, 14, 15, 16, 17, 18, and 19 will also be searched. For a count of 15 or lower, a tolerance of ±2 is considered adequate.

Other criminal files include the "Released Prisoner File," the "Nickname File," various special indexes of the "'Mug' File," and the "Known Gambler File." The files of any large police department will vary, particularly with respect to the auxiliary sections. The general problems, however, will remain the same, namely: the housing of large numbers of units with a view to availability, rapid file search, and supervisory control.

Some of the mechanized units adaptable to this purpose are shown in the accompanying illustrations, which display Remington Rand equipment. Mechanized filing equipment is also available from Diebold, IBM, and other companies. The functions of these units are indicated in the caption; details and relative advantages can be found in the literature of systems companies.

Reference searches can be made simultaneously with the original search. These can include primaries, secondaries and final classifications. The machine prints the primaries searched, as well as the total number of cards handled, the date of birth, and the serial number of possible identifications. Printing of the primary serves as a check on reference searches; printing the serial number and the date of birth permits a quick check of prints for purposes of comparison.

The IBM system of searching is adjustable to either ridge counts or pattern types. With the latter, the number of fingerprint items placed on a card can be restricted to permit a set of other identifying data to be added in the form of punched holes. Serial number, date of birth, race, and similar items can then be added.

The problem of rapidly searching fingerprint files will probably find a more satisfactory solution by the application of the methods of microcopying and scanning. Within the last decade, considerable progress has been made in the development of microcopying processes for the collection, classification, and finding of information. The methods of document microcopying employing a narrow gauge motion picture film can be used for criminal records in conjunction with machines for selecting information of a specified kind from entries in a large filing system.

Thus, copies of criminal records can be attached to the cards of an IBM machine, for example, which selects cards on the desired subject by the operation of a coding system keyed to punched holes.

A far more rapid way of achieving the same result, while avoiding the excessive wear of cards, is suggested by a scanning method such as that used in the Rapid Selector project initiated by Vannevar Bush. Each frame of microfilm contains a record composite and a reference code consisting of an area of black film with a system of clear spots. The film is moved rapidly past a projector, which causes the image of the spots to be superimposed on an "interrogating card" bearing black spots on a white background, corresponding to the subject matter for which the reference records are sought. The combined images are scanned photoelectrically. When two patterns coincide, an electronic circuit causes the images of the desired frames to be printed on an unexposed film by means of an electronic flash.

The prototype of this apparatus scanned film at the rate of 72,000 frames per minute. Improved versions have achieved scanning or searching rates of 120,000 frames per minute.

It should be noted in this method that microfilm is no longer restricted to the storage of "dead" material and that careful prearrangement is not needed to permit finding the information. The Rapid Selector method permits the random addition of new material as it is received. Each entry is filmed and coded as for normal film. Thus, microfilm is used to replace both the files and the indexes to the files and in such a form as to permit a search at the rate of 100,000 entries per minute. The additional advantage of reduction of storage space for the actual working file is obvious, since this is now in the form of microfilm.

Another approach to the desiderata of accessibility and storage capacity is offered by the "Minicard" system which uses 16-mm film with an image reduction of 60 diameters. Four images of an 8-inch card can be placed end to end within the width of the 16-mm film. In the "Minicard" system the film is used in a special camera equipped with an additional unit for exposing part of the film to form a coded system of clear or opaque dots. The disposition of these dots yields the information necessary to each card. The information itself is derived from a paper tape previously punched in a machine using a typewriter keyboard. Automatic devices can be obtained for converting code from punched cards or magnetic tape. The use of a binary code permits the application of a digital computer to sorting and searching. Finally, the system uses a low-contrast process, a feature that makes not only for legibility of text but also for imaging fingerprints without sacrifice of detail and for recording "mug" shots, which require, even in crude reproduction, a continuous-tone process.

The foregoing methods rely on coded fingerprint symbols, date of birth, and like data. Greater storage capacity and reduced search time suggest the feasibility of a much more broadly based single-print file using line-light interruptions, within the near future.

COMMUNICATIONS

Devices like the Speedphoto that transmit facsimiles of fingerprints over communications lines have been available for some time. These pictures look like the wired photographs seen in newspapers, and are ordinarily used in emergencies, for example when a rapid check with FBI central files is needed. When only fingerprint classifications need be sent, a telephone call, or, for wider circulation, the teletype system, can be cheaply and effectively used. The difficulties of transmitting classifications accurately over wire were studied as far back as 1919, when Wentworth first devised a code system to reduce the probability of error.

Another problem in fingerprint communications that has received study is that of rapidly reproducing a great number of copies of fingerprints for distribution in cities throughout the area. An associated problem is the quick production of "wanted" posters bearing fingerprints.

The difficulty in mass reproduction lies in the tendency to lose detail. Although a number of processes are available for this type of reproduction, many of them fail to meet the standards of clear and full replicas. One of the more satisfactory methods is Eastman's Ektalith.

X

LATENT FINGERPRINTS IN CRIMINAL INVESTIGATION

A FACTOR of frequent importance in the field of criminal investigation is that of so-called "latent fingerprints." The word "latent" is derived from the Latin, and means "something hidden." With evidential finger-traces, this is not invariably the case; but in recognition of approved usage, any discussion of the subject must accept the expression, at least in its current significance. Therefore, throughout this text, the term "latent fingerprints" will be applied alike to impressions both discernible and less apparent.

Latent fingerprints have been defined as the markings of oily matter or perspiration from the skin glands, left upon any surface which the hands and fingers may have touched. These are often perceptible to the unaided eye, although in other instances they are actually "latent," being indistinct or even invisible, and require developing or "disclosing" treatment to establish their utility.

Much has been written on the subject of latent fingerprints, but unfortunately a great deal of this matter is in the form of popular fiction, and of little practical value. The veritable fingerprint technician may not always display the invincibility of story-book sleuths. Nevertheless, average readers still credit

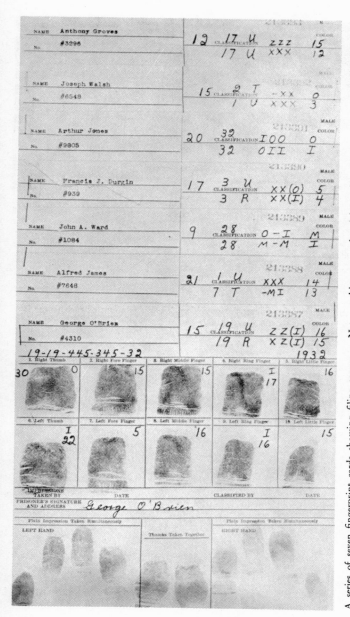

A series of seven fingerprint cards showing sequence. Note machine-stamped serial number above the fingerprint classification number: 213387, 213388, 213389, etc. Cards in this electronic system are filed by serial number, not by fingerprint classifications. Hence, a card with a classification of 1/7 may be filed in back of one with a primary of 19/19. The print classifications shown are according to the American system used by the New York State DCI

Dial controls designed for fingerprint searching. The ridge count of each finger is dialed, beginning with the right thumb and continuing on through to the left little finger

This illustration is a view of 8x8 fingerprint records in the New York State DCI. As can be seen by the numbers on the guides, these cards are now filed by serial numbers rather than by fingerprint classifications. This method of filing makes it possible to fill each drawer completely, thus conserving filing space

Electronic data processing machine used by the New York State DCI for fingerprint and personal appearance searching. The control panel of twenty dials on the
top left-hand side of the apparatus is designed especially for fingerprint searches

these exaggerated achievements, and thus are sometimes led to demand overmuch from the real investigator, who labors under the handicap of physical limitations.

Despite all this, success may be expected from the expert whose training embraces the many arts and devices that have been usefully employed in fingerprint procedure. The compilation of data in this work has been made with the object of including the more effective of these methods.

The potential aids offered to law-enforcement by fingerprints are numerous. This is especially true of latents. Though perhaps not so frequently involved as the conventional "ten-finger" methods, when latent traces do have a place in some investigation, it may be that the case's ultimate issue will depend upon their testimony. The finger-markings on some lethal weapon often determine whether the act was that of suicide or murder; skin patterns, faintly visible on a ransom note, may identify the perpetrator and speed the rescue of an imperiled captive; while digital impressions on an important document may affect the course of national destiny.

It has been aptly said that the criminal's own hand is his greatest enemy. As the most important aid to the sense of touch, the hand and fingers meet frequently with surrounding objects and surfaces, thus producing evidential markings that may serve either to condemn or to vindicate the accused. The tiny ridges which nature has provided upon the human hands and feet, appear in patterns that are unique with every individual; an autograph never duplicated, that will often be recorded, since the hands are the part of the anatomy essentially exposed to contact.

A circumstance frequently overlooked, but none the less noteworthy, is the fact that the skin is an organ; it is, in reality, the largest of all the organs. It would be impractical to present a highly technical discussion of the skin at this time; it is very necessary, however, to recognize here some few of its characteristics, and especially such as relate to latent fingerprints.

Misleading statements have been published to the effect that "latent fingerprints are made from the oil which the skin of the fingers secretes." Oil is secreted and exuded by the sebaceous glands, which are usually adjacent to the hair follicles; in consequence, the skin of the palms and fingers exudes relatively little oil. The normally hairless friction surfaces of the human hands may accumulate oil through touching the other oil-exuding areas, such as the face, neck, hair, scalp, etc. The normal excretion of the palms and fingers is perspiration, which contains 98.5 to 99.5 per cent water, and 0.5 to 1.5 per cent of solids. Of these solids, one-third is inorganic matter, chiefly salt, while two-thirds are urea and such organic components as volatile fatty acids, formic acid, acetic acid, butyric acid, and occasionally a trace of albumin, about 0.045 per cent.

Individuality is presented not only in the general forms of friction-skin anatomy, but also in their more intimate peculiarities. Under magnification, the apex of each friction ridge will be seen to display numerous minute openings, the exits of the skin glands, or pores. These are extremely variable as to size, formation, and position upon the friction ridge. But, despite their smallness, they still feature importantly in the field of latent fingerprints, since they too constitute a definitely individual characteristic (Fig. 151, *A* and *B*).

With the study of latent traces left by human hands and fingers, a little common-sense consideration will reveal more possibilities here presented than may at first be recognized. The feet and hands are obviously the chief instruments of the mind, and are connected with the brain by many nerves. Life is a union of mind and body, and the mind most certainly can not be considered without recognition of its reference to, and effect upon, the body. At birth, each person is endowed through inheritance with certain possessions, mental and physical. These assets are, in principle, common to all humanity, but in kind and degree they differ with the individual. Since body forms vary in appearance, providing visible personalities, experience associates outward signs with certain inward qualities.

Upon entering the world, each individual is the product of his many ancestors; the molding of every tissue fiber, every brain convolution, and every physical endowment, is an ancestral legacy which must be accepted without choice. This complex creature is quite different from all his fellows, and is recognizable as such. Furthermore, he is certain to display much of the individuality stamped on his exterior, just as a bottle is labeled. This is easy to understand, since every form taken by matter suggests at least some of its latent elements.

Fig. 151A   Fig. 151B

Enlarged view of a fingerprint showing the personal characteristics of ridge structure and pore formation.

Thus, common sense would insist that the patterns in the human skin, like other features of the anatomy, must inevitably reveal not only hereditary influences, but also more intimate descriptive indications with every individual.

Obviously, evidence here displayed would suggest those attributes with which the subject began his career. The rule is qualified, however, by skin alterations resulting from illness, injury, and occupation. It would be strange if this were not the case. As already indicated, the skin is continually exposed to modifying contacts; it includes an important part of the excretory system, that must be affected in varying degrees by bodily conditions; and it is closely involved with both the circulatory and nervous systems, which are constantly in tune with every transient physical state.

Fig. 152   Fig. 153

Fig. 152. Fingerprint showing pronounced skin creases. These frequently occur as a result of illness

Fig. 153. Fingerprint of an elderly person showing distinctive skin conditions indicating advanced age

Where the possibilities are so many and various, an inclusive enumeration would be impractical. Nevertheless, it seems advisable to cite a few representative examples. Every fingerprint technician is familiar with the white lines often seen in ink-recorded fingerprints, and resulting from tiny creases in the skin (Fig. 152). These skin-folds may be caused by both age and illness. However, the age-wrinkles are usually manifest as such (Fig. 153). In the lower skin levels are present tiny clusters of fatty tissue that resemble minute bunches of grapes. With abrupt losses of weight, these fat clusters are rapidly absorbed, and the skin shrinks, thus forming folds, or pleats. These folds cause the fine, white, transverse lines in fingerprints.

The pore openings usually react conspicuously to high body temperatures. With feverish conditions, the pores dilate, and in severe cases, remain permanently enlarged. When pore-enlargement becomes pronounced, as it does in some ailments, the ridges will assume a broken or interrupted appearance, being cut or separated at many of the pore exits, which have grown so large as to cut completely through the ridge (Fig. 154). Also, a patient convalescing from serious illness of any kind, will frequently display in the skin a distinctly "mottled" appearance where small areas of the cuticle have scaled off in patches.

Some maladies leave the friction ridges reduced or flattened, so that there is little difference between the ridges and the furrows. In such cases,

Typical example of broken and interrupted ridges. This condition often results from excessive pore-enlargement

Fig. 154

the print shows but small indication of ridge structure. In certain trophic disorders, the skin becomes seriously affected, taking on the semblance of paint that is checked and cracked from overexposure to the sun. Many diseases show their most pronounced symptoms in the skin, and for further discussion of this aspect, the student is referred to standard texts on dermatology.

A scientist familiar with the field of paleontology has little difficulty in reconstructing an accurate likeness of some long-extinct animal from nothing more than a few fossilized bone fragments. It is conceivable that the skilled fingerprint techni-cian may approximate this accomplishment, and deduce the description of an unknown suspect from some informative digital impression. The skins of men and women are distinc-tively different, while an intimate examination of recorded ridge structure will often reveal indications of not only sex, but also race, age, occupation, past and present ailments, to-gether with many other personal characteristics and condi-tions. Obviously, the establishment of but a few common facts concerning an unknown subject will be of considerable as-sistance in determining his identity.

Although it is true that the general configuration of skin patterns remains constant, it has already been shown that temporal causes may produce at least superficial, but none the less discernible, alteration. In this connection, it has been determined that the diameter of the friction ridges of an adult is usually about two-and-one-half times their diameter at birth. A somewhat more definite standard is furnished in the follow-ing table, which indicates the number of ridges to be expected in the average finger patterns at various ages:

Age	Ridges to Be Counted in the Space of 5 mm.
Newborn	15 to 18 ridges
Eight years	13 "
Twelve years	12 "
Twenty years	9 to 10 "

In cases of adults with extremely large hands, the ratio may drop to 6 or 7 ridges at the age of twenty years.

It must be remembered that this table should not be taken as final in all instances, since the number of ridges will vary slightly with different persons. However, from a latent fragment of even limited area, it is usually possible to state with some assurance whether the subject is a young child, an adolescent, or a male or female adult.

Further indications of age are recognized in the skin creases already mentioned, and also in the ridges themselves, which in elderly persons are frequently flattened, or ragged, and with the edges no longer smooth and sharply defined as in youthful skin.

An important circumstance to be noted is the fact that there is often a relationship between the general physique and the structure of the skin. Large, burly persons are more likely to have friction patterns of a coarser quality than those of a small, delicately formed individual, whose skin patterns may approach the appearance of a woman's fingerprints. Furthermore, with abnormally small male adults, the friction ridges are not only narrower, but also fewer in number than in the hand and finger surfaces of taller persons. Although this may not be inevitable in all cases, it is a general condition.

Another useful indication is found in the comparative length of the fingers, a tall person's usually being elongated and decidedly unequal, while the hands of one who is short and stout may display fingers that are also short and stubby, none being much longer than the others.

There is little doubt that skin patterns do display some general race characteristics, especially in pure-blooded groups of little intermingling. This is notably true of Negroes and Orientals, whose patterns are commonly distinctive enough to be recognized in any accumulation of miscellaneous prints. With familiarity, the skilled technician finds it possible to discriminate, although the aptitude is more easily acquired than described. The evidence found in latent prints may offer only occasional suggestions as to an unknown's nationality, but when combined with the many other indications, even this fragmentary information adds materially to the clue's collective value.

A more definite source of information is seen in occupational markings, since a great many kinds of activity cause decisive changes in the skin and hands. For example, when numerous tiny pits or spots show in a fingerprint, it may suggest the subject's being a tailor, a seamstress, an upholsterer, a sail maker, a shoe repairer, a maker of artificial flowers, or a cleaner and presser, whose thumb and index finger have been superficially burned by hot pins removed from the steamed garments on which he was working. Numerous other forms of work occasion similar damage, which is often more precisely classifiable by the disfigurement's exact location; that is, just which of the fingers have been involved.

Broad, vertical wrinkles indicate the hands of a dishwasher, a tanner, a laundress, or other person whose hands are kept constantly in liquids or astringents. Although calluses are usually found on the palms, it often happens that the constant use of a tool or other appliance will leave recognizable traces pointing to a certain vocation. Even the absence of occupational blemishes offers indications of at least negative value, since it tends to eliminate suspects engaged in disfiguring labor.

The fingerprints of musicians are sometimes recognizable, notably those of the violinist and bass-fiddle player. The pianist's fingers are frequently large and square; and the saxophone or clarinet player develops a heavy callus on the inside of the right thumb.

Latent prints are often representative when left by hands that habitually use the hammer, pickax, chisel, saw, and various other implements, and although it may not be possible to determine the precise tool involved, the presence of occupational alteration in any form constitutes an important class characteristic. As already indicated, the thickness of the epidermis may alter with circumstance, and the skin of a workman will be much thicker than that of a clerical employee, or one accustomed to inaction.

With the cellular replacement of epidermal tissue, superficial abrasions are eventually repaired by nature. However, when a skin damage penetrates both layers and destroys or disturbs the underlying structure, a permanent disfigurement results. In view of their endurance, these scars have high identification value. Also, their nature, degree, and location may indicate the injury's possible cause, thus intimating the subject's probable activities.

When considering any wounds disclosed in a latent fingerprint, the student must exercise care in distinguishing between temporary and permanent damage. The reasons are plain; should a latent trace, displaying scars, be offered in evidence, its legal value would be nullified should the accused's currently recorded fingerprint include no such blemish. This situation could arise if the original skin disturbance had resulted from a wart, hand-corn, mole, or similar growth, which had since healed. A wart may alter the course of ridge structure, and yet disappear leaving no trace. Ordinarily, a temporary abrasion does not disturb the course of a friction pattern, and leaves the ridges ending evenly; whereas a lasting scar leaves the ridge-endings drawn and puckered (Fig. 155). Discrimination is needful to recognize these conditions. A helpful hint may be offered in the case of warts and such abnormalities, since they usually "push the ridges apart" rather than pucker them, much the same as thrusting a pencil-point through a piece of cloth fabric.

Various authorities differ as to the period of time that fingerprints may endure upon touched surfaces. Obviously, the atmospheric conditions must affect this duration, but the physical state of the person who left the traces, and the nature of the surface where the prints adhere, are also of high importance. Fingerprints will usually remain viscid for several days when left upon glass, steel, or other smooth and non-porous surfaces, and may be developed by any one of a number of simple methods. The most favorable results are obtained when the impressions have been made but a short time, and while the exudation is still sticky and not as yet contaminated by dust or other foreign matter. But despite the time element, fingerprints may be developed, under certain favorable conditions, and by the

Fig. 155

Scarred fingerprint. This is a typical example of permanent damage proper methods, even when all the moisture has dried; this may be years after they were recorded.

In the business of criminal investigation, fingerprints are frequently discovered that were made with materials other than perspiration. Blood, soot, ink, paint, oil, grease, common dirt, and many other substances, feature as recording mediums. It sometimes happens that the presence of one or more of such materials offers considerable aid in making legible the especial impressions. The problem is more difficult when the touching was done with clean hands; this usually requires special treatment. But even in such instances, it is often quite possible to achieve success. A touch, however light, must have an effect upon the surface where it falls. This may be illustrated by writing upon a window or mirror with a clean, dry match. Breathing over the surface will render the markings visible. A similar experiment may be performed with an ordinary rubber stamp. Clean its face carefully, or better still, select a stamp not previously used; then press it upon a sheet of white paper. Breathe upon the paper, and the impression may be seen, since the delicate film of moisture-droplets left by the breath will show a decisive difference of condensation in the places where pressure was made.

Thus a finger-touch may leave recognizable traces, even though the skin surface be quite free from any visible substance. Under normal conditions, healthy fingers are covered with a residue of oil and sweat, known as "body wax," which is transmitted to any surface touched. This exudation is sufficient to produce a picture of the ridge pattern that may be developed by chemical, mechanical, photographic, and other processes, in nearly every case. A more difficult situation exists when the touch falls on some dry or dusty surface, thus producing "negative" impressions of the finger ridges.

Many different conditions affect the recording of fingerprints. The touched surface may be smooth or rough; the fingers may move while in contact and leave smeared impressions; the skin surface may be wet with blood, oil, paint, or may be coated with dry matter such as sand, dust, flour, powder, etc. Dry substances prevent the ridge's transmission by interposing between the fingers and the touched surface, while blotches usually result from fingers that are overmoist with sweat or other liquids.

Latent impressions may display a spotted appearance resulting from bits of foreign matter on the skin, such as grains of dirt, bits of tobacco, fragments of wood fiber, textile fabrics, or similar residue. When fingers are excessively oily, covered with blood or other coloring matter, the recorded lines may have the broken appearance of ridges composed of rows of dots. Although these and many other circumstances may interfere with the recording process, the proper method will usually develop the traces to a state of legibility.

XI

INVESTIGATING LATENT FINGERPRINTS

FORTUNATELY for the investigator, those who habitually commit illegal acts are often below the normal intelligence level. This, however, is by no means true in all cases. From time to time, enforcement officers are harassed by criminals who display a remarkable cunning in evading detection. Here the technician pits his skill against that of the criminal, and success will depend upon the expert's competence and his available resources. But despite the lawbreaker's occasional ingenuity, he is sure to forget discretion in some vital moment, and leave a clue that can bring about his downfall. It is the business of the successful investigator to discover that clue.

The criminal is at all times at a decided disadvantage. The forces opposing him are many and powerful, while he has few if any allies whom he may trust or call upon at need. His acts are customarily committed by stealth, and under the emotional stress of fear, which is certain to inhibit his normal ability. And besides all this, as pointed out, he is frequently mentally subnormal, and thus less able to best the situation.

On the other hand, the criminologist has at his command every known facility of modern science. He may enlist the cooperation of skilled specialists in all fields of human endeavor to aid him when necessary. He has the option of conducting his research amid salutary surroundings and under the most favorable conditions. And above all, he is acknowledged as the delinquent's intellectual superior. Under these circumstances, the nonsuccess of criminal investigation, when occurrent, can be attributed to little else than negligence.

The quality of persistence is important in conducting criminal investigation. The technician should employ every possible effort and utility to accomplish his purpose. Furthermore, his enterprise should be conducted methodically. No fixed set of instructions could be compiled that would answer in every situation; however, there are some basic policies that will apply usually.

When the expert learns that a crime has been committed, his first care should be that the locale be left undisturbed pending his arrival. At the actual scene, if it be a dwelling or any enclosed structure, the technician should exclude all other persons from the place of his investigations. Should the location be an outdoor area, as when a body is discovered in some open field or lot, or when an importantly involved motor vehicle is to be examined on the street, the zone should be enclosed as soon as possible to protect it from invasion. This may be done by stretching a rope or wire about the scene, or by stationing officers at suitable points to keep away intruders. Without such precaution, valuable evidence is sure to be damaged or destroyed by the ignorant and curious, the would-be helpers, and by other troublesome persons.

The actual business of examining a crime scene can be expedited by employing a few simple tactics. Having secured all the first-hand information, select a "starting place" which, in the case of a burglarized building, could logically be the presumed point of entry. Beginning here, make a preliminary survey of the entire premises, noting the general conditions, position of all objects, and other geographical features. At this time it is important to recognize anything that may seem unusual. One of the most helpful factors in criminal investigation is incongruity. Informative clues may exist in disarranged furniture, scattered objects, unexplained damage, and many other indicative circumstances. As a matter of fact, anything that seems in any way out of the ordinary deserves closest consideration.

It is scientifically true that no person can even walk through an empty room without leaving recognizable traces. A dust particle, stray hair, thread from clothing, or other residual fragment, may be inconspicuous but present, and waiting to tell its intimate story. Many crimes have been solved through the scientific analysis of footprints, shoe marks, fired bullets, cartridges, tire-tread marks, bits of broken headlight glass, blood, hair, fingernail dirt, soils, textiles, clothing, powder marks, stains, burns, etc., and in numerous instances the solution was accomplished from such bits of evidence when no other evidence was available. Passing recognition of this brings clearer appreciation of the more obvious assistance offered by latent fingerprints.

In all instances, and especially when the case is involved or important, it is well to make written notes describing the locale and its included objects. These can be supplemented by photographs that show everything as it was at the time. Obviously, nothing should be moved, altered, or even touched, until such notes and photographs have been made. A more intimate discussion of photography is presented elsewhere in the text.

Following the preliminary survey, the investigator should return to the suspected place of entry, and again go over the territory more methodically; a left-to-right or "clock-wise" course is recommended. At this time, all suspected surfaces should be carefully examined for fingerprints, both visible and latent. Having traversed the outer boundaries of the area, then examine such objects as may be more centrally located. By following this procedure with each enclosure or area inspected, nothing should escape the investigator's notice.

With the examination of buildings, the exterior also demands careful attention. The proved place of entry may not be the only point displaying evidence, since the intruder may have made a number of unsuccessful trials before finally effecting his entrance. Hence, minute inspection of all doors, windows, or other possible avenues of ingress is mandatory.

A good plan is to consider the situation from the intruder's viewpoint. The investigator should ask himself: What would *I* have done in attempting or gaining entry here? Having gotten inside, what would have been my next move? How would I have made my exit from the premises? Then picture the thief's probable reaction to the surroundings; the kind and amount of purloinable loot, together with his dread of apprehension and other likely mental processes. To some, this may prove difficult, since it requires the investigator to imagine himself as the criminal. However, an active imagination is vital to the success of criminal investigation.

As suggested, it is an excellent plan to picture in detail the most probable way in which the act was committed; how the criminal may have made his entrance and exit, and what objects and surfaces he would have touched or handled. Especial attention should be directed to door- and window-fastenings and their neighboring areas, to window sills, broken-glass fragments, and other recently damaged or displaced objects.

Highly important is the actual point or object of the crime; this may be a cash box, a jewel case, a desk or trunk, a safe or strong box, vault, or other repository. In many cases the intruder's tools may have been left behind, either by design or accident, or some available object may have been impressed into service. All these should be examined carefully.

Articles of furniture may have been moved to clear the intruder's path, or for other reasons; these also may prove productive. In his search for desirable loot, he may have touched the tops of dressers, cabinets, closets, or chests of drawers. He may have explored high and unused shelves, and unwarily left his imprints in the dust adhering there. Washbowls and drying equipment are fruitful fields, especially in cases where the subject had reason to cleanse his hands of blood or other stains.

If the crime was committed at night, close attention should be given to all lighting fixtures and equipment. Investigation may disclose that the invader sustained an injury, perhaps on broken glass, in which event bloody traces may be of vital importance. Furthermore, should a suspect later be arrested, any recently acquired wounds would be indicative.

In his investigative enterprise, the technician should be provided with certain equipment in the form of a "field kit," including a number of necessary articles.

ITEMS TO BE INCLUDED IN A FINGERPRINT FIELD KIT

A variety of fingerprint powders
2 brushes, for dark and light powders
2 feather "dusters" for light and dark powders
Supply of rubber latent-print lifting material
Iodine fuming outfit complete (separately contained)
Supply of transparent lifting tape and mounting material
Supply of cards (black and white) for mounting latents
Supply of 8x8 fingerprint record cards
1 metal holder for holding 8x8 cards when used
5X fingerprint magnifying glass for classifying
Henry and Battley discs to be used with the above
4" round magnifying glass for latent examinations
Supply of cellophane envelopes
Portable inking outfit for inking fingers
3" soft-gum rubber fingerprint roller for inking
2 oz. tube of fingerprint ink
4x10 glass plate for inking
Complete post-mortem outfit for printing corpses
1 pr. scissors
1 pr. rubber gloves
3 ft. rolling rule (steel)
25 ft. steel tape (registered)
Note book
Flashlight
Atomizer for applying powder
Atomizer for applying chemicals

The nature of the case may suggest objects that should be scrutinized for latent fingerprints. In a suspected poisoning, glasses, spoons, and medicine chests should be carefully examined. In the case of a stabbing, the investigator should examine all sharp objects, including broken dishes and glassware. In burglary, areas of strong interest will be recessed places where the thief might feel about for money, keys, or other small objects. Latent traces are often found upon the pages of books and magazines, on cards and documents, letters, the inside of brief cases and purses; in fact, in all places that may have been of interest to the criminal.

It is a habit of some burglars to eat or drink while on the premises. Consequently, close scrutiny should be made of any food utensils used. Glasses, cups, plates, bottles, and all table ware, are promising fields for search. Cases are on record wherein evidential prints were successfully developed from the peelings of fruit, from sausage skins, and broken bits of egg shell.

A factor frequently overlooked, especially in homicide cases, is the victim's fingerprints. When an occupant has met death on his own premises, it is highly probable that most of the fingerprints found near-by are his own. Even the fingerprints of an unknown victim may not only establish his identity, but also involve an associate or acquaintance as the probable culprit.

In searching for fingerprint evidence during the examination of a stolen and recovered motor vehicle, the investigator will find skin impressions in vexing profusion. However, even here there may be some few areas which were last touched by the thief. Contrary to popular belief, the steering wheel is not always the best possibility, due to the failure of fresh latent prints to adhere upon any surface already coated with skin exudation from frequent handling. Nevertheless, the steering wheel may yield important traces. A more promising source of evidence is the rear-view mirror. It is a fact well-known to motorists that the mirror in a stranger's car is seldom set at the angle desired by a new driver, who will be sure to change its position. In auto stealing, this adjustment is usually made almost immediately following the actual theft, and while the fugitive is occupied in effecting his escape; thus, the act will be more or less subconscious, with no thought as to subsequent hazard. For this reason, it often happens that the right lower corner of an adjustable rear-view mirror in a stolen car will show at least one clear imprint of the thief's right thumb.

Of course there are numerous other likely places, such as the horn button, the gear-shift knob, the dash fixtures, the door handles, the window molding, the windows, the cigar lighter or radio, if present, together with many miscellaneous articles, such as bottles, cigarette packages, cards, road maps, etc., which may have been handled or even discarded by the thief.

In the commission of auto theft, it often happens that the larcenist may hesitate to drive the vehicle away under its own power and may seek to avoid detection by pushing the car some distance before starting the engine. This may result in well-defined impressions on prominent areas of the machine. Furthermore, it is a favored recourse among auto thieves to remove the original license plates and substitute others less likely to be recognized. In these cases, fingerprints may be left upon some of the surfaces during the exchange, or may be found upon the original plates, should they be recovered later.

In searching for latent prints, especially indoors or at night, a flashlight will be effective. The light should be held so that its beam falls across the questioned zone at a sharp angle. In this way otherwise invisible marks may be seen in relief. When this reveals no prints, a promising spot should be further explored by dusting, fuming, or by other methods, all fully explained later in this text. It may be remembered that, except on paper, prints entirely invisible to the naked eye are comparatively rare.

The question could arise as to why prints are left by the human fingers, and especially at the scene of crime, when the

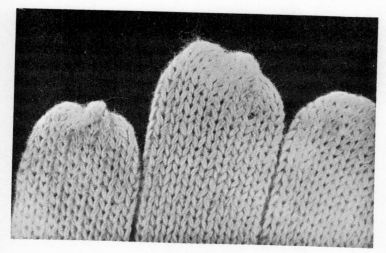

Fig. 156A

Glove impressions

These photographs, A, B and C, illustrate the type of markings that may be left when gloves are worn. Fig. 156A shows the texture of the gloves themselves. Fig. 156B shows glove impressions left upon a white surface and developed with black fingerprint powder. Fig. 156C shows glove impressions in a plastic surface. It will be noted that the weave of the glove material is plainly recognizable in the evidential traces.

(For continuation see next page)

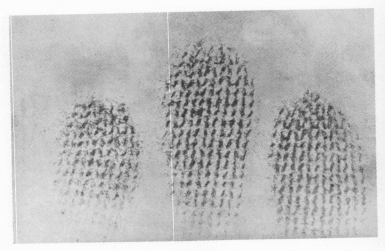

Fig. 156B

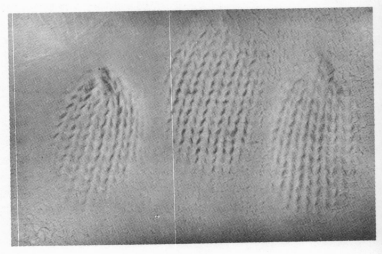

Fig. 156C

friction areas exude relatively little solid matter. This is explained by prevalent and peculiar circumstances. The criminal's hands are customarily dirty, and may be smeared with various foreign substances. During the commission of an illegal act, he is likely to be nervous, which will promote an excessive flow of perspiration. It often happens that he reaches within places that are dusty or dirty. He may be using oily tools; those employed in burglary are usually greasy. In the process of forcing bolts and locks, his hands may become generously smeared with lubricants. Also, the burglar is habitually lacking in refinement, and may be expected to daub his hands and fingers with food fats and other telltale residue at mealtime.

Although the intruder may have been known to wear gloves when entrance was gained, this circumstance does not prove that he left no prints on the premises. In the haste of burglary, gloves may be easily torn, or removed in an unguarded moment or at some special need. Acts such as burglary, and kindred crimes, are popularly committed in darkness, where the sense of touch must play an important part. Although an investigator may at first be discouraged at failure to find latent prints, and come to the conclusion that the criminal wore gloves throughout the entire time of his act, this can easily be a wrong conclusion, and a little patience may discover useful latents that were left by the intruder. Furthermore, cases are on record wherein the conviction of a criminal wearing gloves was materially aided by the marks from the especial gloves which he wore (Fig. 156, *A*, *B*, and *C*). Many glove fabrics have a distinctive texture, and it is quite possible to show marked similarity between some residual trace and the glove subsequently found in the possession of a suspect.

A great many conditions are unfavorable to the recording of fingerprints. It is usually a waste of effort to look for prints on rough or rusty metal, undressed wood, soft leather, coarse cloth, and all uneven, highly absorptive or porous surfaces. Another baffling situation is that wherein the object thought to hold evidential finger markings has been handled promiscuously.

Rough and unplaned boards are not usually favorable, but all papered, polished, or smoothly plastered walls offer possibilities of latent prints. The suspect may have felt his way in the dark with hands previously soiled or contaminated. As just stated, with those who commit burglary, a dirty hand may even be considered symbolic.

Persons with oily skin leave more enduring impressions, while prints formed mainly with sweat are transient. In a closed room, fingerprints left upon glass remain more or less viscid for several months; and even in the open, exposed to the elements, they may be developed after some weeks. Fingerprints upon objects submerged in water have been dried and successfully developed later. Water tends to retain the body wax, and helps to prevent its otherwise rapid evaporation.

Upon paper surfaces, "dusting" processes are usually successful only when the prints are fresh. Even after twenty-four hours' time, the moisture in the body wax may have evaporated to such an extent that ordinary "fingerprint powders" will not adhere. Fuming methods have proved effective after lapse of years; however, it must be admitted that not only development but also the discovery of latent prints becomes more difficult with increasing time. There are exceptions to this rule, since fingerprints left on brass, though quite invisible when recorded, may appear later, due to etching caused by corrosion of the metal.

So-called latent fingerprints may be found in three general classes; namely, the "molded" print, the "visible" print, and the truly "latent" impression. Molded impressions are those imprinted in a plastic surface or material, such as tallow, wax, pitch, tar, putty, partially dried paint, glue, the adhesive gum on envelopes or postage stamps, dried paste, grease, butter, soap, etc.

Visible impressions are made by fingers impregnated with coloring matter such as blood, grease, or dust mixed with perspiration, etc. Many of the prints thus recorded are so badly smudged that the ridge patterns are indistinct or indiscernible. It is common for a victim, witness, or would-be detective proudly to point out such impressions to the investigator, and become indignant when informed that the discovery is of little value. Bloody or dirty palm impressions are often discovered by inept police officers, who insist upon an identification despite the fact that no skin patterns are visible. Although of less value, even such sparse evidence offers an indication of the form and dimension of the criminal's hand, and consequently is a key to his general proportions.

In some instances, the visible print may be clear and legible. This happens when the coloring substance is not too thickly spread, or is of a favorable nature. Traces left by inky fingers may fall in this class, and in the case of questioned documents, can be of welcome assistance, identifying the author of anonymous letters, and so on.

Latent fingerprints may be present, even invisibly, on all manner of surfaces, but are more likely on glass, plates, mirrors, unfrosted electric-light globes, bottles, glazed utensils, smooth earthenware, porcelain, varnished or polished wood and metal, or safes, locks, firearms, various areas of motor vehicles, smooth leather, paper, celluloid, shell; a complete list of the possibilities here would be considerable. Paper may retain many finger markings, but still show no sign of the traces. However, even these can be made visible, as will be explained presently.

Since it is almost impossible to perform any act without some physical contact, fingerprints are a probability at the scene of crime. It is regrettable when overeager or careless persons touch and handle important objects which should be left unmolested. In every case where fingerprint evidence is thought to be present, intruders should be debarred pending the technician's arrival. And when possible, the expert's investigation should be conducted with all other persons excluded. Though this point may be stressed repeatedly in the text, it is one that deserves emphasis.

The actual search for fingerprints has certain requirements. The technician should be thorough and persevering; he should be circumspect, cautious, and conscientious. He will learn that when investigating a crime, it is desirable to secure comparison fingerprints of all those in or about the premises, or in any way connected. Assurance from an individual that he has touched nothing should be ignored at the outset. It is common experience for the expert to discover that prints thought to have been made by the criminal, are those of a legitimate occupant, or some careless police officer.

Following the discovery of latent fingerprints, the next problem is that of their suitable disposal. Some treatment usually will be necessary to prepare the evidence for future use, and, when possible, this should be done at the laboratory. All portable objects, thought to bear impressions, should be brought to the technician's workroom for development and photographing. Although this sometimes may represent a considerable undertaking, it is a wise policy. Lack of needful facilities, probable local interference, and many other disturbing factors, make the actual crime scene unfavorable for such operations.

Of course latent prints may be upon a heavy safe, a vault, or other location that renders removal out of the question.

But such cases are fortunately rare, and may be handled by emergency methods described elsewhere in this text. Transportation of small objects presents little difficulty, and even when latent prints are present under hindering circumstances, the rule of removal may usually be followed. If the case requires, sections can be cut from walls, windows, floors, or from cumbersome articles of furniture; but this will be at the technician's discretion, and will require special equipment.

The primary purpose at all times is that of preserving the evidence. Hence, extreme care and good judgment must be exercised to avoid damage or contamination, especially with lately recorded fingerprints, which may be sticky and easily smeared. This point can not be overemphasized. Furthermore, the evidential object itself may be breakable and require caution in handling. Contrary to belief, it is unwise to wrap objects bearing fingerprints in cloth or paper. The ideal technique employs a container in which the object can be secured in such a manner as to require the fewest possible contact points. This may be done in many ways, and will depend to a great extent upon the technician's ingenuity. However, a few suggestions may be timely. Wooden or cardboard boxes of suitable size may serve to hold such things as jewel cases, weapons, glass fragments, cups and drinking glasses, bottles and articles of similar size. In all cases, the box should be sufficiently roomy to allow free space around the object, which may be held in suspension by means of string, pins, wires, wooden braces, gummed tape, or other facilities. For the safe handling of evidential objects, the technician's field kit should include rubber gloves. Tweezers are also useful when picking up small articles, while for large objects, pliers or surgical hemostats are best.

In this as well as other stages of investigation, an important point must be remembered, which is that the evidence be handled by no one except the technician, or by as few persons as possible. The reasons for this are several, but the chief motive is a common legal requirement. When objects are introduced as court exhibits, it is necessary to show who had the evidence in possession from the time it became involved in the case. With defense attorneys, this is a favorite point of attack. If it can be plausibly contended that promiscuous handling may have altered the evidence, it may be rejected. The need for discretion here is apparent.

First, a Photograph

Regardless of the method employed to develop a latent impression, it is well first to photograph the trace as it appears prior to retouching. This is especially recommended when the evidence is likely to be presented in court. Although photography will not be fully discussed until later, its advantages at this stage must be emphasized. Securing a good likeness of an untreated latent may be an exacting task in some cases; the impression may be poorly defined or may be adhering to an unfavorable background. Nevertheless, oblique-ray light-sources, color filters, and specially sensitized films are available for many requirements; skill and persistence can usually produce a successful photograph.

A picture of the impression as it first appeared may also include the surrounding areas, even showing a complete view of the object touched, and where it was situated. This information may be of great importance later. In court, it is frequently desirable to show where the latent prints were found, and to indicate their position upon the surface handled, as well as the touched object's relation to its surroundings. Such data may be recorded in a handmade sketch, but this at best is a makeshift, and only recommended as an emergency measure.

It is often possible to secure a photograph that will show

details not discernible to the naked eye. Fine minutiae of this kind are sure to undergo some change of appearance through developing treatment. Many times the picture of an undeveloped latent impression may be so representative that no further restoration is needed, and an enlarged print of the negative will answer all requirements.

Another advantage is the informative nature of an intimate reproduction. As earlier indicated, the structure and condition of friction skin sometimes offer clues to the subject's further description. Obviously, this utility is endangered by developing treatments that may change the pattern's aspect.

Apart from these facts, it is a common misfortune for some important latent trace to sustain damage or even destruction during unsuccessful development, or by other accident. In that event, the forethought of taking an original photograph will be recognized as timely. Latent impressions left in loose dust and similar substances, are notable examples wherein, aside from photography, any attempt to reproduce the perishable evidence may not be an unqualified success.

An important step in latent-fingerprint technique is to make indistinct or invisible traces legible. This is usually done through the agency of developers in the form of solids, liquids, and gases. There are many methods employed for this purpose, the more common being that of "powdering" and "fuming," although numerous others have found favor.

The search for latent impressions also involves obtaining the fingerprints of all persons who have legitimately frequented the area or room where the crime was committed and who may have left their fingerprints. Only by this method can it be determined which fingerprints were left by a person who had not legitimately had access to the area previously and therefore could be a potential suspect.

XII

POWDERING LATENT FINGERPRINTS

WHEN exploring some suspected surface, latent prints may sometimes be made visible by simply breathing over the area; and also by exposing the surface to smoke from a burning match or candle. However, the latter method is not encouraged in all cases, since it may cause some damage to the evidence. A normal and fresh fingerprint is sticky, and when finely powdered material of a favorable nature can be made to adhere, the pattern outlines are more legible. There are numerous developing preparations available. To insure good results, the substance should not only adhere, but also be in contrast with the surface where the prints are situated; that is, dark powder for light backgrounds, and vice versa. When latent prints are present on multicolored backgrounds, viscid surfaces, cloth, and other unusual areas, special treatments may be needed; these will be taken up presently.

For general utility, there is little doubt that fingerprint powders hold first place as a means of developing latents. However, the success of this method will depend to a great extent upon the kind of powder used, the brush or applicator with which it is applied, and the skill of the operator. Under casual inspection, most fingerprint powders appear more or less alike, especially before they have been tested on an actual latent fingerprint. Experiment will show that this is not the case; sometimes one powder will best serve the purpose, and sometimes another.

It will be discovered that almost any kind of powder with a strictly physical action will adhere readily enough to a fingerprint freshly made with plenty of skin oil, and upon a favorable surface. But unfortunately this is not always the sort of print to be expected. Only the right powder can assure the best results on chance or casual latent prints.

Many latent fingerprints have been partially destroyed, damaged beyond recognition, or entirely obliterated by faulty technique and by using the wrong powder, particularly powders with "cutting" tendencies, of which little is known by many users. With unsuitable material, some questioned surface may be brushed carefully, but with no apparent results, whereas there may have been present faint or invisible latents which were destroyed in the process. Perhaps a bit of glass fragment may be found at a crime scene; reflected light reveals a barely discernible but promising latent print, very probably the criminal's. Should this be dusted improperly and with the wrong powder, after development the finer details may be blurred and valueless, yet the unpowdered print, when first examined, was potential useful evidence. In such an instance, failure may have resulted from the use of some powdering preparation that lacked the right agents in correct proportion; an unsuitable brush or applicator may have caused the damage; or the fault may have been with the operator. In any event, incorrect procedure has destroyed a latent print that may have been the only available evidence against the criminal.

All types and kinds of powders have utility in certain requirements; but no one powder will answer every need for developing powders. A good powder must first have sufficient adhesiveness to cling to the ridges; it must also have sufficient "wetting" characteristics to keep the formed or developed ridges from being broken by brushing or by gravity; it must also have incorporated in its compounding process an agent to keep the inner spaces between the ridges clear so that "extra" characteristics, such as the appearance or semblance of short ridges, dots, and other fragments will not be formed by accident.

A particular powder may work very well in one case, and not so well in another. Some powders, in certain circumstances, actually "cut" the ridge film impressed on paper or smooth surfaces. Others, in special cases, may work exactly opposite to the way a fingerprint powder should work. Instead of being absorbed by the oil and adhered to the ridges in a latent pattern, a powder not adapted to the case in hand may absorb the perspiration and oily matter from the ridges, and an extra stroke of the brush will then cause the ridges to "break"; particles of the brushed ridge may stick and form in the inner spaces, and many other unfortunate results may occur. A microscopic study of a latent print during development with powder and brush will reveal what actually occurs during this process.

With the simple methods of applying powder to a latent, little difficulty is encountered; however, caution is essential. The impression is composed largely of viscid body wax, to which the powder is likely to adhere readily enough, but the pattern's fine minutiae may easily be damaged by excessive friction during the powder's application. Furthermore, a too generous spread of powder may cover the background also, thus submerging the pattern. The extreme delicacy of such evidence must be remembered, and care taken to preserve all of its value.

Chance impressions at a crime scene are usually very fragile and must be handled skillfully. Regardless of what consistency the salt, organic substances, or plain perspiration may be in the individual's sweat pores, charcoal, lampblack, talcs, chalks, and many other powders, including aluminum and gold bronzes, may have "cutting" tendencies or smearing qualities in some especial instance, and, while not noticeably harmful to a well-recorded print, may destroy a most important casual impression at the scene of a crime.

Many latent prints are rendered useless through improper development. Their finer characteristics are blended or clouded; bifurcations no longer appear as such, recurring lines seem angular, islands become bifurcations, short ridges and dots show in the powdered latent when nothing of the sort is present in the inked impression; also, dots and other ridge fragments which exist on the subject's fingers, are not to be seen in the evidential impression. Some badly developed latents are smudged, others show their ridge structure deceptively broken. Still others display a greater or lesser number of ridges between the core and delta when compared with the suspect's inked impression. Under magnification, many dissimilarities and distortions are sometimes found in poorly developed patterns which make it difficult to check that latent against the suspect's inked fingerprint, and render the evidence worse than useless for court presentation. All these conditions may be caused by incorrect procedural methods. However, as in most other fields of endeavor and enterprise, assured success comes only through specialized skill and application; with the right technique, such errors can be avoided.

To prevent certain unfortunate results, it is imperative to determine the powder best suited to a given surface. For example, on a window having a slight grease film from cooking fumes, or steam, with layers of dust and residue, which in time dry and form a film, mercurized powders should prove satisfactory, as being more likely to adhere and build up a heavier ridge body, despite the grease film. This film may be found on painted surfaces in restaurants and kitchens. In cold weather, windows are often steamed and moist on their inner sides from condensation. Before finger-traces on such surfaces can be powdered successfully, they must be dried. This may be accomplished by opening the window and allowing the moisture to evaporate with the air, or by directing a stream of air against the glass with an electric fan.

Before placing any powder on a latent print, it is a good plan to experiment with various materials. The investigator makes "trial" prints of his own fingers upon unimportant areas of the same surface, and tests these impressions to determine which powder will best suit his purpose. Finally, having decided upon the material that seems most adaptable, the evidential traces may be treated.

Developing powders may be applied with an atomizer, by sifting, and by brushing, the latter being the generally accepted method. In this treatment, the material is spread with a brush of soft and extremely fine hair; small feather "dusters" are also designed for this purpose. Even these delicate applicators, if used too vigorously, can damage the evidence.

A wide variety of brushes is used for applying fingerprint powders. The flat or varnish type of brush is not usually very desirable. Also to be avoided are brushes with bristles that are too short and stiff. Nor can the best results always be expected with a brush of the excessively fluffy type with extremely long hair. However, these opinions should be considered as general observations, since conditions may sometimes exist wherein such brushes may prove useful for some special requirement. Each technician has his own ideas about the brush most suitable. Nevertheless, an excellent type of brush is rounded and composed of very soft camel hair about one and one-half inches long, with between three and four thousand hairs in the cluster. Better service is insured when the hair has been chemically treated so that the bristle tips do not wear or stiffen with continued use.

Before using any brush it is well to place the handle between the palms and roll it back and forth rapidly. This will separate the hairs and expel any stray bits of foreign matter that may be present. It is unwise to thrust the brush promiscuously into a jar or container of fingerprint powder. This forces the material too high upon the bristles, resulting in uneven distribution when the powder is applied, thus causing smears.

The well-equipped fingerprint kit should include an assortment of brushes and applicators; but in any case at least two brushes or dusters are recommended, one for all light-colored powders, and one for dark materials.

The correct technique of brushing powder on a latent print can only be acquired with practice; however, the paramount demand is for delicacy of touch. Instructions to a beginner are: Dip the brush sparingly in the powder, or better still, shake some of the powder out of the jar upon some clean surface such as a sheet of paper, and pick it up with the brush. A few light taps will shake off the excess material; then draw the brush *very lightly* across the latent print. When powder starts to adhere, the print's configuration becomes apparent. Then, instead of drawing the brush *across* the area, direct the strokes so that they follow the general course of the ridges as much as possible. This will be less likely to distort the print's detail.

Miscroscopic examination of a newly recorded print reveals the reason for this precaution. The design's structure, which may appear to the unaided eye as continuous, is in reality composed of many small, moist globules of body wax, the nature of which has been described (Fig. 157). Experiment

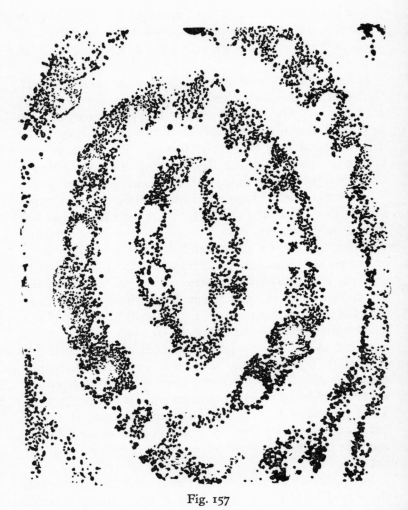

Fig. 157

Magnified view of a newly recorded fingerprint showing its distinctive
structure of tiny moisture droplets. This photograph is an
enlargement of 40 times

will show that, when fresh, this material is soft and sticky, becoming more like dried glue as its moisture evaporates. Plainly, the most favorable time for powdering is while the wax is still viscid. At this time, however, it is also more easily marred.

When enough of the material has adhered to the print, the residue is brushed away, care being taken first to shake the brush free of powder. Best results are attained by allowing only the tip-ends of the brush hair to touch the print, both in applying the powder and in removing it.

If the powdering operation is checked carefully throughout with a good magnifying glass, it will be possible in most cases to secure even distribution with a minimum of alteration. In this connection, minor but unpreventable changes in the print will be noted. For example, two bits of ridge structure may approach each other without actually touching, but powdering may fill the tiny space between, and indicate the formation as unbroken. Other similar modifications result in the powdering process, but are usually of little importance, since they can be discounted in the final analysis.

Another more pronounced form of alteration results from pressure. The flesh of a normal finger tip, and for that matter, throughout the whole body, is resilient and pliable, and may be somewhat distorted like rubber. Under these circumstances, it is plain that fingerprints must vary slightly in their pictorial aspects, depending on the degree and direction of force exerted in their recording. This can be illustrated by pressing the thumb against the underside of a piece of glass, and rotating it from side to side. It will be observed that the pattern is stretched, first in one direction, then the other, as the digit is shifted.

This type of distortion is common to the field of latent fingerprints, and must be recognized at all times, especially with comparative examination. It may produce such changes in the appearance of a fingerprint that its identification with another print taken of the same finger, but under different conditions, may be difficult. Poorly qualified investigators have sometimes been led to wrong conclusions in the presence of a conventionally recorded fingerprint and some evidential fragment left by the same digit, but with pressure of a different degree and direction.

It is difficult to form a true conception of something from verbal description only. Since the smaller details of friction skin are below the eye's resolving power, magnification is necessary for clear understanding. Therefore, the student should make enlarged photographs of finger patterns, variously distorted by the above method. Careful study of these will reveal the type and degree of change to be anticipated.

It is also instructive to make large photographs showing different stages of the powdering technique. For example, the first view may be of the finger itself, with the pattern prominently displayed. Next may be shown a latent impression made by the same finger upon a surface offering enough contrast to reveal the print. Then several photographs of the print may be taken after the powder has been applied in increasing amounts. Through this means, a student will discover the nature and anatomy of a latent fingerprint, and will learn how much powder is necessary and the best method of applying it.

In the pioneer period of criminal investigation, few commercial products were to be had. However, modern enterprise has supplied many of these earlier requirements. Aluminum dust has enjoyed considerable popularity, since it is very finely divided and adheres readily. However, it has a tendency to cling not only to the latent print, but to the background as well, thus obliterating the evidence. This imperfection is known as "painting." The use of any developing powder that "paints" is hazardous. None the less, aluminum powder has a virtue in its reflecting properties. Being silver-colored, it photographs satisfactorily.

FINGERPRINT POWDER FORMULAS

Lampblack ....70 parts
Graphite ....20 parts
Powdered acacia ....10 parts

Ferric oxide ....85 parts
Potassium acid tartrate ..10 parts
Aluminum stearate ..... 3 parts
Talc .... 2 parts

Charcoal (willow) .....75 parts
Graphite ....15 parts
Acacia .... 9 parts
Aluminum .... 1 part

Aluminum ....95 parts
Fuller's earth .... 4 parts
Charcoal (willow) .....¾ part
Lycopodium ....¼ part

Charcoal ....74 parts
Aluminum (fine) ......24 parts
Dragon's blood .... 2 parts

Aluminum ....75 parts
Charcoal ....20 parts
Dragon's blood .... 5 parts

Lampblack ....65 parts
Black carbon ....30 parts
Aluminum .... 5 parts

Lycopodium ....90 parts
Soudan red III ....10 parts

Chemist's gray ....85 parts
Aluminum ....15 parts

Lead oxide (brown) ....60 parts
Charcoal (bone) ....30 parts
Fuller's earth .... 9 parts
Aluminum .... 1 part

Lead oxide (orange) ...90 parts
Acacia .... 8 parts
Aluminum .... 2 parts

FINGERPRINT POWDER FORMULAS

White Powder: Zinc Oxide .... 100% by wgt.

Gray Powder:
Zinc Oxide .... 98% by wgt.
Aluminum Lining Powder .... 2% by wgt.

Red Powder:
Iron Oxide ($Fe_2 O_3$) .... 99.75% by wgt.
Aluminum Lining Powder .... 0.25% by wgt.

Gold Powder:
Lead Chromate (Lemon Yellow) .... 65% by wgt.
Dark Gold Lining Powder .... 35% by wgt.

Black Powder:
Manganese Dioxide .... 85% by wgt.
Graphite (Powdered) .... 14.75% by wgt.
Aluminum Lining Powder .... 0.25% by wgt.

Fluorescence Powder:
Anthracene, finely powdered .... 100% by wgt.
Use both technically and chemically
Pure grades for different colors.

In summary, the choice of powder is determined by several factors. Color should be selected to give optimal photographic contrast. The powder should adhere to the print without "clogging" or "painting" the areas between the ridges.

When exploring areas too large to be "brushed" conveniently, developing powders may be applied effectively with an atomizer of the type used as a nasal spray and for similar purposes. Here, the atomizer's container is filled partially with powder. The container should be perfectly dry, as moisture will cause lumps. Squeezing the bulb over the questioned surface may reveal latent traces. Although this is recommended in some cases as a preliminary step, the brush method should be employed lastly for the print's more refined development. Another preparatory method for large, more-or-less horizontal, surfaces employs a "sifter" such as that used for powdered sugar. A technique especially useful for paper applies the powder directly, sliding it back and forth across the suspected area. This method is especially successful with black powders. Latents thus developed may be impaired by even a light touch from a brush. Excess powder is removed by a few brisk taps of the finger. In the Magna-Brush method, the powder is a ferromagnetic mixture which is moved across the print by a magnet passed beneath the paper. Excess powder is removed from the developed print by the magnet.

The aerosol method of spraying fingerprint powder was marketed a few years ago, and is an improvement over the brush method in the hands of an incompetent technician. The spray, however, is no substitute for the brush in the hands of a skilled identification man. Indeed, its manufacturers recommend the supplementary use of the brush, at least for the removal of excess powder. Fingerprint spray is mainly useful on large areas. Since the broad and indiscriminate application of fingerprint powder is often demanded by suspicious complainants and nervous supervisors, the spray will do much to improve public and departmental relations for the identification man. However, for the effective development of latents, he will rely mainly on the brush to apply powder with discrimination, skill, and purpose.

The major criticisms of the aerosol method are that it clogs at the nozzle and sprays unevenly. These are problems concerned with the nature of the powder. Recently a fluorescent powder has been packaged in the form of an aerosol bomb.

XIII

LIFTING LATENTS

Owing to the variable circumstances under which latent fingerprints are recorded, it sometimes happens that impressions may be present in places where they can not be photographed successfully. In such cases it is often possible to secure and preserve the evidence by a process known as "lifting." This method is popular with fingerprint technicians, and offers numerous advantages.

The technique employs a variety of pliable, adhesive materials that are utilized by pressing the sticky surface against the latent impression that has been dusted with powder. The powder on the print adheres to the viscid "lifter," which is peeled away, bringing the powder with it. The latent print is thus "lifted" and remains on the lifter. The sticky side of the lifter is then covered with some transparent substance, and the operation is completed.

Lifter material is sold commercially in a variety of types and colors, a popular kind being of sheet rubber, similar to that used for patching automobile inner tubes. As a matter of fact, this same patching rubber can also be used with fair success as a lifting sheet. However, an advantage of the commercial lifter is the transparent cover which is provided to protect the sticky surface until ready for use, and to cover the print when it has been lifted. Also, commercially prepared rubber lifters are superior, since their active or "tacky" surface is smooth and free from breaks, wrinkles, and porous conditions often present in rubber sheeting not intended for fingerprints.

To use the conventional lifting material is simple. The latent print to be lifted is first carefully developed by dusting, care being exercised to brush away as much of the excess powder as possible. Next, a sheet of the lifting material is selected and trimmed to the desired size. The color of the lifter chosen will depend upon whether the powder used is light or dark. A dark-colored lifter will agree with light powder, and white lifters will furnish better contrast when dark powders have been used. The transparent covering of the lifter is removed, and the sticky surface is pressed firmly against the powdered print. The lifter is then stripped away and the transparent covering replaced over the lifted print. If the process has been applied correctly, the "lifted" latent will be clearly visible under the transparent cover. It is important to expel the air bubbles both in applying to the print and when covering the lifted impression with the transparent sheet.

As already stated, tire-patch rubber will be a good makeshift for this purpose. When this is used, a transparent covering must be provided. This can be of thin celluloid, photographic film from which the emulsion has been removed, heavy cellophane, or acetate. To use patch-rubber as a lifter, select a piece of suitable color (it usually is obtainable in red, blue, black, and white), cut a piece of the right size, peel off the fabric covering, and apply to the dusted print as with the regular lifting material. When the sticky surface has been covered with whatever has been selected, it is well to trim both the covering and the lifter to the same size, since this will help to prevent their separation.

An important point to remember is the fact that rubber

lifters are not advisable when the latent print has been developed with mercurized-white or mercury-with-chalk powders, since both of these preparations blend into the rubber's surface and darken it. Nevertheless, as indicated, this technique insures success in many instances where photography is impractical.

The question might reasonably be asked why latent fingerprints can not be photographed in all cases. Experience will show that latents are sometimes found on the inner surfaces of jewel cases and other small containers, on the inside of jars and vases, in narrow crannies, nooks and corners, and in numerous other recesses that are difficult of access and quite out of the camera's direct range. Furthermore, latents are sometimes present on surfaces that may be accessible, but which hinder or prevent photographic methods, owing to the background's characteristics. The area may be of some unfavorable color, it may include many colors or be composed of intricate design, or the factor of illumination may render photography impractical. The questioned surface where the print adheres may be curved, corrugated, rough, irregular, or otherwise unfavorable for photography. However, none of these conditions are likely to hamper the lifting process.

With this method of preserving latents, a most important factor must be recognized. When a fingerprint has been lifted by the means just described, the result will show the pattern in reverse, that is, the powdered outline adhering to the lifter's surface will be a "mirror image" of the print as it appeared on the surface where it was originally discovered. This "reversal" can be rectified by photographing the "lifted" pattern and then making a print from the resultant negative, with the negative's "emulsion surface" turned away from the printing paper.

This difficulty is more effectively eliminated by the use of transparent lifters. An inexpensive material of this type is found in clear cellulose or "Scotch" tape, such as may be obtained in stationery stores. With its use the technique is varied slightly. The powdered print is covered with a strip of the tape, which is then peeled off and pasted on a card, either light- or dark-colored, depending upon the powder used in developing the latent. The print then may be seen through the clear tape, and not reversed as in the other instance. More care is required when using Scotch tape, since it is very viscid, and adheres to any surface with which it comes in contact; so much so, in fact, that it is not always successful in lifting prints from some kinds of paper, portions of which may cling to the tape and tear away when the tape is removed. However, on most surfaces, Scotch tape will be found quite effective as a lifting tissue.

Despite its usefulness for lifting latents, Scotch tape is only a cheap material popularly used for binding and sealing packages, mending torn paper, etc., and although convenient as a "second choice," it has some disadvantages. The base upon which the adhesive substance is affixed is usually not so clear as could be wished, and the coating may be too sticky in some cases, as indicated. Furthermore, the type of Scotch or "mending-tissue" so called, commonly sold in stationery stores, is usually in narrow widths only, a wider material being more desirable for lifting latents.

A similar but much better grade of transparent tape has been designed especially for fingerprint work, and is obtainable from a number of firms that deal in fingerprint supplies. It is of an adequate width, is manufactured in a continuous roll, and if used properly, produces excellent transfers from which can be made practical comparisons, direct photographic prints, and enlargements without the use of a camera. With this type of lifting tape there is provided celluloid or acetate cover material to which the tape may be affixed after the latent impression has been lifted. This covering material is also prepared with one side frosted, which permits writing beneath the latent any desired data such as case numbers, dates, names, etc. When the lifted latent is used to make photographic prints, as explained, the writing thus recorded will appear, together with the fingerprint, in the finished picture.

The technique of using this transparent lifting tape is easy, but requires care to insure good results. After the latent has been powdered and is ready for lifting, several inches of tape are unwound from the roll, but without cutting. When unwinding the tape, which, like ordinary Scotch tape, is also very sticky, it should not be jerked loose, but pulled away slowly and gradually, not straight out, but with a backward motion. The roll is held in one hand and the tape's free end in the other. The end of the tape is placed, sticky side down, about one half-inch in front of the latent print, and the strip is smoothed backward over the latent with a firm and even pressure, care being taken to expel any tiny air bubbles that may be present beneath.

The tape should be removed from the surface by pulling slowly and steadily on the roll to which it is still attached, the direction of pull being the same as that in removing the tape from the roll. The tape will thus peel away and bring with it the powder from the developed latent. The tape should not be pulled quite clear from the surface, a small end or corner being allowed to adhere. The "used" portion of the tape is clipped off and the roll laid aside. The short strip with its latent print may then be affixed to the celluloid cover. It is a wise precaution after cutting the "used" strip of tape free from the roll, to fold the loose end back on itself, thus making a convenient, nonadhesive tab for unwinding more tape for future requirement.

If desired, the lifted print may be backed with paper or cardboard, either light or dark, to contrast with the powder used in developing. It is not advisable, however, to attach the tape directly to thin cardboard or paper, since both the backing and the tape will be likely to pucker after a time and thus distort the print. It is more practical to use only the celluloid covers for this purpose; the covered print may be backed with colored cardboard if desired. By using the lifted print as a negative, photographic "contact" prints and also projection enlargements can be made if necessary, as previously indicated.

In some cases, the "lifting" process will successfully preserve latents that have been left in dust, or when the fingers are stained with some moist coloring matter, such as blood, paint, etc. These, of course, would be "lifted" in their original condition, since any attempt to "powder" such evidence could be destructive.

An earlier method of "lifting" latent fingerprints employed ordinary gelatine-coated photographic printing paper. This was first "fixed" in hypo, then washed and dried. Just prior to using, it was immersed for a short time in warm water, the superfluous water was absorbed by blotting, and the moist paper was then applied in much the same manner as with other types of lifting material. The adhesive quality of this transfer paper was considerably increased by placing it in a bath of 50 per cent water and 50 per cent glycerin.

For a transparent lifter, photographic film can be used. A sheet of ordinary film is soaked in warm water until the emulsion can be removed. On drying, the clear film is coated with a solution of 15 grams of salicylic acid in 100 cc. of water to which 30 cc. of glycerin is added, allowed to dry for 24 hours and covered with celluloid.

Among the newer lifting products on the market is Lift-Print, a material specifically made for lifting faint dust prints, even from paper surfaces, and providing them with a suitably contrasting background for photography. Lift-Print is well suited for lifting prints of larger area, such as palm prints and footprints. Spray materials are available for several purposes. One product is designed for spraying over prints which have already been developed, as, for example, fingerprints developed with black powder on paper. A spray of this nature serves to protect the print by covering it with a thin, transparent coat of acetate. The print should, of course, be photographed before applying any specialized protective measures. Another form of spray material is used to lift fingerprints. The spray is applied carefully to the print until a satisfactory thickness of the transparent film has been built up. After drying, the material may be withdrawn from the surface in the usual manner. Nylon Spray, one of the more recent of these materials, is considered an effective lifting medium.

When possible, it will be found advisable to photograph lifted latent fingerprints; due to many variant factors, the specimen's future condition is unpredictable. As already indicated, photographic prints may be made directly from latents lifted with transparent lifting material. Furthermore, photographic negatives may be made without the use of a camera, if so desired. A special film has been developed commercially for this purpose. To employ the method, procure two small pieces of glass and attach them at the edges with adhesive tape so that they will open like a book. To make the exposure, open the glass sheets and lay the latent print on one of the glasses with the fingerprint film placed over it. The emulsion side of the film should be next to the print. Close the glasses and hold them firmly to insure a perfect contact. Expose them for six or seven seconds to the rays of a 25- or 30-watt lamp at a distance of four feet. These operations, of course, should be performed in a darkroom. Care should be exercised in placing the latent against the film to insure the finished image's being turned in the right direction as to its ulnar or radial slant.

Regardless of the relative merits of the "lifter" process in the preservation of latents, its use is more advisable in cases where other methods are impractical or unavailable, and more especially when the evidence is likely to be used in court. For various reasons, this type of evidence seems to have less legal weight than the conventional photographic reproduction, and in some instances may be disqualified as inaccurate. However, the occasions when fingerprint evidence is offered before a judge and jury are relatively few as compared with the constantly arising identification problems in which fingerprints feature indispensably. Any timely advice here offered as to the legal limitations of "lifters" should not be taken as a discouragement of their general use, since they are both effective and convenient, and frequently afford a ready solution to problems yielding to no other method.

Despite the wide utility of powders in developing latents, this method will not answer all the needs that arise. When the prints are old and dry, there are little or no adhesive properties present. It is difficult to powder prints successfully on can and bottle labels, on old documents and letters, magazines and book pages. Good powdering results are improbable where surfaces are covered by grease or oil, which condition may be present on oil-polished furniture, greasy machinery, surfaces in garages and those exposed to cooking fumes, and all areas filmed over with oily residue. There are many conditions under which useful latents may be even visibly present, but practically unpowderable. Some of these problems can be solved by fuming.

XIV

CHEMICAL METHODS

As STATED, powders inevitably change the original design, whereas fuming and chemical treatments often afford greater resolution of detail. This is important when only part of a print is found, and identification depends on intimate features of ridge structure and pore formation.

IODINE FUMING

Small portable objects such as documents can be treated in an iodine fuming chamber made of a wooden box with a sliding glass front. The chamber is preferably placed in a chemical hood. A crucible containing iodine crystals is placed in the circular opening at the bottom of the chamber, the document is suspended at least six inches above the crucible, and the glass front slid down. The fumes from the crystals will reveal any latent print with a dark brown pattern. Since iodine sublimes slowly at room temperature, an hour or more may be required. The process can be speeded by heating the crucible but this is less satisfactory owing to the localized effects of the thick curling fumes. Iodine vapor is poisonous, and care should be exercised in its application.

For processing large surfaces and for treating objects at the crime scene, a portable iodine fuming apparatus is used. This consists of a glass tube containing iodine crystals, calcium chloride, and glass wool arranged as shown below. As the operator blows into the rubber tubing, the breath loses moisture as it passes over the calcium chloride to reach the iodine crystals. The warmth of the breath serves to enhance sublimation, and iodine vapor emerges from the other end where another piece of tubing may be added to direct the vapor toward the surface to be processed.

The nature of the iodine fuming operation restricts its use to relatively small surfaces. Iodine vapor is specifically useful for prints on greasy surfaces. Powder in these situations tends to adhere indiscriminately, clinging to the spaces between the ridges as well as to the ridges themselves.

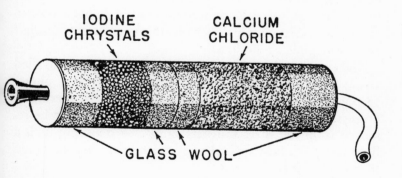

Fig. 158

Iodine fuming apparatus for chemical development and investigation of latent fingerprints; to be handled with caution as iodine fumes are poisonous

Unfortunately, the images produced by iodine vapor are not permanent, and to meet this situation, additional facilities have been provided in the form of silver "transfer" sheets. These are flexible, and may be used on uneven surfaces. In making a transfer, the latent is fumed to its maximum contrast, and the silver sheet is applied directly and held in place for a brief period. Although somewhat dependent upon the amount of iodine which the latent has absorbed, the correct time of contact will be approximately a second. Usually a faint brown image will be seen when the sheet is removed. A few minutes' exposure to direct sunlight darkens the image, which is then permanent. A photo-flood bulb will produce even more rapid results, although ordinary electric lights are too weak for this purpose.

When the method has been successfully applied, at this stage there is a clear, black image of the latent print upon the silver. If the reproduction is too weak or too strong, however, the entire process may be repeated, making such corrections in fuming and exposure as seem necessary. It is possible to make a number of transfers from the same latent, the last being as legible as the first.

The exposed silver sheets are placed in envelopes and filed away; the images will remain permanent. When photographic copies are desired, these can be made by the use of process film and side lighting. Also, the images may be removed from the silver transfers simply by polishing with a little moist whiting applied with the finger. The sheets are then ready for further use.

Although impermanent without the silver transfers, an iodine image will remain visible for a little time after fuming, and may be photographed immediately, if necessary. This eliminates the need of silver transfer sheets, which are convenient but not indispensable. In such cases it is advisable to have the evidential object and camera in place and all in readiness. Then, when the fumed image shows its highest contrast, the exposure can be made without unnecessary delay.

The iodine method may be used upon a variety of surfaces, many of which would present an unanswerable problem ordinarily. Silver-iodine transfers from all types of paper are practical, with the possible exception of newsprint, and even here, transfers have been taken from surfaces carrying writing or printing, that showed but insignificant interference from that source. The method has such wide application that under favorable conditions serviceable prints have been reproduced from certain kinds of cloth. When the material is coarse, soft, or loosely woven, it is not likely that it will receive a fingerprint, and consequently there will be no image to develop by any means employable. However, when the texture is smooth and fine-grained, especially on tightly stretched furniture covering, the iodine method may react favorably.

All types of hardened paper such as stationery, typing paper, and the smooth stock of books and magazines, respond well to this application. A unique employment is the examination of intercepted documents; since the latent print is not noticeably affected by the iodine fumes, there are no visible traces to arouse suspicion. In some special requirements demanding secrecy, the entire process of fuming and lifting the latent on the silver sheet may be accomplished practically in darkness, and in a few seconds.

Effective and rapid examination of miscellaneous scraps of paper may be made with the versatile iodine process. Remarkably clear reproductions have been made of prints on bright and variously colored backgrounds that would be hopeless with many other methods. Fingerprints upon the surfaces of mirrors usually offer difficulties; in some cases the silver must be removed in order to secure a good photograph. Here is a case where the iodine method is applied effectively.

With iodine, greasy surfaces present no problem. There is usually a marked difference between the absorption rate of iodine by a latent print and that of a greasy background. This may be demonstrated by coating a sheet of clean glass with a thin film of lubricating oil, and recording some fingerprints. When fumed, it will be noted that the iodine is absorbed much more readily by the latents than by the oily background.

The chemistry of the iodine-silver process is simple. The substances composing latent traces absorb iodine vapor. Silver, being highly sensitive to iodine, receives the image by chemical reaction, producing silver iodide. When silver iodide is exposed to strong actinic light, it is decomposed, and brings out the image in black silver.

Iodine vapor has little lasting effect upon a latent print, aside from a slight hardening action, which has even been known to improve its qualities for powdering. Thus the investigator employs the method with perfect assurance that he may later resort to powdering or any other treatment, until all possibilities are exhausted. With latents that occasion a doubt as to the best means of reproduction, iodine-silver may be used confidently, since it does not in any way damage the evidence or prevent other recourses.

A marked advantage in the fuming-tube is the fact that it applies the vapor only where necessary. With older methods, clouds of iodine gas were often profuse, and while not harmful in small quantities, the fumes are unpleasant. Metal objects, especially steel and iron, tend to corrode more rapidly when exposed to iodine vapor; such articles should be carefully cleaned and oiled following examination.

As stated, the images produced by iodine fumes fade quickly after development. However, in certain instances, it may be desirable to preserve the original print without the use of photography or the silver-transfer sheets. For this purpose a solution is available, which, when sprayed upon the fumed prints, will "fix" them permanently. The formula for this preparation is as follows:

Calcium chloride	½ oz. avdps.
Potassium bromide	50 grs.
Water	4 oz.

This solution will keep well for several weeks, but gives better results if made up fresh and in small quantities; only a little is required for an application.

The user may encounter some difficulties unless the right type of atomizer is chosen for applying the solution. A special instrument for this purpose has been developed by the De Vilbiss Company; its use is preferable.

Immediately after the latents have been fumed to their maximum contrast, they may be sprayed with the above solution. The excess moisture is absorbed with a clean blotter; this is most necessary, as an overdampening of the surface is undesirable.

When working with fingerprints on paper surfaces that also contain written matter, care is required not to blot the ink. It is advisable to prepare a mask of heavy paper or cardboard, with a small opening just large enough to expose the prints to be treated. Thus, the solution will be sprayed only upon the prints, very little if any of the writing being affected.

The commercial fixatives commonly used for spraying charcoal drawings, have been advocated for fixing iodine images, and still another method recommends brushing the fumed prints with 10 per cent tannic acid, although these procedures are not as effective as the calcium chloride and potassium bromide solution. However, a practical method of preventing iodine prints from fading upon paper specimens is described as follows: Secure two sheets of glass of the same size and large enough to enclose the paper upon which the prints are present. When the iodine images have been fumed to their maximum density, place them at once between the glass covers and bind the edges of the glass with adhesive tape so that the joint is airtight. In the absence of air, the iodine images will not disappear. The iodine image will fade should the glass covers be removed later; this could be a desirable factor in the case of an intercepted document. The image's disappearance may be considerably hastened by warming the paper or by exposing it to ammonia fumes.

When the iodine process has been used to develop latents on paper, and there is a considerable amount of starch present in the paper's sizing, it is possible to "fix" the prints by passing the paper momentarily through a current of steam. The reaction between the iodine in the print and the starch will give a deep blue coloration which will persist for several days. Another method of "fixing" latent impressions employs a spray composed of gum arabic, alum and formaldehyde. This is recommended for general use on prints where fixation is desired. In the same category, the following mixture has proved effective:

	Per cent
Acetone	20
Gun cotton	7
Absolute Alcohol	20
Ether	53

In describing certain of the included methods of developing latent fingerprints, the techniques outlined may not be unconditionally recommended in all cases. However, it has been deemed advisable to present them here at their face value, since inclusive familiarity allows a wider selection.

Furthermore, it sometimes happens that a less popular method may prove quite effective in some unusual circumstance. When possible, the limitations as well as the advantages of the various procedures have been discussed frankly, to dispel possible illusions and also to acknowledge any utility that may deserve recognition.

Nearly all methods for developing latents depend upon the components of skin exudation, such as perspiration, salt, oil, protein, etc. Imprints left by the fingers invariably contain traces of organic matter, notably fatty compounds. Therefore, osmic acid suggests itself as a good reagent; however, it has some disadvantages. If desired, it may be applied directly by brushing a 1 per cent solution on the suspected area and leaving the surface moist, preferably while exposed to bright sunlight. This treatment produces a developed image in which the ridges are black.

Tetroxide of ruthenium also deserves passing mention as a fuming agent, though its results are not entirely satisfactory in all cases. Mercuric iodide as a fuming agent has the advantage of producing images that are much less fugitive than those produced by iodine alone. The result is obtained by exposing the latents to the vapor from a heated mixture of 4 parts of mercury to 5 parts of iodine. Care should be taken not to breathe the fumes, as they are harmful. Under this method, the latent patterns first turn dark, then presently change to yellow. An objection to this method is that it may discolor the entire surface as well as the prints.

Bromine vapor produces faint yellow images, and iodine chloride gives a somewhat darker result, but not as dark as iodine alone. Mercuric bromide has been employed, but is less satisfactory than mercuric iodide.

Osmium tetroxide, which boils at 130 degrees C., has proved to be a sensitive agent. A 1 per cent solution evaporated in an open container produces a vapor that brings out the finer detail in a latent. The fumes are harmful, and should not be breathed. This method is not as sensitive as the straight iodine method. The patterns produced by this process are gray. Ruthenium tetroxide, or volatile ruthenium salts, already mentioned, also reacts by darkening upon contact with organic substances.

Latents on paper may sometimes be brought out by dipping in a 10 per cent solution of hyposulphite of soda, 10 parts of sodium hyposulphite and 90 parts of water, with a few drops of alcohol added; but for requirements of fine definition, this treatment is not recommended, as the patterns are likely to be blurred and hard to photograph. Eosin is sometimes used in the development of latents by the dye method. A 2 per cent solution gives fairly desirable results; an alcoholic fuchsine solution (aniline red) also has been utilized.

THE SILVER-NITRATE METHOD

The fact that perspiration contains a certain percentage of sodium chloride, common salt, permits the use of a reagent such as silver nitrate for the development of fingerprints by converting the sodium chloride to silver chloride, a substance which darkens on exposure to light. Silver nitrate is widely used for latent fingerprints on paper and other porous substances. Of the various methods of applying the reagent, simple immersion in a 3 per cent solution is preferred.

By dissolving four ounces of silver nitrate in a gallon of water a solution of satisfactory strength is obtained. The paper or other object is dipped in the silver nitrate solution and left to dry in a darkened room. When the paper is dry it is exposed to sunlight, or artificial illumination rich in ultra-violet, until the print areas have darkened sufficiently.

The fingerprints are now photographed in the usual manner. If it is desired to preserve the prints, the document is placed between black sheets of paper and placed in an empty photographic film box of appropriate size.

Sometimes it is requested that the paper be restored to its original condition if no prints are found. This is done by immersing the paper in a solution of mercuric chloride, after the silver-nitrate examination has been completed. The reaction products are white and readily removed by rinsing in water. Naturally, visible effects can be detected in the sizing of the paper and occasionally in ink writings.

Another application of the silver-nitrate method, more especially designed for cloth surfaces, advocates the placing of the questioned material in a 10 per cent solution of silver nitrate to which 2 per cent of acetic acid has been added. The surface is then exposed to a strong artificial light source or to bright sunlight. The silver chloride then darkens and the latent patterns are visible. As stated, the preliminary steps of this method must be conducted under a red light. The developed images may be fixed in a hypo bath, as already explained.

It is obvious that the success of this method will be governed by the texture of the cloth, a finer weave offering higher probability of securing legible prints. Another important point is the material's color; the developed latents would not be recognized on a dark background. For light-colored fabrics, silver nitrate may give good results, but should the material be dark, finely powdered calcium sulphite may be employed. This is dusted over the surface with the same technique as that in ordinary powdering processes. This type of powder adheres to the fatty substances in the body wax, and causes the patterns to emerge in white lines against the dark surface.

A similar technique, usually more successful on paper surfaces, advocates powdering the latents with calomel or lead acetate, and then exposing the area to the fumes of hydrogen sulphide or of ammonium sulphide. The resultant images will be dark brown and permanent. Dusting with dry, finely powdered chloride of silver and exposing to sunlight has also been used as a means of developing latents on paper.

NINHYDRIN

Another chemical method for the development of latent fingerprints on a surface such as paper employs the chemical ninhydrin, a substance which is known to react with amino acids. The document or other surface is sprayed with ninhydrin in the form of a solution with ethyl alcohol or acetone (0.2 to 0.4%). A fine mist is produced over the document by means of a spraying device such as the De Vilbiss Atomizer. Optimal spraying is desired, since an excess may dissolve the latents.

Subsequently the paper is placed for some minutes in an oven at a temperature between 80°C and 140°C. The period of heating will depend on such factors as the nature of the surface and the amount of solution deposited. The document should be removed when the surface begins to turn pink. The fingerprint itself will acquire a deeper shade of pink with the passage of time. Several days may be required to attain the best results.

In the ninhydrin technique it is vital to avoid all finger contact with the questioned surface at any time after treatment, or new fingerprints will develop, even though the paper be dry. When using the ninhydrin technique in conjunction with other methods, such as iodine or silver nitrate, the use of ninhydrin sometimes prevents the subsequent development with iodine fumes: however, it apparently does not decrease the sensitivity to silver nitrate. In fact, fresh prints sometimes appear to be more sensitive to silver nitrate, the older latents responding better to ninhydrin. In this connection, ninhydrin is not practical *after* the use of silver nitrate.

As indicated in the preceding paragraph, the employment of this technique is somewhat demanding; however, despite the difficulties, the ninhydrin process has decided advantages, since it has been possible by this method to develop prints after a lapse of many years. Ninhydrin is said to be especially effective with old fingerprints. Success has been reported in developing fingerprints on paper after an interval of many years.

The initial use of ninhydrin does not interfere with the effectiveness of a subsequent processing with silver nitrate. The converse, however, is not true. The choice of method for relatively fresh fingerprints should lie with silver nitrate.

Other techniques can be used to apply ninhydrin. Some technicians prefer to use it in the same manner as silver nitrate, that is, by dipping the object in a solution. Ninhydrin is also being marketed in aerosol containers.

Various Other Methods

A process that depends upon the presence of oil in the bodily exudations employs hydrofluoric acid. This substance has the property of etching upon glass. When latents are present on glass surfaces, they may be exposed to the vapors of this acid, which attack the unprotected areas, leaving the oily ridges on the latent more or less untouched. Although this is an interesting laboratory experiment, it is not recommended for practical application. The acid is dangerous to handle, and the prints that it develops are frequently indistinct, the results in some instances being entirely negative.

Another more useful method of utilizing the oil content in latents is the application of an alkaline-alcohol solution consisting of a mixture of sodium hydroxide with alcohol and coloring matter. Within certain limits, the quantity and strength of the soda-lye appear to have little effect. The formula is as follows:

Alcohol, absolute	70 parts
10% sodium hydroxide*	20 parts
Water	10 parts

To this is added a saturated solution of Scarlet-Red.

This solution dyes the oil deposit a deep red in a few minutes, and the reaction may be hastened by warming the liquid. After coloring, it is necessary to rinse in pure alcohol, otherwise the background also becomes colored. Other dyeing methods have been suggested in which Scarlet-Red and Sudan III are employed, but their application is somewhat involved and is hardly recommended.

Latent prints found upon nonporous surfaces such as metal, glass, etc., may be treated by dusting with powdered albumin, and staining with blue or red coal-tar dyes. Prints produced by skin excretion containing moisture of oil composites are adaptable to this coloring method. The process is the same as with bacteria-dyeing, the dusted print being "fixed" by passing it through an open flame before subjecting it to the coloring medium. Care should be observed in the application of heat, should the specimen be of glass. The method is not suited to porous surfaces such as wood or paper, since the dye will color the entire area. Inflammable materials should not be treated by this method.

There are many exceptional cases which present especial

* Made by dissolving 10 grams of sodium hydroxide in 90 grams of water.

difficulties in the process of developing and recording latent fingerprints. Viscid or "tacky" backgrounds offer a common problem. Prints thereon obviously cannot be developed by dusting, as any powder will adhere not only to the ridges but to their surroundings as well. These surfaces are all too common, being found in stables, barns, kitchens, barrooms, garages, factories, etc., where sticky coating of grease or vapor film more or less covers all exposed areas.

The complex mixture which constitutes the perspiratory excretion has given rise to a number of ingenious suggestions for the development of latent fingerprints. Each of the methods described below avails itself of some special physical or chemical property of perspiration. The procedures are, however, mainly of academic interest, and rarely applicable in place of those previously recommended.

Heat—The organic material present in the perspiration can be charred with the application of heat. A hot iron, for example, can be applied to a sheet of paper to develop the latent print in a dark outline.

Colored Solutions—The preferential wetting of paper by a colored solution such as ink will reveal a fingerprint by contrast. In effect, this technique is an offset process. One recommended mixture consists of 2 ml osmic acid, 2 ml water and 0.05 gm pyrogallic acid.

Dyestuffs—A print can be powdered with a dye and fixed by exposure to acetic acid and steam. Waxoline dyes, yellow, red, or violet can be used.

Hydrofluoric Acid—Fingerprints on glass can be made legible by treating directly with hydrofluoric acid. The area between the ridges is etched while the ridges themselves repel the acid because of their waxy content.

Reducing Agent—This technique effectually enables the operator to produce a negative of the fingerprint without using a camera. An organic reducing agent of the photographic class such as amidol, pyrogallol or hydroquinone is brushed on the print. A piece of photographic film is pressed against the print, developed in ammonia and water vapor, and fixed in hypo.

Tannic Acid—The albumin present in a fingerprint becomes visible when set by a 10 per cent solution of tannic acid.

Fleming's Reagent—This reagent is a mixture of osmic acid and glacial acetic acid. The print is first treated with a liquid which fluoresces in ultraviolet light. The fatty substance present in the fingerprint will retain the liquid after being treated with the reagent. A photograph is made with ultraviolet light.

CASTINGS

A perplexing situation that sometimes arises is one wherein quite promising latent traces are present in dust, flour, or other finely powdered material. It may be that the finest detail of the ridge structure is plainly visible, but any attempt at powdering may at once destroy the evidence. Of course, photography will usually solve such a problem; however, it may be that this recourse is not available.

An excellent method for preserving such delicate traces is to make a "casting" directly from the impression. This can be accomplished by one of several procedures. A popular commercial preparation known as "moulage" may be used. This substance is a synthetic material resembling rubber, that may be melted with moderate heat, and poured upon the impressions. When cool, it may be removed, and will furnish a reproduction of the tiniest minutiae present. This useful preparation also is employed for making castings of tire marks, tool impressions, wounds, weapons, death masks, and for countless other purposes in the law-enforcement field. If moulage should not be obtainable, a liquid solution of white gypsum may also be used in much the same fashion. Practical reproductions have been secured with dental plaster of Paris.

In spite of their favorable results, all of the substances mentioned require some preliminary preparation before using, and in case the time element is important, there is another material available that is even more convenient in its application. This is a metallic alloy known as "Woods metal." When cold, it is hard, fairly nonpliable, and has a smooth finish. However, it melts at an extremely low temperature (68° C.), the heat from a candle or cigarette lighter being sufficient to liquefy it in a few seconds. A bit of Woods metal may be melted thus in a spoon or other container and poured over the latent traces. After cooling, which occurs immediately, the pattern's finest design will be seen in sharp relief upon the metallic surface.

Nor is this remarkable substance's utility limited to fingerprints in dust. As a matter of fact, it may be successfully applied to almost any surface where prints have been recorded with body wax, the only requirement being that the surface is fairly level. In applying the hot metal, it is well to surround the area with a tiny "coffer dam" of wax, clay, chewing gum, or any similar substance that may be at hand. This will retain the metal during the brief period while it hardens. Since it cools rapidly, there is little danger of damaging the surface, regardless of its nature.

This alloy is obtainable in any chemical supply house, as it is a material extensively used in automatic fire equipment wherein the increased temperature caused by fire melts the metal and releases a trigger that sets the extinguishing mechanism in operation. Woods metal is composed of 50 per cent bismuth, 25 per cent lead, 12½ per cent tin, and 12½ per cent cadmium. The element "indium" is another metallic substance with a very low melting-point (155° C.) that has been recommended by some for use in the same manner as Woods metal. However, Woods metal is to be preferred, since indium is handicapped by almost prohibitive cost and scarcity.

In addition to casting, several of the other methods previously mentioned have application in special circumstances—namely, the use of heat and the ink process, which was included under "colored solutions."

Ink Process

A quite effective method of developing latents on paper is the so-called "ink process." This treatment is based on the fact that there is normally a slight secretion of oil on the fingers, picked up from the oil-exuding skin surfaces, and with finger impressions thus produced, some of the oil will have been conveyed to those parts of the paper with which the ridges of the pattern come in contact. Hence, when the paper is subsequently treated with ink, the oily ridge markings will repel the liquid, whereas the intermediate furrows and the rest of the paper will be stained. In this way a negative fingerprint will be produced, as opposed to the positive print given by adhering powders, in which the ridges receive most of the pigment and the furrows remain relatively uncolored.

Slightly diluting the ink sometimes yields better results. The questioned surface is then painted lightly and evenly with a small, soft brush dipped in the solution. Owing to the grease and oil forming the pattern to which the ink does not adhere, the pattern becomes visible, as indicated. Ordinarily, these developed prints are permanent, and a further advantage is the circumstance that ink, the developing medium, is usually available. This process frequently yields excellent results even with very old prints to which powders will not adhere.

Discrepancies in the ink method, as noted by some technicians, may be due in many cases to the fact that all writing fluids are not of the same definite chemical composition, varying widely in their constituents. A carefully conducted test on this question showed that the amount of total solids in 25 samples of writing inks had variance of 1.89 to 7.94 per cent, while copying inks showed even greater variance.

The drawback to the use of ordinary iron-gall ink is that it is applied to the paper in an unoxidized condition, so that even those parts which appear very pale at first may eventually become darker, with the result that it is difficult to control the final coloration.

The blue color given by ferric salts with gallic and gallo-tannic acids, phenol, etc. may be attributed to the presence of hydroxyl groups, and the intensity of coloration depends upon the number of free hydroxyl groups in the organic compound. To produce a permanent coloration with iron salts, resulting in ink, a substance must contain three hydroxyl groups in juxtaposition. For example, hydroquinone with two hydroxyl groups does not yield ink, whereas gallic acid and pyrogallol with three adjacent hydroxyl groups, do. This law of atomic grouping also applies to permanent coloration produced by ammonium vanadate with similar compounds, and the same rule is applicable to the color reactions of osmium tetroxide.

The ordinary 1 per cent solution of osmic acid and gallo-tannic acid produces inks with violet-gray coloration, but the most suitable ink for developing fingerprints is obtained by adding pyrogallic acid to osmic acid in solution. In very dilute solutions, the osmic-pyrogallic acid is at first violet, but almost immediately becomes greenish blue, and when applied to paper, gives a rich violet-black coloration.

Ink of a suitable dilution for treating fingerprints may be made by diluting 2 cc. of ordinary osmic acid reagent with the same quantity of water, and adding 0.05 grams of pyrogallic acid. The liquid is ready for immediate use, and should be brushed across the paper with broad sweeps of a camel's-hair brush.

In the ink method of developing fingerprints, good results may sometimes be attained by adding a small amount of creosote to the ink. This causes the reagent to run rapidly over the surface of the paper so that the period of contact is much shorter than when ordinary ink is used. Also, the differential staining is more pronounced in a recently-made fingerprint than with one made some time previously, which gives some approximation of the age of the marks in question.

A marked difficulty must be recognized with the ink process, namely, latents so developed do not photograph well. For photographic reproduction, the iodine process is superior. Another fact to be noted is the damage to the surface. If the process fails, it is difficult or impossible to employ other methods, and failure of this method is not unusual. Many papers, such as ordinary writing paper, give good results, while others fail completely. No rules can be offered, since the grade and texture of papers show so great a variation.

Impressions produced by excessive pressure, as well as those made by exceedingly oily fingers, do not lend themselves readily to the ink method. For such conditions, the iodine or dusting process is recommended, and more especially the iodine, since these impressions, when dusted only, may yield blurred black dots in which the ridges cannot be recognized. The ink process usually develops clear images when the latents are the result of the normal touch of normally oily fingers.

Latent impressions upon paper may often be brought out by a treatment of heat, which produces a dark brown pattern upon a lighter brown background. This is due to the fact that the organic substances in body wax, under heat, become carbonized in the absence of sufficient oxidation, since they are enclosed largely by the saline components which are present in all bodily exudations. The organic particles in the salt crust char more readily than does the paper. This reaction is stimulated by the heat-conducting property of the salt. The organic particles, hermetically enclosed in the salt, are very small, and with the application of heat, receive much more warmth than the paper, hence the resultant action.

Temperatures of from 200 to 300 degrees Centigrade will produce the desired results. The paper may be protected by placing it between two sheets of mica held together with metal paper-clips. If the specimen so prepared is moved back and forth over a flame, the impressions will appear without the paper's being burned. The development should be carefully watched and interrupted as soon as the impressions are sufficiently legible. Care must be exercised in applying the heat, as the mica tends to expand or blister where the most heat falls. This leaves the paper unevenly protected, and blurred places result. A heat source is recommended which furnishes hot air without bringing the paper in contact with an open flame; if so desired, the paper may be placed for treatment on an asbestos plate. This method is adapted especially for the examination of large documents.

Often good results may be secured by merely smoothing the questioned surfaces with a hot iron, the temperature and manipulation being precisely the same as in ordinary damp-wash ironing.

When the latent imprints have been produced by excessively oily fingers, the heating process is not recommended, and such traces are better developed by other methods, such as the iodine treatment.

Considering the fact that all bodily exudations contain a percentage of salts, notably sodium chloride, this substance also offers some possibilities in the development of latent fingerprints. Ordinarily, a considerable amount of chlorides are present on the hands and fingers, and frequently in much higher percentage than may be found in free perspiration, which leaves a more concentrated deposit as it evaporates. Thus, recognizable traces of sodium chloride are left upon surfaces which the fingers touch.

Since chloride deposits migrate slowly, here is seen a possible means of estimating the age of latent fingerprints. However, it is not advisable to place too much trust in this indication, owing to its variability. The chloride migration is certain to be influenced by temperature, humidity, organic materials in the perspiration, the nature of the surface touched, etc. But notwithstanding this, the factor of migration should not be ignored summarily, as it is informative in some degree.

XV

LATENT FINGERPRINT FILES

LATENT impressions should be kept in a special file for a prescribed period: until they have been identified or the trial is over. If still unidentified, they may be removed after a lapse of time indicated by the statute of limitations. If the impressions were developed on a portable object, they should be protected by a celluloid strip taped at the ends, and the object should be wrapped and stored. Negatives and lifts should be filed with the case folder.

The photographs of the latent prints, however, should be pasted on 3 x 5-inch cards with the case number and classification typed on the top line. Two cards should be made for each fingerprint. One will be filed by serial number, the other by pattern type, and daily compared with newly acquired prints of similar pattern.

When the record bureau includes a single-print unit in which each of the subjects has a separate card filed for every finger, the identification of an unknown person from a latent pattern is more probable. There have been a number of single-print methods employed for classifying and filing single impressions, of which the Battley is the most widely known. A point to remember is the fact that the file's utility depends on the prints placed in it. The most promising prospects are those subjects who seem likely to commit future crimes in which latent prints may be left. Plainly, a defendant arrested for drunkenness would be less desirable for the single-print file as compared with one guilty of house burglary. A little consideration will serve to limit the single-print file's inclusions to the most appropriate subjects.

Even if a single-print file is not included in the local bureau, it is good practice to preserve and segregate all latents found during local investigations. These should be placed in envelopes bearing the case number, the date, and a brief résumé of the circumstances, and filed chronologically. Also, it is necessary to file copies of the same impressions according to their pattern types. In this way it will be possible to compare newly discovered latents with others of similar design which have been found in previous instances. It will often be shown that several unrelated crimes were all the work of one person. Thus, with the arrest of a suspect, the latent file may indicate his responsibility for a number of prior acts in addition to his current offense.

Unfortunately, those who leave latent prints at a crime scene seldom furnish a sufficient number of their impressions to permit an accurate classification of all ten digits. To be sure, in rare instances, this actually has happened; but usually only a few legible traces are available. Although this scanty evidence may seem inadequate for a conclusive search in a ten-finger file, nevertheless, such a search is often quite possible with but one or two latents as a guide.

At the outset, it is plain that should the evidential pattern be a loop, there would be little use in searching in the all-whorl division, just as a latent whorl would exclude everything in the section devoted to loops only. Thus, at least a broad segregation is possible in every instance. Obviously, if it can be determined with any degree of certainty which finger made the latent in question, it then is possible to comb all parts of a ten-finger bureau wherein such a pattern might be filed.

DETERMINATION OF FINGER INVOLVED

When a latent trace is unidentified as to the finger involved, the problem is more complicated. Nevertheless, recognition of certain facts is helpful in this connection. The majority of persons are right-handed, and in ordinary circumstances, the thumb, index, and second fingers are those most often used.

Experience will show that latent prints are not always found singly, but frequently in combinations; two, three, and even four or more impressions sometimes appear. These are usually the thumb, index, and second fingers, although groups including the index, second, ring, and even the little finger, are discovered. To determine accurately which fingers have been involved requires careful consideration. It will be necessary to visualize how the object or surface may have been handled, the position which the fingers probably assumed, the degree and direction of pressure applied, and all other related circumstances.

There are certain physical facts which are helpful in this requirement. It is known that in the white races about 65 per cent of all finger-patterns are loops, and that the large majority of these have an ulnar slope, that is, toward the little finger. Radial loops appear most frequently in the index fingers. Thus, a group of loop patterns all slanting toward the right, would inevitably have been made by a right hand (Fig. 159-*a*); should the first impression slope toward the left and the other three to the right, it would still indicate a right-hand print in which the index finger displayed a radial loop, the other digits ulnar loops (Fig. 159-*b*). The opposite, of course, is also true;

Fig. 159A

Imprints of the four fingers of a right hand, all displaying ulnar loops

Fig. 159B

Imprints of the four fingers of a right hand wherein the index finger is
radial and the others ulnar loops

Fig. 160A

Imprints of the four fingers of a left hand, all displaying ulnar loops

Fig. 160B

Imprints of the four fingers of a left hand wherein the index finger is
radial and the others are ulnar loops

if all the patterns are loops sloping to the left, a left-hand print is indicated (Fig. 160-*a*); and should the right-hand impression of the group slope toward the right, with the other three sloping left, it would suggest a left hand with a radial loop in the index finger (Fig. 160-*b*). Radial loops rarely occur in the little fingers.

These indications are found in the pattern forms; however, another conclusive denotation will be the length and position of the fingers in relation to each other, together with the comparative size of the impressions. This matter of size is important when only a single latent is available. A thumb-print is nearly always distinctive for its superior size and for the distance from the core to the pattern's upper edge, which normally is much more than in the other fingers. Also, the ridges at the thumb's extreme tip are sure to have a decisive "ulnar" slope, regardless of the pattern type. This is a very

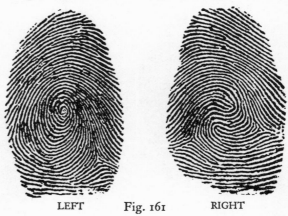

LEFT   Fig. 161   RIGHT

These right and left thumbprints illustrate the characteristic ridge slope usually recognizable in the tip of a thumb impression. Also, it will be noted that a clockwise spiral is present in the left thumb, and that the ascending loop in the right thumb displays an ulnar slope.

marked characteristic; if the right and left thumbprints are recorded side by side, as they appear in the "flat" impressions at the bottom of a fingerprint card, the tip ridges will slope away from each other like the two sides of a roof viewed from its gable end (Fig. 161).

This "ulnar" direction in thumbprints has other aspects; when twin loops are present in the thumbs or other digits, the "ascending" loop will be likely to have an ulnar inclination (Fig. 162); and should the design be a whorl of the elongated or "almond" type, it too will probably slope toward the little finger (Fig. 163). In whorls having a spiral form, the direction of the curvature will usually be "counterclockwise" in the right hand, and "clockwise" in the left, in the recorded patterns. Another phenomenon of unusual significance is the formation of radial loops occurring in the thumbs. As a matter of fact, radial loops are not commonly seen in the thumbs, but when present, they may identify the digit un-

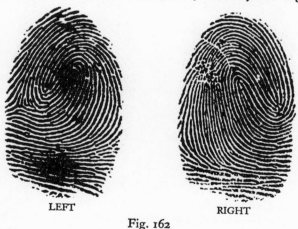

LEFT   RIGHT

Fig. 162

These impressions from right and left hands display the characteristic ulnar slope of the ascending loop in both of the twin-loop patterns

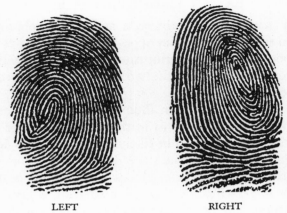

LEFT   RIGHT

Fig. 163

These impressions from right and left hands display elongated-whorl
patterns which have an ulnar slope in both instances

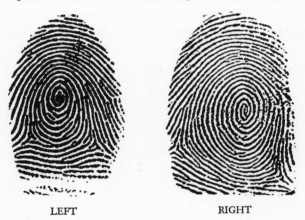

LEFT   RIGHT

Fig. 164

These spiral-whorl patterns from right and left hands illustrate the
directional twist commonly encountered in such designs. It will be noted
that a right-directional or clockwise spiral is present in the left-hand
pattern, and that a left-directional or counter-clockwise spiral is seen
in the right-hand design

mistakably. Loop patterns present many different arrangements in design, a unique form being the so-called "nutant" or "nodding" loop, in which the structure, instead of pointing upward, has a bent or curved appearance that causes the tip end to point downward, much the same as a slanting metal bar might appear were it caused to soften and sag from intense heat. When loop patterns of this formation occur, they are usually in the thumbs and almost invariably radial (Fig. 165). True, radial loops may be present in the thumbs and not be "nutant," but these exceptions do not minimize the rule's importance.

The index fingers show the greatest variance, since all types of pattern are found in these digits. Nevertheless, should whorls be present, the same rule holds as with the thumbs, namely, right-directional spirals on the left hand and left-directional on the right, when the impressions are recorded, and with the marked "ulnar" inclination of oval whorls and the "ascending" cores in double-loop designs. These indications may be recognized in the other fingers also.

The index finger's position on the hand is such that when grasping or touching surfaces, its imprint is likely to include less of the pattern area on the "thumb side." Thus, if the latent print be that of a right index displaying a broad whorl, the right delta will probably be conspicuous, whereas the left delta may not even be included.

This illustration shows a typical nutant loop. Usually, when this pattern form is present in a set of fingerprints, it will be in one or both of the thumbs, and if so located, is almost certain to have a radial slope.

Fig. 165

There is, perhaps, more chance of confusion between the middle and ring fingers than with the others. However, the middle finger is distinctive for its superior length, and also for its pattern area, which usually is greater than those of the index and ring fingers; the little finger, of course, has the smallest pattern area of all. It is possible, in exceptional cases, to mistake the imprint of the right middle and right ring fingers for those of the left index and left middle; nevertheless, a careful examination will usually correct this error. Also, the middle and ring fingers alone are less likely to be recorded.

As stated, about 65 per cent of fingerprint patterns of the white race are loops; approximately 30 per cent are whorls, and 5 per cent arches. Incidentally, there seems to be some indication that arches appear more frequently on the fingers of women as compared to those of men. In regard to the distribution of these various designs on the fingers of both men and women, certain pattern arrangements do have more frequency than others. However, an ample consideration of this would be involved, and perhaps not conclusive in all cases. The technician will note a large percentage of fingerprint cards showing all loops, as well as many that show all whorls. Whorls in the thumbs are common.

Experience in classifying and filing fingerprints will teach the student what to anticipate in the way of pattern arrangement far better than any written text. Nevertheless, there are other aspects of skin design which deserve at least passing mention. In looking over any sizable number of fingerprint cards, certain characteristics will be noted. Although, of course, no two designs can ever absolutely agree in their finer detail, there usually will be a general similarity throughout in the ten patterns of any person, as to their pictorial aspects of form, structure, slope, line quality, etc. It will be noted that a given set of fingerprints will display a "related" appearance, indicating their common origin or "parentage," like ten children in one family. Also, should one of the patterns be in disagreement with the others, as when a radial loop appears in a thumb, it probably will assume a different appearance from the rest, thus indicating that this disagreement is the evasion of a natural law under which the skin designs assume their form. In violating this law, the pattern has lost some of its pictorial harmony.

There seems to be a marked "radial" influence present at the indexes, diminishing toward the little finger. Also a "twinning," or similarity of patterns, is noted at this point, as well as in the thumbs. The ring fingers, too, display a tendency toward twinning.

DETECTING FORGED FINGERPRINTS

From time to time, considerable attention has been directed toward the question of so-called "forged" fingerprints. "Forgery," in this sense, would seem to mean making copies of fingerprints by some method and with unlawful purpose or intent. Many opinions have been advanced on this; some pseudo-experts have even advocated renouncing the subject as taboo, and not to be discussed under any circumstances. Such obvious futility needs no comment, aside from recognition of the advocators' probable incompetence.

Common sense well understands that fingerprints can be copied, just as other concrete objects may be reproduced or imitated. However, the skilled technician will recognize these reproductions as imitations, no more, no less. To contend otherwise is an insult to the intelligence. Counterfeits of any description are still counterfeits, and detectable as such by those possessing the necessary familiarity in that especial field.

This is true of currency, art objects, personal signatures, in fact everything, including fingerprints.

Simulation of fingerprints can be made in a number of ways, by etching, with transfer materials, rubber stamps, photography, etc. One enterprising enthusiast wrote a small book on forging fingerprints in which he described his choice of technique, the results of which, incidentally, should not have deceived the rankest amateur. All of the above and many other methods can produce imitated or "forged" fingerprints; but they still are forgeries, and recognizable as such.

One of the reasons why "forged" fingerprints may seem terrifying to some is the fact that these persons may have overlooked the finer detail in skin structure. To detect forgery of any kind it usually is necessary to examine the questioned object carefully and to scrutinize its less conspicuous characteristics. For example, a counterfeit bill may seem genuine to a casual observer, but under the expert's inspection, its defects are obvious. If a counterfeit bill can be recognized, the detection of an imitated fingerprint is understandable, since the fingerprint is a natural phenomenon, and the hardest to simulate. Another factor militating against the possibility of successful fingerprint forgery, is the would-be forger's probable lack of needful skill and necessary facilities.

A "forged" fingerprint may be likened to a personal signature made with a rubber stamp; the general appearance is similar, but under closer inspection, its spurious origin is unmistakable. A fingerprint under the microscope is seen to be an extremely complex subject. To the unaided eye, its structure may appear to be composed of more or less symmetrical ridges, all much the same in appearance, and with few if any individual characteristics. When magnified, a quite different picture is presented. The ridges which at first seemed uniform throughout, are seen to be composed of marked irregularities of a unique nature (Fig. 166 *a, b, c* and *d*).

Fig. 166A

An outstanding feature of friction skin patterns, and one that defies successful imitation, is the pore openings (Fig. 151, *a* and *b*). As explained elsewhere, the exudation from these tiny orifices is deposited upon finger-touched surfaces. The magnified view of a normal fingerprint shows the moisture in tiny pools or droplets, the size, shape, distribution, and general appearance of which, if naturally recorded will be unmistakable (Fig. 157). The pores' placement and formation will be indicated by the larger moisture globules together with smaller droplets representing the oily substance which the fingers have accumulated by touching oil-exuding areas of the body where the sebaceous glands are present. In its natural state, this moisture deposit is extremely fragile and will be certain to sustain irreparable damage from any contact whatever (Fig. 167 *a* and *b*). A comparable situation is the surface of a dew-drenched leaf upon which the slightest touch disturbs the natural arrangement of its liquid beading. Plainly, it would be impossible to "transplant" this delicate and destructible coating of droplets without crushing them out of all semblance to their original form. Also, any adhesive substance used in making such a transfer would be certain to leave some traces that microscopic examination could recognize.

A normal fingerprint is an impression from the living skin, and made with natural body secretions and exudations. It is of such a nature that any attempt to remove it from one surface and replace it upon another is certain to fail for many further reasons than those already given. Since a genuine

Fig. 166B

Figs. 166A, B, C and D show progressive enlargement of a fingerprint
showing its intimate structure more conspicuously as the degree
of magnification increases

Fig. 166C   Fig. 166D

fingerprint can not be "transplanted" successfully, the only other alternative open to the would-be forger is to produce a convincing simulation of a genuine fingerprint by artificial means. To do this, a living finger must serve as a model from which a "negative" impression might be made in wax, moulage, or other plastic medium. Then, from the "negative" mold, a "positive" casting could be made, thus furnishing an artificial finger of rubber or similar resilient substance. Its surface would be skinlike, and from it could be made fingerprints, of a sort.

As compared with the "transfer" technique's futility, the making of perfect fingerprint "simulation" is simply out of the question. An artificial "finger," no matter how carefully made to approximate the skin's true texture, certainly can not include what is most necessary to the recording of a normal fingerprint, namely, the sweat ducts. Therefore, though the false finger be moistened with real body wax, any impression made with it will have little resemblance to a genuine fingerprint. Under magnification, the moisture globules which in a normal fingerprint appear in irregularly distributed ellipsoids, will be seen in extremely small spheroids distributed evenly, and in no way resembling the natural deposit of the human skin. Nor will the rubber-stamp fingerprint's general appearance seem genuine; it will look like a rubber stamp, and that most decisively.

Quite apart from their physical aspects, additional evidence of forged fingerprints' unnatural origin would certainly be seen in their placement; also, their inevitable appearance upon the surface allegedly touched, the direction and degree of pressure indicated, their number, the plausibility and even possibility of their being there at all, together with many other conspicuous factors, would be highly informative. As stated at the outset, fingerprints, like anything else, can be "forged," but the results attainable by any process could never be more than crude and obvious copies, easily recognized by the qualified investigator.

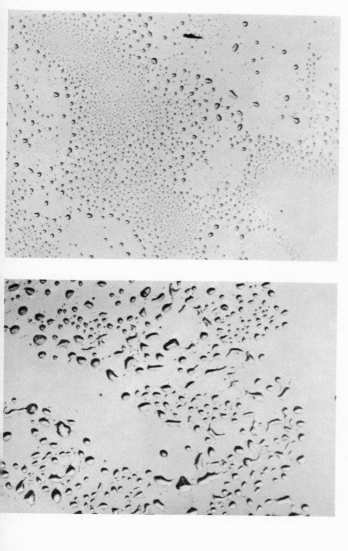

Fig. 167A

Fig. 167B

Enlarged view of the moisture deposit in a fingerprint before and after its transfer to another surface. Fig. 167A shows the normal appearance of the globules of body wax. Fig. 167B shows the same area of the pattern with the moisture globules crushed and scattered by the transfer process. It will be noted that they have lost their natural form, and present a decidedly abnormal aspect

XVI

FINGERPRINTING DECEASED PERSONS

WITH the investigative program of law enforcement, it is sometimes necessary to compare an evidential impression with the skin patterns of a deceased person; in certain cases this is difficult, and may require special technique. Thus, any comprehensive work on the subject of latents should include some description of these methods.

When fingerprinting deceased persons, the technician will meet with a variety of conditions. Nevertheless, legible prints usually can be obtained by some means, even in situations which at first seem discouraging. Despite the differing states of preservation in which dead bodies are discovered, they may be grouped in three classes, generally speaking. When death has but recently occurred, taking fingerprints is usually simple, and can be accomplished in much the same manner as with a living subject. This may be considered as the first class. However, in the second class, more difficulty may be encountered when rigor mortis has appeared, or in the early stages of decomposition. In the third class, serious problems are often presented in advanced stages of disintegration, maceration, decomposition, or putrefaction.

Technique in Simpler Cases

It would seem appropriate to discuss these three classes separately. In the first instance, when the fingers of the dead subject are flexible, sometimes it is possible to secure the fingerprints through the regular inking and rolling process, and upon a standard fingerprint card. Nevertheless, it is more convenient to use a separate piece of paper for each finger to be printed. Later, these may be trimmed and pasted in the correct squares on a fingerprint card. For this purpose, ordinary typing paper will furnish good results. Care must be observed to make notation on each of the paper squares, designating which finger has been printed thereon.

It is, of course, much easier to take the impressions of a living subject than of a dead one, since the hands and fingers are flexible. In a corpse, post-mortem rigidity will usually appear in from four to seven hours. Before this condition develops, the fingers can be manipulated readily. As when printing a living person, the skin should be clean to insure the best outcome. When the body is in perfect preservation, the skin may be cleansed with any good solvent such as alcohol, benzine, etc., or with soap and water; and after cleaning, the fingers should be thoroughly dried. This will demand extra care, as there is no body heat to aid the drying; the skin of a corpse ordinarily is dank and clammy. It is an excellent plan to submerge the hands in hot water for a short time before printing. This will make the skin easier to dry; also, the fingers will be more pliable.

After washing and drying, the joints of the wrist and fingers should be subjected to vigorous extension and flexion to attain as much pliability as possible. In applying the ink, it may not be convenient to "roll" the finger on an inking plate in all cases. Various methods have been advocated for this procedure. The ink may be applied directly to the finger with a small rubber roller. Also, inking may be accomplished by the use of a tool similar to a wide, blunt knife or spatula, either flat or curved. The ink is first rolled on the surface of the spatula, and thence to the finger. A small, portable ink plate may be employed, the finger being held against its surface while the plate is "rolled."

In any case, the purpose is to spread a thin and even film of ink on the finger's pattern area. In this procedure, it will be found expedient to ink and print the fingers one at a time rather than to ink all the fingers before printing. When recording the impressions of the inked digits, it must be remembered that the object is to secure records that are both legible and inclusive; that is, the finished print should include all of the pattern area in every instance. Since finger patterns are often wide, extending well up and around the sides of the digit, this will demand care and attention both in inking and printing.

Since the fingers can not be "rolled" upon the paper, the paper must be "rolled" around the finger. By holding the paper in the palm of the hand and pressing the finger that is being printed against it, a satisfactory impression may sometimes be obtained. Also, curved metal "spoons," especially designed for this purpose, are sold commercially. These are customarily provided with slots or grooves to hold the paper (Fig. 168 *a*). As a matter of fact, a number of firms dealing in fingerprint supplies, offer complete outfits for the fingerprinting of dead bodies.

A useful device for holding the paper can be improvised from an ordinary shoehorn (Fig. 168 *b*); two channels cut lengthwise with a hacksaw will serve to retain the paper, which may be cut in a strip to thread through the slots of whatever type of holder is used. In this case, the paper strip

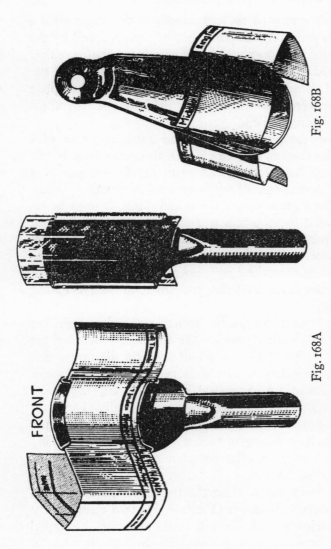

FRONT

Fig. 168A

Fig. 168B

A shows two types of curved "spoon" for taking the fingerprints of dead bodies. B shows how an ordinary shoehorn can be adapted for finger-printing dead bodies

(Reproduced from the "Finger Print and Identification Magazine")

is moved forward as each finger is printed, the finished result showing all the impressions in a row; this has some advantages.

When fingerprinting well-preserved bodies in the manner herein described, it usually will be possible to record not only the "rolled" impressions, but also the "flat" imprints as well. These may be placed directly on the fingerprint card, or upon separate paper to be mounted on the conventional card later. The latter technique is advocated, since it will be found in taking the prints from dead bodies that several trials may sometimes be necessary in order to secure a useful record.

AFTER RIGOR MORTIS HAS APPEARED

When the body to be printed falls in the second classification, somewhat different techniques are necessary. It may be that the fingers can not be rendered flexible by the methods described. The skin may be shrunken, or peeling away, and portions of the friction areas damaged or missing. Frequently the subject's hands are stiff and clenched. If the flesh is still firm and the ridges intact, it may be possible to insert the "spoon" under each digit, both in inking and in printing, and thus secure the impressions. However, to release the fingers, surgical attention may be necessary, such as cutting the controlling tendons. Since the business of printing a deceased is usually conducted at the morgue, it is possible that the services of an autopsy surgeon will be available. In the absence of such aid, the technician may perform the tenotomy himself by cutting the flexure tendons at the fingers or wrist.

When separating the sinews at the wrist, the operation should be performed by one skilled in surgery; but cutting the tendons at the fingers is much the simpler procedure, and can be accomplished with but little experience. With a narrow bistouri or lancet, a small incision will sever the sinews beneath the skin, leaving an inconspicuous wound. Once the fingers have been freed, the prints may be taken, as already described.

So far, this discussion has dealt with the taking of impressions when the flesh is fairly well preserved. A different problem will arise when decay has started. The technique of treating fingers in such instances varies greatly, depending upon the conditions. When available, the cooperation of a surgeon or embalmer will be found very helpful, since these skilled specialists will be certain to have at hand many needed facilities.

Frequently the skin of a corpse will be softened and shrunken, perhaps from submersion, with the friction skin in folds and furrows. This condition may respond to plastic restoration, which involves the introduction of a suitable substance beneath the skin that will round out the finger and eliminate the wrinkles. For this purpose, various materials are used, such as vaseline, hot water, glycerin, melted paraffin, etc. Good results have been obtained with a solution of glycerinated gelatin. To a hot solution of gelatin is added glycerin in the proportion of about one part of gelatin to seven of glycerin. This heated mixture is injected into the finger tissues hypodermically; a syringe with a large needle will be necessary.

Another quite simple technique employs a hypodermic with a very fine needle, through which air is injected to inflate the shrunken tissues. The spot selected for insertion should be the extremity of the longitudinal axis of the finger at a point on the bulb about 4 to 5 mm. back from the tip. The necessary amount of air to be injected will usually be about 1 to 1½ c.c. When the tissue of the finger bulb is sufficiently inflated, the needle is withdrawn abruptly and the opening massaged to close the perforation and retain the air.

When the fingers are sufficiently rounded, inking and print-ing may be accomplished in the usual manner.

When the fingers are hard and desiccated from long ex-posure to the sun, as with bodies found in the desert, soaking the fingers in a solution of caustic potash will cause the tissue to swell. This may require the fingers' amputation, in which event, precaution must be taken to identify each finger by a serviceable tag or other means, since it is absolutely neces-sary to know the fingers apart when their impressions are finally placed in the squares of a fingerprint card. A treatment of caustic potash has proved successful with dried bodies after a lapse of years.

Desiccated bodies also become mummified when lying in some sheltered place not exposed to the elements and where the air may circulate freely. In any case, the hands and fingers are more likely to resist decay, since their underlying parts are mainly bones and tendons.

In treating the shrunken tissue, results can not be expected too quickly, but restoration will usually be possible with a solution of potassium hydroxide. It will be found convenient to secure ten beakers or similar containers of about 150 c.c. capacity, and mark them according to the ten fingers. The fingers, having been removed as suggested above, are then placed in these receptacles and covered with a 3 per cent solu-tion of potassium hydroxide. The solution may be varied from $1\frac{1}{2}$ to 3 per cent, according to the condition of the specimens; if the outer skin is intact, a stronger mixture may be used with safety.

When the fingers have been immersed in the liquid, they must be watched carefully, as the solution, if too strong, will attack the tissues and the ridges will be eaten away, thus mak-ing it impossible to secure any prints. Should the fingers ap-pear to be distending too rapidly, which may cause the skin to rupture, they may be removed from the solution and washed in distilled water, which will check absorption.

When the fingers are distended to normal size, they should be removed from the solution and washed in distilled water. If necessary, the tissues may be hardened by soaking in a 1 per cent solution of formaldehyde. Inking and printing may be accomplished in the manner already described.

It is difficult to state how long the fingers should remain in the potassium hydroxide; this will depend upon the condition of the skin and the strength of the solution, but will probably be from four to ten or more hours.

Where Decomposition Has Set In

Cases falling in the third group are the most difficult to handle. The skin may be peeling away, with only portions of the patterns available. The body may be in a more or less advanced state of putrefaction and the skin tissue so badly decomposed that, regardless of careful treatment, particles would adhere to any inking instrument, or at best only blurred prints could be obtained. In some cases, the skin may be carefully cut away from the pattern areas, and the fragments placed in bottles of formaldehyde, using a separate bottle for the skin of each finger and labeling them accordingly. The formaldehyde, besides being a preservative, has a hardening effect upon the tissue. These bits of skin may later be placed over the technician's own fingers, protected by rubber gloves, and rolled impressions taken from them in the customary manner.

In the event that the outer ridge structure is no longer discernible, the design may still be seen upon the skin's under surface. This, of course, also necessitates the skin's removal. In some circumstances the skin will separate from the under tissue quite readily, but will occasionally be more tenacious.

Loosening of the skin from the flesh may often be accomplished by boiling the fingers just as a beef tongue is boiled to remove the skin. When finally separated from the pattern areas, the skin patches should be mounted on cardboard with the inner surface turned outward. The ridge designs will thus be presented for observation. Here it must be remembered that the patterns, if visible, will necessarily be in reverse from the prints' original appearance upon the surface.

Where the condition of the tissue prohibits inking or skin removal, an effective solution may be found in photography. Careful lighting and photographing with a film such as Eastman Panatomic-X or Ansco Isopan can sometimes yield a classifiable image of the fingerprint.

A 1:1 size photograph should be made using the fingerprint camera or, if special lighting is required, a larger camera, such as the 4 x 5 press-type camera with a long bellows extension. If the ridges are clear and the skin devoid of wrinkles, direct lighting is satisfactory. Side lighting from carefully selected angles will serve to provide relief in more difficult cases.

The use of radiography as a means of obtaining the fingerprints of a deceased person is mainly of academic interest. The surface of the fingers is powdered with a mixture containing a heavy metal salt such as bismuth or lead carbonate and brushed lightly so that the powder is left between the ridges for the most part. A radiograph is then made in the usual manner, with an X-ray intensity of about 30 kilovolts. The resulting negative will be opaque in the outlines created by the powder. Bone structure, of course, will also be apparent.

If the procedures to be used in fingerprinting a dead person involve dissection, amputation, or other postmortem surgery, it is essential to fulfill the legal requirements of the controlling jurisdiction. Most state codes (e.g. California Health and Safety Code, Secs. 7102-7114) contain provisions prescribing the conditions for exhumation, surgery, or other special processes needed for identification. A common preliminary condition is the permission of the coroner or comparable state or municipal official.

XVII

PHOTOGRAPHY OF LATENT TRACES

IT IS a fact well known to law-enforcement officers that many crimes remain unsolved, and many cases that do come to trial are lost, because of the absence of important evidence. For recording, preserving, and objectifying most forms of evidence, and especially that of latent fingerprints, there probably is no method superior to photography. It is one of the most essential steps in latent fingerprint technique. Not only is a well-made photograph a factual reproduction, but it is also recognized as such in the eyes of the law. Although other forms of latent-print evidence may sometimes be challenged by an opposing counsel, a good photograph is usually immune from successful attack, since its veracity is self-evident. A good photograph needs no other witness or supporting testimony; it is incontrovertible, and constitutes in itself a preponderance of evidence.

Unfortunately, space does not permit a discussion of all the aspects of photography in this text. Nevertheless, some of the approved applications are presented, and it will be assumed that the reader is familiar with the primary procedures. The scope of photography, even in the field of latent fingerprints, is so broad that it would be impossible to cover its every phase in any single work; however, the student should be fully acquainted with them. In this connection, the following books are recommended for supplementary reading:

Photography in Law Enforcement, Eastman Kodak Company, Rochester, New York, 1959.

An Introduction to Criminalistics, O'Hara and Osterburg, New York; Macmillan, 1949.

Fundamentals of Photography, TM-2324, U. S. Army Field Manual.

Photographic Evidence, Preparation and Presentation, Charles C. Scott, Kansas City, Missouri; Vernon Law Book Company, 1952.

By the use of photography, some inconspicuous detail in a latent trace can be made prominent through enlargement, and shown to be identical with the print of a suspect. Photography permits of reproduction, thus providing copies of the evidence for each member of the jury, as well as for the court and the several attorneys. By photographic methods, the fingerprints of a defendant can be placed beside the latent markings, with their points of identity clearly indicated.

Not only the fingerprint itself, but also the entire crime scene can be illustrated by a photograph that may show many important features, together with the handled object. In this way, information may be included that no other presentation could render possible. This is most important, since it may be difficult to describe verbally some involved situation in such a manner as to make everything clear to a group audience.

Although latent-print evidence may commonly be of more importance to the technician for his personal study, it is well to remember that this same evidence may also feature in court. This is especially true of latent-fingerprint photographs. Here a pertinent circumstance demands attention. Before evidence of any sort may serve to demonstrate the facts of a case before

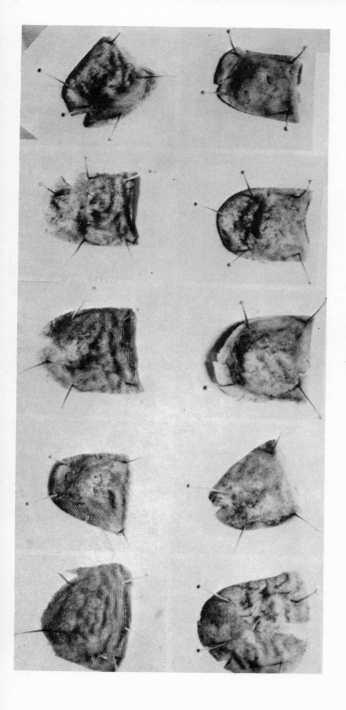

Fig. 169

Sections of skin removed from the fingers of a partially decomposed body. The complete fingerprint formula in this case was:

$$\frac{5)1 \ aT \ (-10) \ 18}{)1 \ tT \ (-11) \ 14}$$

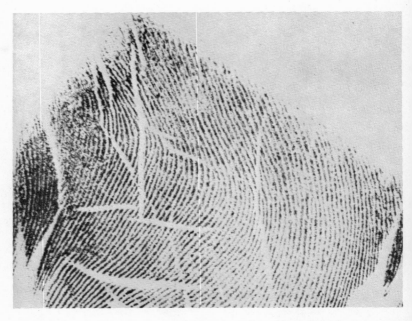
Palm-print enlargement showing friction-ridge detail. See Appendix, page 369, **for** further discussion

judge or jury, it must first be "admitted" in court; that is, it must be officially recognized as evidence, and its introduction sanctioned by the judge. Good evidence is described as being relevant, material, and competent. It should be relevant, as relating to the case; material, in being of importance to the case; and competent to demonstrate facts in the case. Of all fingerprint evidence, a photograph is most likely to qualify in these respects.

When taking photographs of a crime scene, it must be remembered that although the pictures may be intended to show latent fingerprints, this does not necessarily mean that they may show nothing else. As a matter of fact, *anything and everything* can be of vital importance as photographic evidence, and still be related to the primary issue, namely that of latent fingerprints; no possibility should be overlooked.

In legal procedure, there is a policy called "law of evidence," stipulating that the actual object shall be produced in court when possible. However, in the case of latent fingerprints, the impressions themselves offer little information to inexperienced observers. Consequently, such evidence is best presented by photographic exhibits.

All too frequently, fingerprints have been introduced in court by photographs that showed no more than the latent traces. This often is a regrettable oversight. Such evidence requires considerable explanation, is more likely to be attacked by a defense counsel, and at best may not convey all the facts to judge and jury.

When presenting fingerprint evidence by photography, it is desirable to offer photographs not only of the fingerprints, but also the object or surface where they were present, as well as the location where they were found. The reasons for this are simple; it may not be possible for the court and jury to visit the crime scene in all cases, and even when this can be arranged, it is certain they could not know exactly how the locale appeared when the crime was first discovered. This appearance can be preserved by photography.

In addition to the actual latent prints, other views are recommended. In these pictures, nothing should be included except that which is related to the case, and all objects should be photographed in their original condition and positions if possible. For example, illustrations in detective magazines and similar publications often show a crime scene wherein an officer or other person is observed pointing to a fingerprint or similar evidential object. For legal purposes, this inclusion is decidedly wrong, and may result in the photograph's being disqualified in court. No foreign marks, arrows, printed cards, or similar devices of any sort should be introduced to call attention to anything in the photograph; and most certainly no person should be permitted to intrude. Should the location be a street or other public place, the casual presence of pedestrians or vehicles is not likely to constitute a restriction; but none the less, they too should be excluded if possible.

PHOTOGRAPHIC FIELD KIT

Since it is frequently necessary to photograph a number of latent fingerprints at the crime scene, the methods and equipment should be designed to simplify and expedite the photographic process without sacrifice of picture quality. After an appropriate selection of camera and film, photographic and darkroom procedures can be standardized by an identification unit within a short time to insure reliable and rapid production of fingerprint photos having the necessary contrast and resolution.

The characteristics of an ideal fingerprint negative should be familiar to the photographer. The negative image should be the same size as the original fingerprint. Negative contrast should be somewhat higher than medium so that the fingerprint is clearly distinguishable from the background without sacrifice of fingerprint detail. The definition of the negative should permit a 5x enlargement with no obvious graininess. An appreciation of these criteria is necessary for an intelligent approach to the selection of camera and photographic materials.

Most cameras can be adapted to fingerprint photography but only a few are suitable from the point of view of simplicity, convenience, and rapidity of operation in field use. Noteworthy among these is the fixed-focus type of camera such as the Faurot and Search fingerprint cameras which contain their own lamps and battery. This camera accepts a 2¼ x 3¼ sheet film or film pack. In operation the exposure lever is also the illuminant switch. The camera is placed flush against the surface bearing the fingerprint and held steadily during the few seconds required for exposure. The fingerprint can be examined in the ground glass before exposing to insure proper coverage and also to check on the adequacy of light or the need for a filter. The depth of field is usually small at the typical setting, but will be found sufficient to photograph surfaces of moderate curvature such as quart bottles.

The fixed-focus fingerprint camera is in general use in police departments large enough to possess an identification unit. Very little knowledge of photography is required for its operation, since the lens aperture and the lights are preset. In the hands of an experienced identification man, however, this camera is quite versatile in its applications. Side-lighting, for example, can be achieved by unscrewing one or more lamps. Filters can be constructed for placement within the front part of the camera. Thus, an infrared photograph can be made with very little difficulty, since infrared sheet film is now available in 2¼ x 3¼ size. Obviously, this camera has a number of uses in photographing signatures and other writings on documents.

The convenience afforded by the fingerprint camera lies in its fixed-focus feature, namely, the fact that the bellows extension is preset at twice the focal length of the lens. Other cameras can be adapted to this use either by adjustment or by means of attachments in the form of additional bellows extension or a framing device of appropriate length. The function of these auxiliary devices is readily understood if we keep in mind the two conditions for a one-to-one or natural size photograph: the distance from the lens to the film plane must be two focal lengths and the distance from the lens to the fingerprint must also equal two focal lengths.

The 4 x 5-inch press-type camera, which enjoys an extensive popularity among investigative agencies as a versatile camera for field use, can be adapted to fingerprint work in several ways. If the camera has a long bellows extension, the lens board can be lifted from the inner track section and replaced on the front of the track without disturbing the track stops. The camera can now be adjusted to a bellows extension of twice the focal length of the taking lens. The camera bed should be marked at the point to which the bellows are extended to obtain a 1:1-size image with a given lens. Preferably this marking should be accomplished at the identification bureau where the image can be determined by illuminating a ruler in the field of view.

At the scene the camera is quickly adjusted by extending the bellows to the place marked on the camera bed. If the lens is now placed at a distance of two focal lengths from the print-bearing surface, the fingerprint will be in focus. The image size can be checked by putting a ruler in the plane of the fingerprint and measuring the length of the image by placing another ruler against the ground glass of the camera back.

Since camera f-numbers can be taken at their face value only when the object is at infinity, allowance must be made in exposure time for the bellows extension required in 1:1-size photography. The effective aperture should be taken as two stops smaller than the indicated f-number. The exposure time is then four times that indicated by an exposure meter.

Another result of the long bellows extension will be a limited depth of field. Focusing, which in this case is a matter of accurately determining object distance, now becomes quite critical. An aid for the use of the 4 x 5 Speed Graphic in fingerprint work has been made by Faurot Inc. in the form of a metal frame and extension which can be attached at the lens. When the end of the frame is in contact with the surface, a fingerprint in the indicated area will be in focus.

The smaller cameras, especially the 35-mm such as the Leica, Contax, and Kodak Bantam, have also been adapted to fingerprint work. The Leica, for example, is fitted for this purpose by placing an extension tube between the lens and the camera body to provide the appropriate bellows length. Three rods are then attached to the camera to hold a frame equal in area to a frame of 35-mm film. The camera is now held so that the frame is in contact with the surface bearing the fingerprint. Similar attachments are available for the Bantam, Contax, and other 35-mm cameras.

The fixed-focus camera designed specifically for fingerprints is the obvious choice among the cameras described above by reason of its ease of operation and its reliability. It should be noted, however, that the fingerprint camera is limited for practical purposes to surfaces against which the front of the camera may be placed. It is conceivable that a fingerprint may be found on a surface inaccessible in this way. A camera with an adjustable focus should then be used. The

4 x 5 press-type camera is quite suitable in situations like these.

Another advantage offered by the variable-focus camera is control of lighting. Occasionally a latent print is found to be clearly visible only when illuminated obliquely from a specific direction. Here, again, the 4 x 5 camera has the advantage of permitting the photographer to experiment with the lighting until the critical angle is determined by observation in the ground glass. Although problems of this nature can be encountered in the form of latent plastic prints or other prints which do not respond to powder, they occur too seldom to detract from the general utility of the fingerprint camera.

An interesting piece of supplementary equipment for photographing fingerprints is the Polaroid-Land Film Holder. By means of this attachment a camera such as the 4 x 5 Speed Graphic can be used to produce a finished positive photograph of a fingerprint in less than a minute. Where the rapid production of a positive print is desired to expedite investigative work, a Polaroid photograph has obvious advantages. The necessity of making a negative, however, is not eliminated by using this method, and another photograph must still be made so that a negative will be available as a permanent record and as a source of additional contact or projection prints. A combination of positive-and-negative material is available for this purpose; its cost, however, may prohibit its use in routine fingerprint work.

CLARITY AND CONTRAST

Contrast is of critical importance in fingerprint photography. The latent trace is often found on a neutral background which offers little contrast for either black or white powder. The print may be further obscured by grime or other foreign substance.

The latent print should ordinarily be developed with a powder selected for the contrast which its color will provide against the background. If there is doubt as to the most effective color, test fingerprints should be placed on a safe area and developed for observation.

A film of higher than average contrast is ordinarily used in fingerprint photography, since a clear, sharp, black image against a light background is required in classification or comparison. Films such as Eastman Panatomic-X and Ansco Isopan are representative of this class of film. In addition to satisfactory contrast, these films lend themselves readily to enlargements greater than 5x.

If the subject matter is unusually devoid of contrast, special methods should be employed to enhance the visibility of the fingerprint. Contrast can be improved by one or all of three different means: namely, proper choice of photographic materials and processing; suitable illumination; and the use of appropriate filters. Films and papers can be chosen to yield any reasonable degree of contrast. Photographic development will also affect contrast. The use of directional lighting and of invisible radiations will sometimes promote visibility. Finally, a judicious choice of filter will serve to render the background surface of the fingerprint darker or lighter as the case may require.

Panchromatic process film such as Eastman Contrast Process Pan can be used to provide maximum film contrast. Extreme contrast can be achieved with a special purpose film such as Kodalith. Contrast films, however, have the associated disadvantage of short tonal range; consequently the effort to achieve contrast in this way often results in a loss of fingerprint detail.

Improved contrast can often be obtained by means of careful lighting. Faint traces on a knife blade, for example, may be relatively invisible under uniform lighting. A controlled sidelight, however, may supply the needed contrast. The light is carefully manipulated while the image of the latent is observed in the ground glass until the correct angle is reached. At a suitable glancing angle the light will be totally reflected from the latent print with a relative minimum of reflection from the blade itself.

Another technique readily applied in the studio is the use of the spectral regions on both sides of the visible spectrum. The infrared region is occasionally useful for fingerprints developed with black powder but insufficiently visible against a background such as a brown leather suitcase. The visibility of the fingerprint will be improved if there is a marked difference in the reflectivity of the carbon black and the leather with respect to infrared radiation.

The procedure is simple. Infrared film is used together with a deep red filter such as Wratten No. 25, or, better, a Wratten No. 87, which excludes most of the visible light. Tungsten lamps are used. Some adjustment in focus may be necessary for a true infrared photograph taken on a 1:1 scale. Reducing the lens aperture two additional stops will usually take care of this slight variation. An alternative procedure, after focusing in visible light, is to extend the back of the camera by 0.5 per cent of the focal length.

In actual practice, satisfactory results can be obtained by using the fingerprint camera with the 2¼x3¼ size Eastman Infrared Film. The filter is placed inside of the "nose" of the camera. The camera is positioned as usual and a twenty-second exposure is made.

Ultraviolet radiation is found in the shorter wavelength region just beyond the visible spectrum. Its use in fingerprint photography is quite different from that of infrared radiation where the directly reflected invisible rays were recorded on a specially sensitized emulsion. With ultraviolet radiation a derived effect is used, namely, fluorescence. Substances are said to fluoresce when they become luminous under ultraviolet radiation. A powder such as anthracene, which appears as a light-colored powder under ordinary light, will become brilliantly luminous in a darkened room under the rays of an ultraviolet lamp.

In fingerprint work, fluorescent powders such as anthracene can be used to produce contrast against a multi-colored surface or other background that interferes with the subject contrast necessary to discern the print. A fluorescent powder of suitable composition is used to develop the print. The print-bearing surface is then illuminated by an ultraviolet source in a darkened room. The brilliant fluorescence of the powder will show the fingerprint distinctly against a non-fluorescing surface, regardless of the brightness or coloring of the background in ordinary light.

No special films are required to photograph a fluorescent fingerprint under ultraviolet radiation. Eastman Panatomic-X or Ansco Isopan will yield excellent results. The photograph is usually taken at the identification bureau since a 4 x 5 press-type camera or a studio camera is used to permit the ultraviolet radiation to reach the print-bearing surface. Since an excess of blue light is ordinarily reflected from the surface, it is advisable to use a light yellow filter, such as the Wratten No. 2A, on the camera lens to render the background darker. The exposure time may sometimes run to several minutes.

The most common way of improving fingerprint contrast is to use a filter which will darken or lighten the background color. Initially, the powder chosen to develop the fingerprint is of a color calculated to contrast the fingerprint against the surface on which it is found. For example, a black powder will be used on a light-color surface, while on a dark background a white powder will be used. Intermediate colors are also available in powders, but less commonly used. Regardless of the powder color, it will be found that some surfaces do not offer satisfactory contrast. Visibility of the print can often be improved by using the correct filter in front of the lens.

The selection of such a filter should present no problem. By viewing the fingerprint through the filter itself or by means of a filter chart the appropriate color can be readily determined. For example, if a latent print has been developed with black powder on a yellow surface, it will be found that a yellow filter will make the background lighter and, hence, improve the contrast. On the other hand, if a white powder has been used on a yellow-brown surface, it will be desirable to darken the background and a blue filter might be found satisfactory. Visual inspection by means of a filter chart will give a reliable correspondence to photographic results with panchromatic film.

Occasionally the problem of contrast can be partially solved by the use of color film. A latent fingerprint developed, for example, on a can or bottle with a label of contrasting colors may present a confusing pattern on black-and-white film, regardless of the color of the powder used. The use of color film in this situation will provide a more accurate picture of the fingerprint as seen by the eye, and permit the identification expert to discern fine detail. Color film, however, is only a supplementary technique, since the photographer must eventually produce a black-and-white picture. For this purpose he will usually resort to the use of filters or fluorescent powder.

VALUE OF ENLARGEMENTS

Regardless of the other methods and techniques employed, photography is certain to play some part in nearly every case involving latent fingerprints. The ways in which photography may prove useful are many. One of the most important is that in this manner latent traces can be enlarged so that all of the included characteristics may be studied. Even from the technician's viewpoint, a latent trace offers less information in its original appearance.

When photographic enlargements are offered in evidence, they are sometimes assailed by representatives of the defendant with the contention that the pictures include something not to be seen in the original latent traces. In the absence of any explanation, this form of attack may damage a case. It should be pointed out that in order for tangible things to be seen at all they must be of discernible size. The purpose of photographic enlargement is to make visible the details in a latent which ordinarily are too small to be seen. When examining something tiny, if a larger view of the subject is available at the same time, the smaller specimen's characteristics will be the more readily noted. With these points made clear, any further objection is added proof of the evidence's value; those who do not fear a disclosure of the truth have no objection to photographs.

MATCHING PATTERNS

During the examination of a latent print, it may be desirable to "match" certain portions of the pattern with that of a suspect. This can be accomplished by cutting photographs of the two designs and fitting them together, a recourse especially helpful when explaining the identification to others. The untrained eye is unable to look at two images, even if they are but a short distance apart, and recognize all the resemblance or disparity. It is a well-known law of optics that similar objects appear more alike the closer they are together, and when objects which are different are brought near each other, their dissimilarity seems even more apparent. Thus, when some latent fingerprint is enlarged and shown beside a reproduction of the subject's skin design, the identity can easily be recognized. As a matter of fact, the most practical way to show whether two objects are alike or different, is to look at them side by side; in latent-print comparison, photography makes this possible.

When the identifying characteristics in a latent are not obvious to the untrained eye, their contended resemblance to the prints of a suspect may be disparaged as "opinion" testimony. However, with the detail of both patterns made clear through photography, the pictures become convincing witnesses, not of opinion, but of fact.

The camera is a scientific instrument, and requires competent handling for best results. Improper manipulation can produce unintentional distortion; when using wide-angle lenses, especial care and discretion are necessary. However, when photographs have been made correctly, any legal criticism on the grounds that they are not true representations of the original, may be refuted, since modern lenses are constructed so accurately that they are certified by the Government Bureau of Standards as "making reproductions without any appreciable distortion." Photographs *can* be true reproductions, and when this fact is clearly shown, all objections are removed. Mistaken impressions sometimes result when a photograph is viewed incorrectly. The proper distance for viewing a photograph is equal to the focal length of the camera lens times any magnification of the negative in enlarging.

PHOTOGRAPHS AS EVIDENCE

Photographs are admissible as evidence when verified by the photographer or other competent witness who was pres-

Fig. 170

Eastman Commercial View Camera

Fig. 171

Fixed-Focus Fingerprint Camera

ent at the scene and can attest to the fact that the photograph is a satisfactory representation of the scene or object. Photographic evidence must be free from optical distortion and must be sharp, clear, and relevant. Investigative photographs must be accompanied by complete notes and sketches in order to fulfill their purpose. The negative and data card should be available to assist in furnishing full information on the photograph in case a question of accuracy should arise. Evidence of chain of custody of the negative and prints should be available. If an enlargement is introduced as evidence, a contact print from the negative should also be available.

The chain of custody of investigative photographs must be as carefully maintained as that of other types of physical evidence. Continuity of possession is shown by making a complete record of the location and possession of films and prints from the time the camera shutter snaps until the print is introduced at a hearing. The simplest chain of custody is established when the investigator takes the pictures, develops and prints the film, and marks and files the photographs. In situations where the processing cannot be accomplished by the investigator or his unit, handling and receipting procedures should be initiated to preserve the chain of custody of films and prints when the investigator cannot be present during the processing.

Best Prints for Court Use

Since it is impractical to offer latents in their natural size as court evidence, the impressions will require some treatment before they are presented. A number of techniques have been employed for this purpose. Of course, enlargement will be necessary, the degree most desirable depending upon conditions. Since the seeing ability of different persons will vary, this factor may be hard to determine. A photograph too much enlarged may defeat its purpose by actually obscuring or confusing the detail it was designed to reveal. Some specimens are such that enlargement only serves to emphasize their detail, while others, perhaps less legibly recorded, may lose their significance as the picture increases in size. This demands nice discrimination; only experience can tell the size of pictures most likely to be convincing in any given circumstance.

An important point is the selection of prints most suitable for evidential purposes, when several specimens are available. The audience will be likely to understand a pattern that is distinct, and although other traces may include more points of identity which can be recognized by the technician, he must remember that many of those poorly defined similarities would be quite beyond the jurymen's perception. Therefore, sometimes it may be best to sacrifice quantity for legibility.

Having chosen what seems to be the most promising specimen or specimens, the next step is their preparation. An effective mode employs a medium enlargement of the evidential print beside which may be presented another view, of considerably increased dimension, wherein certain characteristics have been marked for special attention.

The most popular method is that of enlarging the latent and the suspect's corresponding print to the same size, indicating the points of identity on each photograph with lines drawn from the detail to the edge of the picture, each of the line endings being numbered (Fig. 173). With this arrangement, enlargements of 36" x 36" and over have proved effective. If this presentation is employed, it is prudent to place the latent together with the suspect's print on the same mounting. Thus they can be observed in close proximity at all times. Both photographs should be mounted at the same angle, and with their characteristics, as nearly as possible, in the same relative positions. Also, when drawing the lines to indicate the points for consideration, added emphasis may be had by placing the corresponding marks at the same angles and making them the same length on each of the illustrations. This is important; the technician knows that both prints were made by the same person, and any legitimate measure that he may employ to stress this fact is permissible. In short, it is justifiable to use any reasonable means of making the pictures look as much alike as possible.

When the two prints have been prepared in the manner described, it is an excellent plan to re-photograph them, making a "master" negative on an 8 x 10 Commercial film. From this, any number of photographs can be produced in which the lines marking the points of identity will, of course, be identical.

Another matter requiring care and discretion is the selection of points for comparison in the latent impression. Obviously, the most legible features are appropriate; however, should some unusual or distinctive formation be recognizable in both designs, its unique characteristics must not be overlooked even if less clearly registered. The number of points required for proof of identity has been viewed differently by various jurists. Naturally, the object is to secure as many as possible, although the desire for quantity should not overrule discretion. Legal opinions on this question are presented in a subsequent section of the text that deals with court procedure and legal precedent.

With the latent print and the subject's print placed close together on the same mounting, and their similar characteristics numbered as described, a useful piece of evidence has been prepared. However, it has its limitations, since all of the interested parties cannot examine it simultaneously. Some presentations employ a stereopticon and a screen upon which photographic evidence can be shown to the entire audience, and it must be admitted that this technique has many advantages. Nevertheless, it also has its restrictions. The time permitted for observance will be at the operator's discretion. Some near-sighted spectator may not see distinctly, and yet hesitate to admit it. A juryman's reaction to evidence thus presented is frequently not so favorable as when he holds an enlarged photograph in his own hands and scans it more leisurely. In this manner he will be certain to note much that would otherwise be overlooked. To enjoy the full advantage of this circumstance, an ample number of photographs should be prepared so that each member of the jury as well as the judge and the attorneys may have individual copies. To some, this may seem superfluous; but none the less, experience will show that it is better to furnish a little more evidence than may actually be demanded, than to have an important case lost through not providing enough.

The photographic copies prepared for the judge and jury should not be too large for convenient handling; 8″ x 10″ is a good size. However, it is an excellent plan to prepare also a much larger view of the subject. This can be mounted on an easel where all may see; with this enlargement, the technician can indicate the various points that he wishes to emphasize.

To supplement the popular technique of indicating points of comparison in a latent with numbered lines, a unique addition has been devised. In this method the lines are ruled and numbered as usual, but at the outer extremity of each a circle is inscribed, within which a likeness of the indicated ridge detail is illustrated (Fig. 174). These circled sketches may be drawn with pen and ink, and since they are not on the photograph of the latent itself, are not likely to cause any legal objection.

Fig. 172

This illustration shows a fingerprint that was developed with fluorescent powder
and photographed with ultraviolet light. The powder used was a mixture of
two-thirds anthracene and one-third uranyl phosphate. The light source was a
small, portable U.V. lamp. A B58 and a 2A filter were used. The exposure was
60 minutes on Super Ortho film at f:16. The print was on a brightly colored
cigarette package. It will be noted that the colored background is almost entirely
eliminated

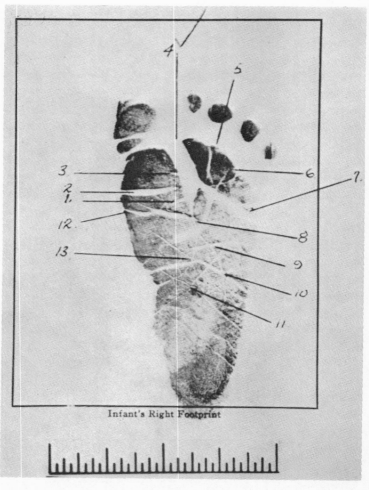

Infant's Right Footprint

Infant's footprint showing flexure creases. See Appendix, page 369, for discussion

The treatment has several advantages, since both the latent and the suspect's print may be treated in the same manner. The drawings in both cases should be made to resemble each other as nearly as possible, thus emphasizing the actual likeness. Also, each of the circled sketches can be enlarged enough to portray clearly the particular point, such as a dot, fork, ridge-ending, enclosure, or some peculiarity. For further clarification, it is a good plan to draw inside each circle not only the actual ridge detail, but also some of its surrounding structure as well, although it will be found more effective to ink the detail heavily and indicate the adjacent structure with dots or lightly-shaded lines.

Should the enlargement be approximately 18" x 20", the circles can be from two to four inches in diameter, which will provide ample room in each for considerable design. The drawings in the circles should be several times larger than the actual ridge structure in the photograph, regardless of how much the latter may have been enlarged. The observer will thus be directed to the point for consideration and may also see a larger reproduction of it.

Another effective arrangement of this technique places the latent and the suspect's print side by side on the same mounting, with the circles enclosing the indicated minutiae in a vertical line between the two (Fig. 175). By this method, one circled sketch illustrates the same corresponding point in both prints, the guide lines from each being drawn to the same circle in each instance, but from opposite sides.

This treatment will help to lessen any unavoidable dissimilarity existing between the latent and the suspect's evidence print, that may be due to illegibility of the latent, an unfavorable surface, unsuccessful development, and so on. In making the photographs of latents compare with the prints of a suspect, the two reproductions should look as much alike as

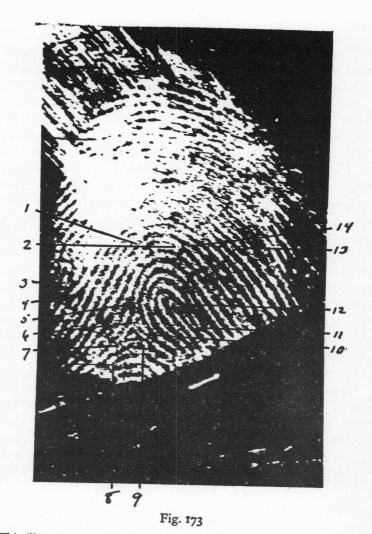

Fig. 173

This illustrates the conventional method of preparing a latent fingerprint for presentation in court. It will be noted that the evidential print
(left) and the print of the suspect (right) are placed side by side, and
the points of identity indicated by lines similarly drawn and numbered.

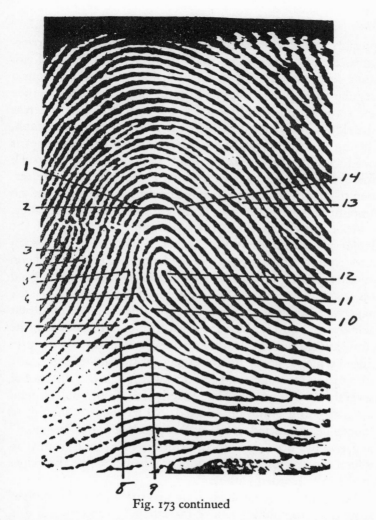

Fig. 173 continued

It will also be observed that the evidence print has been "reversed" so that the ridges are white in agreement with the latent print wherein the ridges are also white, having been developed with a light powder against a dark background possible; though repeated, this requirement cannot be over-stressed; and here an important point is noted. The defend-ant's fingerprints will, in all probability, be taken from a regular fingerprint card, in which the ridges are black, as they are recorded on a white surface with printer's ink, whereas the ridges in the latent may appear white in the photograph, having been developed with light powder, or other means producing similar results. Introducing photographs with such marked differences is to be avoided if possible. They are cer-tain to be misunderstood by some member of the jury, and no amount of explanation can remove the seeming discrepancy.

All confusion is avoided by making a "reversal" of the latent impression, should the ridges be white. To obtain such a reversal, a "contact print" of the latent negative is made on another photographic film; a Process emulsion gives good results in many cases. The technique is as follows: Place the negative of the latent in a printing frame with the emulsion side down, and lay the unexposed film over it, also with the emulsion side down. In this manner, a likeness will be pro-duced which is not a "mirror" image of the latent. Expose the film to a suitable light source—a 25-watt globe at a distance of several feet will answer. The length of exposure will depend upon the film emulsion selected. All these steps should, of course, be conducted in the darkroom. When the "reversed" negative has been developed, prints can be made from it in which the previously white lines will be black like the ridges in the ink-recorded pattern.

The same result can be had by making a paper "negative" from a photographic print of the latent. To accomplish this, the print is placed in a printing frame with the "picture side" down, and a sheet of sensitized paper placed over it, emulsion side down, as in the previous method. Exposure to a light source will provide a print which is a reversal or "negative"

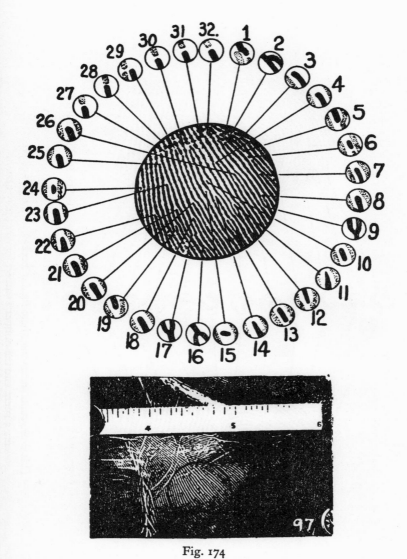

Fig. 174

This illustrates an unique method of preparing a latent fragment for court presentation

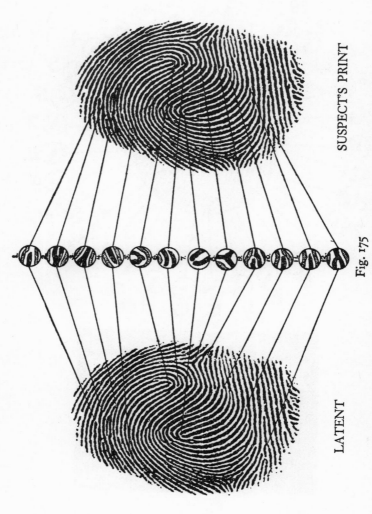

SUSPECT'S PRINT

LATENT

Fig. 175

This illustration shows the Micro-Point Check-chart method of preparing a latent and the print of a suspect for court presentation

of the original, and the ridges, if white before, will be black. This latter plan offers the advantage of simplicity and is feasible with prints up to 8″ x 10″, but if larger sizes are desired, the reversed-film-negative method should be employed.

If the subject matter to be copied is upon some material that is too thick to transmit light, a paper "contact" negative can also be made quite simply by placing a sheet of printing paper *emulsion side up* in the printing frame, and laying over it the material to be copied, *face downward*. When exposed, the light will reflect back against the sensitized emulsion of the printing paper and thus produce a mirror-image negative of the picture.

Should the technician have at his disposal equipment for making photostatic reproductions, the problem will be eliminated, for, with this utility, "negative" and "positive" copies of any subject can be made quickly and cheaply. There are a number of available devices which employ this principle.

There is little probability that any objection or question will be offered when "reversed" photographs are presented in court; but if necessary, the technician can easily explain the process, and give ample reasons for employing it.

Despite popular acceptance of the presentation methods just described, some courts have ruled that lines drawn upon the photograph of a fingerprint constitute an alteration of the evidence, and the introduction of pictures so treated has been overruled in occasional instances. To meet such situations, a slightly different technique has been devised in which the two photographs to be compared are placed one over the other and fastened like pages in a book. The patterns of both designs should, of course, be in as close agreement as possible. This can be attained by adjusting the two images until two or more of the characteristics are in alignment; pins thrust through the pictures at focal points will prove helpful.

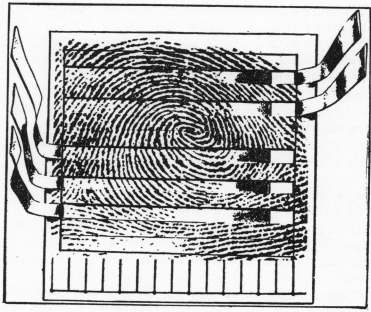

Fig. 176

This illustrates how a latent print may be shown to be the same as that of a suspect by placing one picture over the other and then cutting the upper photograph in transverse strips which can be folded back to reveal the design of the lower print in agreement with the pattern in the upper photograph

When the photographs have been secured, the upper picture may be cut from side to side in horizontal strips; when these are lifted from the lower photograph, it will show the ridges of the under design as continuations of the upper pattern (Fig. 176). It is advisable to place the subject's print uppermost and the latent underneath. In order to employ this method effectively, the two prints must be enlarged the same number of diameters, and fastened together in perfect conjunction.

In addition to the technical skill required, the latent print also must lend itself to this treatment. A different degree or direction of pressure in the two recordings may render the latent unsuitable for this method, which is practical only if the characteristics of both patterns can be made to "line up" when the photographs are superimposed.

In latent fingerprints prepared for evidential purposes, legal precedent requires certain "points of agreement" to prove their identity with those of a suspect. Twelve such points have been considered ample, although fewer may be sufficient in many cases. In this connection, an important factor is apparent. If the points are legible and distinctive, they serve their purpose; the law is concerned with the number of points rather than with the details selected for comparison, provided they are definite and representative.

Although conventional practice may choose only the more conspicuous features of ridge structure in proving identity, the possibilities here are much greater than may at first be realized. In the average fingerprint photograph introduced in court, there probably will be indicated only dots, forkings, ridge-endings, and similar prominent detail. These, though undeniably useful, represent but a minor portion of the pattern's individual characteristics.

For better understanding, it is necessary to establish a rule to determine what constitute "individual characteristics." In the study of latent fingerprints, this term may be considered as applying to the peculiarities in friction skin which make any given fingerprint different from all others. With this definition in mind, microscopic study of friction skin will disclose a wealth of detail that readily lends itself to identification purposes. Some discussion of this has been offered earlier in the text. Although many of their finer points may lie beyond the range of unaided sight, when magnified, dermal designs present a unique aspect.

The wealth of minutiae that exists below the eye's normal vision becomes amazing when revealed through magnification. This fact is well illustrated by the experiments of Mr. J. M. McEwen, of New York City, who, with a super-micropantograph* of his own devising, has made numerous microscopic writings so tiny that with the same size of lettering, the entire Bible could be recorded forty times in the area of one square inch! With this astounding achievement in mind, the practical possibilities of making identifications from small portions of a fingerprint become evident.

When finger patterns are examined under the microscope, numerous individual characteristics will be recognized, not only in the relative size and formation of the pores, their placement and distribution, but also in the width of the ridges, and their intervening spaces, and in the ridges' topography. In fact, the entire friction area is seen to be composed of peculiarities suitable for identification purposes (Fig. 177 and Fig. 151a and b).

Certain foreign texts have discussed this subject under the heading of "Poroscopy;" however, the possibilities here have received little recognition and practically no application in American methods.

MICROSCOPIC TREATMENT

In order to utilize these less-apparent features of ridge structure, it will be necessary to employ a special technique. Also, the latent trace must be adaptable to the treatment; but, should this be the case, it will be possible to prepare microscopic photographs of the latent and the suspect's print, ex-

* The micropantograph was invented by Mr. N. Peters of London, England, in 1852.

treme care being utilized to make both exposures with the same degree of magnification. This can be accomplished by photographing both specimens at the same time with a Micro-Tessar lens such as that recommended for inclusion in the "field kit." With Micro-Tessar lenses, which are available in several focal lengths, enlargements up to and over fifty times can be made, depending on the bellows draw of the camera. In using them, it is advisable to reduce the aperture somewhat, to secure the best definition.

The results of this technique should prove informative. It will be noted that the finer detail of ridge structure will often permit exact matching by superimposing one picture upon the other, as already described. This process will be more satisfactory with tiny fragments than with larger areas of a fingerprint.

Of course, microscopic treatment will be successful only when the latent's finer detail is clearly discernible, at least in some portion of the pattern. However, in cases where a latent fingerprint's individual characteristics can be seen under magnification, it is a simple matter to prove identity from surprisingly small portions of its surface.

In modern printing, each of the letters composing the words on a page closely resembles all similar letters seen there. This is not true of fingerprints. Finger impressions, although made by the same digit, display slight differences in their minor detail. This is often apparent in latents. The subject's fingerprints recorded in the identification bureau may not look exactly like those which were left by him at the scene of the crime. The reasons for this are obvious but unavoidable. Defense attorneys sometimes attack this variation when attempting to discredit evidence; however, a competent technician can readily explain that different conditions, under which fingerprints are impressed, must have some noticeable effect.

Color of Background	Color of Fingerprint Powder	Film
Blue	1) Black	Process
Blue	2) White	Pan
Blue	3) White	Ortho
Blue-Green	1) Black	Process
Blue-Green	2) White	Pan
Green	1) White	Process
Green	2) White	Pan
Yellow	1) White	Process
Yellow (light)	2) Black	Pan
Yellow	3) White	Pan
Red	1) White	Process or Ortho
Red	2) White	Pan or Ortho
Red (bright)	3) Black	Pan
Blue and Yellow	White or Red	Pan
Blue and Red	White	Ortho
Green and Yellow	1) White	Process
Green and Yellow	2) White	Pan
Green and Red	White	Process
Yellow and Red	White	Process
Blue, Green, and Red	Fluorescent	Pan
Black and White	1) Fluorescent	Pan
Black and White	2) Black	Infrared

(Process, i.e., blue-sensitive films, are rarely used in practice. Pan films of medium and high contrast serve for most purposes. When viewed through a filter chart, the appearance of a surface corresponds closely to the results obtained

Color of Filter	Wratten Type	Result	Transparency
None	—	Black print on white	No
Red	F No. 29	White print on black	Yes
Green	B No. 58	White print on black	Yes
None	—	Black print on white	No
Red	F No. 29	White print on black	Yes
None	—	White print on black	Yes
Red	F No. 29	White print on black	Yes
None	—	White print on black	Yes
None	—	Black print on white	No
Blue	C5 No. 47	White print on black	Yes
None	—	White print on black	Yes
Blue	C5 No. 47	White print on black	Yes
None	—	Black print on white	No
Red	F No. 29	White print on black	Yes
Yellow	K1 No. 6	White print on black	Yes
None	—	White print on black	Yes
Red	F No. 29	White print on black	Yes
None	—	White print on black	Yes
None	—	White print on black	Yes
Yellow with ultraviolet light	2A	White print on black	Yes
Same as above	2A	White print on black	Yes
Deep Red	No. 87	Black print on white	No

with pan film. Before using the infrared technique, the background should first be tested photographically for its infrared characteristics.)

A useful recourse which will eliminate this objection in a large measure, is to take the finger impressions of the accused on a surface similar to that where the latents were left. Also, these prints may be developed by the same method as that used with the latents. This will furnish impressions which are more similar to the latent traces.

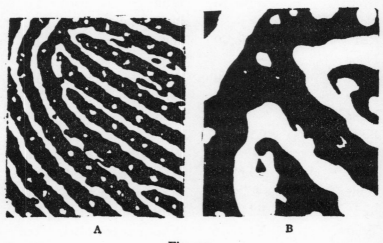

A   B

Fig. 177

This illustrates how a fingerprint can be greatly enlarged to reveal its intimate detail. This treatment is especially appropriate when only a small area of legible ridge structure is available in a latent fingerprint

XVIII

PRESENTATION OF FINGERPRINT EVIDENCE
IN COURT

FROM the foregoing, it will be understood that pictures taken of fingerprints found at a crime scene are likely to feature with considerable importance in the case. Therefore, it behooves the technician to use his best efforts in making and preparing these photographs. Some technicians may not appreciate the care and attention which this special requirement deserves. Inefficiency here is inexcusable, since evidential photographs, indifferently prepared, may endanger a reputation or even a life. Furthermore, both judge and jury will be frankly skeptical of a technician who presents unsuitable photographic evidence, and probably will distrust not only the evidence, but also anything the technician may testify regarding it. With experience, the technician will learn that there is no satisfactory substitute for good photographs, and for the ready and accurate knowledge with which to present them.

As compared with their constant importance in other phases of the law-enforcement program, the occasions when fingerprints are offered as evidence in court are relatively infrequent. To average persons, this may seem strange; nevertheless, the reasons are understandable. Trials by court or jury usually result from a defendant's denial of guilt. Should the subject admit his responsibility, there is little need to offer additional evidence for any purpose other than that of qualifying punishment.

In most cases, an accused will use every resort to avoid a penalty. Pleas of "guilty" are less popular than those of "not guilty." However, when a wrongdoer feels certain of his ultimate conviction, he is more likely to accept the inevitable and throw himself upon the mercy of the court. Obviously, the strongest inducement for a defendant to admit his misconduct, is the self-evident proof thereof. As has been shown, there are few forms of evidence that can offer more convincing attestation than fingerprints. Thus, when confronted with these silent yet eloquent witnesses, a defendant will seldom deny his guilt.

Despite these facts, fingerprints do, from time to time, appear before a judge and jury. If well prepared, this evidence usually can "speak for itself." Nevertheless, the technician must present the exhibits. At this point, the expert witness faces a critical situation. Personally, he is fully aware of the defendant's guilt, but the court and jury are not, as yet. It is his duty to make this fact clear. Furthermore, the testimony that he is about to offer is likely to be vigorously attacked by the defense counsel. But despite the degree of active opposition, his larger problem very probably will be the judge and jury. This assertion is offered without the least intention of disparagement. The court and the twelve jurors, and more especially the latter, can not be expected to possess wide familiarity in the science of fingerprints. Nevertheless, these are the persons who will consider the evidence. Were the technician to display the handled object, and point out the latents thereon in the absence of further explanation, this would convey but scant enlightenment to a lay audience. Consequently, it is important that the technician present evidence which the observers can understand.

Preparing acceptable instructions for a technical witness is difficult; it is easier to furnish advice than to act upon it. However, the technician need not always learn the better course through bitter experience. He must understand that the presentation of physical evidence before a judge and jury is an undertaking quite different from that of securing the evidence. The field of jurisprudence, even as it relates to fingerprints, is so broad that many books would be needed to cover all of its aspects. Nevertheless, some of the more outstanding factors may be discussed here to good advantage.

At the outset, there is a strong point in the technician's favor. With latent fingerprints, there is no uncertainty; either they are those of the accused, or they are not. If the evidence is competent to prove this fact, it is acceptable. Otherwise, it should not be introduced at all. The technician will appreciate the futility of presenting vague, illegible latents, even if he is convinced of their being the defendant's. The evidence should be sufficiently distinct for understanding by any rational observer. Failure in this precaution may result unfavorably.

The presentation of fingerprint evidence in court constitutes a crucial event in the technician's program. The fact that he has been called to testify indicates the occasion's importance. His surroundings in court will differ from the familiar environs of his laboratory. In court, he will be confronted by strangers who may accept his statement with little understanding and even disbelief. But in spite of hindrance, he is obligated to perform his sworn duty, that of furthering the cause of justice.

The technician's success in court will be measured to a

great extent by his capacity for intelligible expression. He will be presenting evidence before persons who, as indicated, are not expected to be familiar with his subject. His testimony will consist largely of replies to questions suggested by the record, and asked by an attorney who, despite his training in law, is not likely to have had much experience with latent fingerprints. Notwithstanding these unfavorable conditions, the witness' responsibility is to remove every possible cause for error.

The technician should prepare his exhibits and present his evidence in a manner calculated to clarify the facts for one who has no previous knowledge of the case or of fingerprint science. He must remember that this will especially apply to those composing the jury; these persons also are faced with difficult requirements. The man on the jury, with no prior interest in the contested issue, is expected to weigh carefully the arguments of the various counsels. He is expected to analyze and assimilate a mass of involved particulars with which he is not familiar. All this and a great deal more he is expected to do in the absence of specialized knowledge. And finally, he is expected to bring in a just verdict. The fingerprint technician should keep these circumstances in mind both in the preparation and in the presentation of his testimony.

The average juryman is earnest and well-meaning, but some point, not made clear, may confuse him. In so far as possible, the technician should eliminate any chance of this. He should use terms not more technical than absolutely necessary, and his statements should be such as he would use in dealing with a class of children. Nor is this any reflection; although the majority of jurymen may have high mentality, some member may be a trifle obtuse and thus retard the others in rendering an honest verdict.

ATTACKS TO BE MET

When the technician presents his evidence in court, he is reasonably certain to encounter opposition. The defense will be represented by one or more attorneys whose purpose, naturally, is to secure a favorable verdict for the client. This will result in attacks on any testimony that may seem damaging; and good photographs of latent fingerprints are always formidable evidence.

In view of its validity, there are few grounds on which bona fide fingerprint evidence can be assailed. As a rule, the defense will be one of several hackneyed forms. The opposing counsel will contend that the latents were not made by the defendant, and will indicate alleged dissimilarity to prove the charge. Pseudo-expert testimony may be offered to substantiate this claim.

It may be freely admitted that the latents were left by the defendant, but not at the time when the crime was committed. It will be asserted that the prints were made on some legitimate occasion.

The defense attorney may boldly contend that the latents were "planted" at the crime scene by the technician or some other interested party, and will offer a strong alibi to prove that the defendant was far away at the time.

In the event that all other deceits prove fruitless, the technician may expect a bitter and very personal attack designed to disparage his qualifications and vilify his integrity.

In defending the latents' authenticity, the technician has little to fear. Here he has every reason for confidence, whereas his aggressor will be on unfamiliar ground. It is unlikely that the defense attorney will possess specialized knowledge of fingerprints; probably he will have at his disposal only such data as he has gleaned hastily from some popular text; and any alleged expert impressed into service is likely to be but little better informed.

In refuting false claims involving a time element, the technician must proceed with caution. An attempt may be made to entrap the witness. However, the expert's knowledge and experience should suffice to avoid such obvious pitfalls, and also at least to approximate the duration of a latent's presence on a questioned surface. Some foresight may be helpful in this instance. When a latent is first discovered, the technician should attempt to determine when it was recorded. This may not prove impossible. The surface may be one upon which dust is continually deposited, and the latent may be free from dust. Should the impression also be overlaid, the thickness of its covering will be significant. If the surface is some piece of household furniture, it may be learned when it was dusted or polished. Should the latent be upon a window, it may be determined when the glass was last washed. Many factors contribute in establishing the time element, to say nothing of the latent print itself, which is sure to offer indications of how recently it was made.

The subject of "forged" fingerprints has been treated elsewhere in the text, and a competent technician should have no difficulty in nullifying any claims which the defense may offer in that respect.

Perhaps the most trying situation which the technical witness is likely to face is a personal attack. This form of offensive, though common enough, has caused the downfall of many otherwise capable experts. It is difficult to suppress righteous indignation, and if an artful defense attorney can goad the witness beyond the point of endurance, he may finally effect his purpose of discrediting the expert's testimony.

In connection with this form of persecution, the technician may be confronted with perjured testimony. It has been aptly said that despite the oath, more untruths are probably uttered in court than in any other place. This is largely due to natural human tendencies, but in many cases it is a vicious and intentional deception. The technician should be prepared to defend his evidence against any malign attack, remembering that his testimony will carry little weight in the face of aggression, if offered in a fainthearted and apologetic manner. However, discretion should always be observed. He must not allow himself to be tricked into exaggeration. The effective course, even when confronted with false contentions supported by outright perjury, is to tell the exact truth simply and convincingly.

FACTS INVINCIBLE

The most convincing evidence that any witness can hope to offer is that of clearly illustrated and relevant fact. When once established, facts are invincible. In the presence of sufficient verifying facts, there can be no alternative other than a just verdict; and the competent fingerprint expert is especially qualified to furnish this kind of evidence.

In addition to their intrinsic value, facts may acquire added importance through association. The technician learns that his testimony will have more weight if favorably presented. A better insight is assured if the related circumstances of a situation are explained in their proper order. At this point, the student is referred to the discussion of photography earlier presented, wherein the approved methods of photographing a crime scene are described. Obviously, the jury will attach more significance to the photograph of a latent fingerprint, if it can be shown by introductory pictures just how and where it was discovered.

Under no circumstances should a technical witness take the stand without prearranging his evidence and testimony. This should be done as a general might plan an important military offensive. Nor should the technician neglect his chief ally, the prosecuting attorney; he too will require knowledge of the expert's forthcoming evidence in order to question the technician effectively. This important need has been neglected in many instances. The prosecuting attorney and the technical witness have often entered the courtroom without previous arrangement or discussion, presumably under the assumption that a perfect understanding should exist through some psychic intuition. This fallacy can only result in confusion.

Justifiable criticism has been directed toward the practice of "coaching" a witness, wherein the deponent is methodically schooled in the part he is expected to play. However, this dubious custom is in no way related to the rational understanding that should be established between the technician and prosecutor, which is not only permissible, but often most necessary. No technical expert, however competent, could be expected to furnish the best possible assistance in a case if not fully prepared; nor, for that matter, could the prosecuting attorney. This will necessitate collaboration. It frequently requires the best combined efforts of these two individuals to overcome fraudulent opposition.

SNARES FOR THE WITNESS

Before a trial, the defense attorney and his client are on most intimate terms, which in some cases descend to an outright conspiracy. Nevertheless, with defense attorneys, a conference between prosecutor and technical witness has been popular ground for criticism; the object is to make such consultations appear blameworthy.

This subterfuge is also sometimes employed as a means of ensnaring a witness. The defense counsel may ask the technician if he has discussed the case with anyone prior to the trial. The unsuspecting witness may reply in the negative, whereupon the lawyer may force the witness to admit that he has conferred with the prosecuting attorney.

Another common version of the same artifice is to address the witness reproachfully, saying, "As a matter of fact, you have discussed this case with the prosecuting attorney, have you not?" Should the technician reply in the negative, his answer, even if true, will be judged a falsehood. Should he give an affirmative reply, the crafty defense attorney will make the admission appear to be a confession of guilt.

This shopworn trick can be defeated quite easily. When asked if he has talked with anyone regarding the case, the technician's reply should be: "Yes, I talked with the prosecutor, and I told him all I knew about the case." At this, the defense attorney will very likely ask, "Did the prosecutor instruct you how he wanted you to testify?" This dangerous question is effectively blocked by the response, "Yes, he did; he instructed me to tell the absolute truth, fully and frankly."

Another trick of the defense attorney is to ask the technician a question which he is told he must answer with "yes" or "no," either of which replies will be certain to compromise him. It usually is easy to anticipate this attack, since the lawyer will probably inquire how long the expert has been engaged in his special field. Next he will probably say, "Now, Mr. Blank, I am going to ask you a question which you must answer 'yes' or 'no'; is that quite clear, Mr. Blank?" Then he will say, "In all these years that you say you have been an identification expert, have you ever made a mistake?" A negative reply to this question would, of course, be absurd; and should the expert answer in the affirmative, the attorney will quickly say in an accusing tone, "Then, as a matter of fact, you *could* be wrong in *this* case, could you not, Mr. Blank?" This leaves the unprepared witness at a disadvantage. However, the success of the trick depends upon the witness' answering "yes" or "no," *which he is not obliged to do*. Despite anything that the attorney may say to the contrary, it is quite permissible for the technician to answer that oversights may occur in any human enterprise, but that he has never been mistaken about any evidence he has ever presented in court. Should the defense counsel demand a "yes" or "no" answer, the judge will no doubt grant the expert permission to qualify his reply.

The technician must remember that the defense attorney's purpose is to refute any evidence which endangers the accused; and it is likely that the onset will intensify with the evidence's importance. Many ruses will be tried, a few of which are mentioned here. However, the technician will always hold a decided advantage in every contest if armed with truth and accuracy. No verbal assault, however vindictive, need be feared if the expert witness testifies only to what he knows, and remembers his own testimony, once he has given it.

Although the expert witness need not, and also should not, always tamely submit to persecution, there are times when dignified self-restraint will be appreciated by those present. In the absence of vehement retaliation, the defense counsel's attack may defeat its own purpose by antagonizing the court and jury; they will probably view the expert's testimony even more favorably if it be unjustly criticized.

On the other hand, there are certain occasions in which a firm retort to some detraction is well justified, and will be sure to receive sympathetic approval from the audience. Although discretion here is most important, no rule could hope to regulate all situations. Nevertheless, a volume of good advice is summarized in the assertion that an expert's appearance in court will leave small grounds for disfavor if his conduct there be that of a gentleman. His testimony will carry conviction if offered distinctly, positively, and impartially; his purpose is the impartial demonstration of truth, as represented by the case facts. His evidence will lose importance if the testimony seems overaggressive or personal. It is usually not advisable to mention the delinquent by name; when necessary, he may be referred to merely as "the accused" or "the defendant."

The expert witness will acquire added confidence and greater dignity if he fully appreciates all the related circumstances of his position in the case. Despite the impressive austerity of a courtroom, when the technician takes the stand he becomes the chief object of interest, and also the dominant factor in the proceedings, at least for the time being. He is the recognized possessor of specialized knowledge which qualifies him to reveal the truth. The facts he is about to present can determine the case's ultimate outcome, which may be an issue of life or death. With this in mind, the competent expert takes the stand frankly aware not only of the situation's gravity, but also of his own necessity.

The capable witness can, if he chooses, exercise a directive influence over the entire courtroom. This intangible but decisive dominance will be felt by all participants. In addition to the technical qualifications expected in an expert, this latter attainment calls for mastery only gained through experience and a knowledge of human nature.

A point often overlooked, but none the less important, is the differing conditions which a technical witness is sure to encounter when testifying in different courts of law. Contrary to common opinion, a courtroom is not the place where justice is certain to triumph in all cases. This unfortunate circumstance results from causes which are numerous and involved, and which are likely to affect the technician's probability of success. It is true that poorly prepared technicians sometimes win in court, not always through their own efforts, but largely because their opponents are even less competent than themselves. All too often the expert who appears repeatedly in but one court, becomes overconfident in the absence of strong opposition. It may require an embarrassing defeat in some unfamiliar jurisdiction to dispel the possible illusion of infallibility.

The qualities desirable in an expert witness are not always inherent, although it is usually possible to acquire them. However, there are still many otherwise competent specialists who are at a marked disadvantage in the courtroom. The individual who realizes his own inadequacy will do well to subject himself to a careful analysis, and take inventory of his assets and liabilities. He should determine where correction is necessary, and set about effecting the same.

The most a technical witness can hope is to convince his listeners; and this requires that they believe in his honesty. It may be that some of the causes of belief and unbelief are beyond his control; however, certain things are known to arouse suspicion, and these can be avoided.

The business of offering expert testimony deserves much consideration. Regardless of the space devoted to its discussion here and in other texts, the beginner and savant alike will find it a profitable field for further research. Regardless of how much knowledge he may already possess, the open-minded investigator will realize that here there is always room for improvement, and that the application of some recently acquired bit of information or courtroom technique in a crucial situation may turn the tide in his favor.

XIX

PRECEDENT COURT DECISIONS

O NE of the earlier court decisions wherein fingerprints
were mentioned was that of *Emperor* v. *Sahdeo*, 3 Nag-
pur, L. Rep. 1 (India, 1904), in which the court states:

The process in our system of justice of identifying persons necessarily calls into use the well-established fact that, so far as human
experience goes, there are no two human beings in the world who
exactly resemble each other in every single detail. . . . Our identification evidence has hitherto been a rough and ready kind. We
have for the most part depended upon oral evidence of witnesses
speaking from memory; upon handwriting; upon photographs;
upon clothes, and so on. The chances of being misled to a wrong
judgment by such evidence are not inconsiderable. . . . The weak-
ness of the system was realized many years ago, and anthropometry
found birth. But the danger of depending on a system of measurements was soon, more or less, realized, owing to the obvious possibility of an approximation in the measurements of two individuals
being so great as to make differentiation doubtful; and this weak-
ness prevented any general adoption of the system, until now its
gradual abandonment in favor of fingerprints may be regarded as
certain.

The papillary ridges presented by the surface of the skin on the
palms of the hands and soles of the feet, have been ascertained to
be the most important of all anthropological data. For identification
purposes, it has been found necessary to deal with impressions made
by the bulbs of the fingers and thumbs. It has been discovered that
systems of parallel ridges sweep in bold curves across the palmar
surface of the hand, and that wherever the boundaries of the two

353

systems of such ridges diverge, the interspace is filled up by an independent compact little system, variously curved and whorled, having a fictitious resemblance to an eddy between two currents. Such an interspace, with a compact system of its own, is found in the bulbs of each human digit. The patterns which are made by the papillary ridges on this bulb afford the means of identification under discussion.

It is from these "dies" that are taken the prints which serve to fix human personality and give to every human being an individuality differentiating from all others. The absence of absolute repetition, which seems to be a universal law of nature, is found to be present here. . . .

By those who have made a study of the subject, though they have made classifications of finger impressions into divisions and subdivisions of types and patterns presenting general features of resemblance, there has never yet been found any case in which the pattern made by one finger exactly resembled the pattern made by any other finger of the same or any other hand. On the contrary, the one may readily be differentiated from all others by comparison. Every such pattern has been found to contain numerous "bifurcations," "origins," "islands," and "enclosures" in the ridges which compose it; and these, while proved to be always beyond change from birth to death, are never wholly repeated in the case of any other pattern.

This case held that where it is proved by competent expert testimony that two finger impressions made at different times, however far apart, contain several points of agreement and no points of disagreement in their minutiae, no further evidence is necessary to prove that they were made by the same finger.

In the case of *Parker* v. *Rex* (Australia) 14 C. L. R. 681; 3 B. R. C. 68 (1912), the only evidence against Parker depended upon a comparison of one of several fingerprints found on a bottle, which was in the shop during the burglary, with a print of the middle finger of Parker's left hand, which was taken in jail. Enlarged photographs of both prints were put in evidence, and the method of obtaining the prints was detailed by the detective in charge of the fingerprint branch of the Criminal Investigation Department, who pointed out to the jury nine points of similarity in the arrangement of the ridges or lines on the prints. The jury having convicted the prisoner, the chairman of the general sessions stated a case for the determination of the superior court of the question whether, when the only evidence of identity against an accused person depends upon the resemblance between fingerprints, such evidence is sufficient to support conviction. The court having answered the question in the affirmative, Parker applied for special leave to appeal to the high court for that decision. This leave was denied and the conviction upheld. The court stated, in part:

Signatures have been accepted as evidence of identity as long as they have been used. The fact of the individuality of the corrugations of the skin on the fingers of the human hand is now so generally recognized as to require very little, if any, evidence of it, although it seems to be still the practice to offer some expert evidence on the point. A fingerprint is therefore in reality an unforgeable signature. That is now recognized in a large part of the world, and in some parts has, I think, been recognized for many centuries. It is certainly now generally recognized in England and other parts of the British dominions. If that is so, there is in this case evidence that the prisoner's signature was found in the place which was broken into, and was found under such circumstances that it would only have been impressed at the time when the crime was committed. It is impossible under those circumstances to say that there was no evidence to go to the jury.

In the case of *People* v. *Jennings,* 252 Ill., 534; 96 N.E. 1077; 43 L.R.A. (N. S.) 1206 (1911), it was held that fingerprint evidence, even though it may not be of independent strength, is admissible, with other evidence, as a means of identification and as tending to make out a case. It was also held that expert testimony is not limited to classed and specified professions, but is admissible where the witnesses offered have peculiar knowledge or experience not common to the world, which renders their opinions, founded upon such knowledge and experience, an aid to the court or jury in determining the issue. It was further held that persons experienced in the matter of fingerprint identification may give their opinions as to whether the fingerprints found at the scene of the crime correspond with those of the accused, there being no question as to the accuracy or authenticity of the photographs. It was further held in this case that the weight to be given the testimony of experts in the fingerprint identification is a question for the jury.

In rendering his opinion in this case, Chief Justice Carter said:

No case in which this question has been raised (*whether evidence as to the comparison of enlarged photographs of the fingerprints found at the scene of a crime with the enlarged fingerprints of the defendant was properly admitted*) has been cited in the briefs, and we find no statutes or decisions touching the point in this country. This class of evidence is admitted in Great Britain. In 1909 the court of criminal appeals held that fingerprints might be received as evidence, and refused to interfere with a conviction below (*in a lower court*) though this evidence was the sole ground of conviction. . . .

All of these (*four*) witnesses have testified, at more or less length, as to the basis of the system and the various markings found in the human hands, stating that they are classified from the various forms of markings, including those known as "arches," "loops," "whorls," and "deltas." . . . When photography was first introduced it was seriously questioned whether pictures thus created could properly be introduced in evidence, but this method of proof, as well as by means of X-rays and the microscope, is now admitted without question. . . .

We are disposed to hold from the evidence of the four witnesses who testified, and from the writings we have referred to on this subject, that there is a scientific basis for the system of fingerprint identification, and that the courts are justified in admitting this class of evidence.

In the case of *State* v. *Cerciello,* 86 N. J. L. 309; 90 Atl. 1112; 52 L. R. A. (N. S.) 1010 (1914), it was contended that it was error to allow testimony by experts concerning finger-prints obtained from the defendant voluntarily, and used as a method of comparison with fingerprints upon a hatchet found near the body of the deceased, when the body was discovered.

Justice Minturn, Court of Errors and Appeals of the State of New Jersey, made the following comments in rendering his opinion in this case:

The testimony in the main in this case was that the defendant, after he had been some time in custody, was taken by two officers to the office of an expert in fingerprint impressions, and was there induced to sign his name upon a sheet of paper, which act inciden-tally impressed his fingerprints upon the sheet. It was contended that the action of the court in allowing the experts upon this subject to testify to their experience in this line of work, as well as to the practical results obtained by use of their art in detecting crime, was illegal and incompetent. We do not so view it. The design of the prosecution, quite obviously was to qualify the witnesses as experts in that particular calling, but the weight of their testimony and importance as evidence in the case, the court quite properly left for the jury to determine. Such is the course pursued in the case of the testimony of expert witnesses in other branches of human effort, science, and progress. . . .

In principle its admission as legal evidence is based upon the theory that the evolution in practical affairs of life, whereby the progressive and scientific tendencies of the age are manifest in every other department of human endeavor, cannot be ignored in legal procedure, but that the law, in its efforts to enforce justice by dem-onstrating a fact in issue, will allow evidence of those scientific processes, which are the work of educated and skillful men in their various departments, and apply them to the demonstration of a fact, leaving the weight and effect to be given to the effort and its results entirely to the consideration of the jury.

In the case of *People* v. *Roach*, 215 N. Y. 592; 109 N. E. 618;
Ann. Cas. 1917-A. 410 (1915), it was stated by the court:

It is earnestly insisted that the admission in evidence of the testimony of an alleged expert as to fingerprint impressions was error
and of such material character as to have wrought grave injury to
the defendant and to necessitate the reversal of this judgment (*of
the Supreme Court of the State of New York convicting the defendant of a crime of murder in the first degree*). This testimony
was given in relation to five separate marks which were discovered
upon the clapboards of the house (*in which the murder was committed*) near the kitchen door. The portion of the boards bearing
these marks was cut out and was submitted to experts in fingerprinting and was offered in evidence upon the trial. The marks
were so placed upon the board and were of such a shape and design
that they could have been made by soiled fingers. It was proved that
the impressions represented by these marks were made in human
blood. . . . Finger impressions of the left hand of this defendant
were taken upon various occasions. In these experiments the left
hand of the defendant was held at the wrist alone, and the hand permitted to assume a natural position, with the fingers extended when
the fingers touched the paper below. These impressions made upon
several sheets of paper were such that the fingerprints of the four
fingers fitted over the four fingers upon the clapboards. . . . Also,
it was sworn by Hamilton (*the fingerprint expert*) that the lineations upon the thumb exactly corresponded with the lineations upon
the lower mark upon the clapboard. Hamilton swears that these
marks were the fingerprints of the left hand of the defendant.

The court continued:

In view of the progress that has been made by scientific students
and those charged with the detection of crime in police departments
of the larger cities of the world, in effecting identification by means
of fingerprint impressions, we cannot rule as a matter of law that
such evidence is incompetent. Nor does the fact that it presents to
the court novel questions preclude its admission upon common law
principles. The same thing is true of typewriting, photography,
and X-ray photographs, and yet the reception of such evidence is a
common occurrence in our courts. The evidence to prove identity

often presents doubtful and unsatisfactory features. One man may be mistaken for another because they look alike, or identity of persons may be inferred from similarity of features, height, expression, or a variety of other circumstances. Under common-law principles whatever tends to prove any material fact is relevant and competent. . . .

The evidence of the expert as to the identity of the fingerprints of the defendant, with the blood marks found upon the clapboards of the house where the murder was committed, was a proper subject for the jury. The weight to be given to this evidence was for the jury, not the court, to determine.

In the case of *State* v. *Connors*, 87 N. J. L. 419 (1915), it was held that it was competent for the State to prove the corpus delecti by showing that the defendant had been seen in the city on more than one occasion on the day of the crime, and that the fingerprints found upon a column of the balcony of the house entered were similar to the fingerprints of the defendant; and it was competent to show the fingerprints upon the column by a photograph thereof, and to identify the fingerprints of the defendant made by experts after the defendant's arrest.

Also, in the case of *Moon* v. *State*, 198 Pac. (Ariz.) 288 (1921), it was held that evidence of the correspondence of fingerprint impressions for the purpose of identification, when introduced by qualified fingerprint experts, is admissible in court cases, the weight and value of such testimony being for the jury.

Again, in the case of *Lamble* v. *State,* 114 Atl. (N. J.) 346 (1921), it was held that it was competent to show in evidence of fingerprints upon the door of an automobile by a photograph thereof, without the production of the door of the automobile; also to identify the fingerprints of the defendant by experts, after the defendant's arrest. Yet, argument in this case was made that this testimony was incompetent so far as the fingerprints on the automobile were concerned, because the door itself ought to have been produced; but it was stated in the court's opinion that this question was decided by the Supreme Court the other way in the case of *State* v. *Connors*, 87 N. J. L. 419, in which case it was held competent to show by a photograph the fingerprints upon the column or balcony post of a house without the column being produced in court.

In the case of *Commonwealth* v. *Albright,* 101 Super. Ct. (Penn.) 317 (1931), a fingerprint expert testified that the fingerprints on a piece of glass, established to be from a pane in a door which had been broken to effect entrance to the house, was the same as the impression of the defendant's left index finger, and he explained in detail the points of identity which led him to that judgment. Furthermore, there was testimony that the defendant, who lived about three blocks from the dwelling which had been burglarized, was seen in the immediate neighborhood the evening of the alleged entry. The court held in such circumstances the case was for the jury, and was sufficient evidence to sustain a verdict of guilty.

The court said:

We do not think it necessary to go into detailed discussion of the facts on which the science of identification by means of fingerprint impressions is based. Its accuracy and reliability are too well established to require elaborate confirmation at this time by courts of this State. It is well settled that the papillary lines and marks on the fingers of every man, woman, and child possess an individual character different from those of any other person, and that the chances that the fingerprints of two different persons may be identical are infinitesimally remote.

In the case of *United States* v. *Kelly,* 55 Fed. (2d) 67 (Jan. 18, 1932), the court indicated that fingerprinting seems to be no more than an extension of the methods of identification long used in dealing with persons under arrest for real or supposed violations of the criminal laws. It is known to be a very certain means devised by modern science to reach the desired end and has become especially important at a time when increased population and vast aggregations of people in urban centers have rendered the notoriety of the individual in the community no longer a ready means of identification.

Note: While the decisions herein included are unquestioned authority, yet in those states which have statutes governing fingerprinting, these decisions would be read in the light of the statutes. This applies to the following cases, and to the claim of infringement of constitutional rights of persons fingerprinted.

It has been contended that the taking of fingerprints and the introduction of the same at the trial of an accused are violations of the constitutional provision against self-incrimination. The question is frequently asked whether fingerprinting a suspect and introducing his fingerprints and record in court are not violations of his constitutional rights as provided in many states, namely, that the defendant in a criminal case cannot be compelled to give evidence against himself. Perhaps the best expression of the Federal law as to the use of a man's body to identify that man with a crime is contained in the opinion of the United States Supreme Court in *Holt* v. *United States*, 218 U. S. 245, page 252, wherein Justice Holmes stated:

The prohibition of compelling a man in a criminal court to be witness against himself is a prohibition of the use of physical or moral compulsion to extort communications from him, not an exclusion of his body as evidence when it may be material. The objection in principle would forbid a jury to look at a prisoner and compare his features with a photograph in proof.

The point has been passed upon in the Federal Courts. In *United States* v. *Kelly*[1] the Government appealed from an

[1] 55 F. (2) 67, 1932.

order directing the United States Attorney to return the defendant's fingerprints.[2] Kelly was arrested by prohibition agents for having sold a quart of gin and was fingerprinted. The Federal law provided an additional penalty for the second conviction. The court held that the slight interference with the person involved in fingerprinting seemed to be one which must be borne in a common interest. Fingerprinting seemed to be more than an extension of methods of identification long used in dealing with persons under arrest for real or supposed violations of the criminal laws. The case distinguishes *Hawkins* v. *Kuhne*[3] because here the defendant was fingerprinted before convicted. The court continued, "We prefer, however, to rest our decision upon the general right of the authorities charged with the enforcement of the criminal law to employ fingerprinting as an appropriate means to identify criminals and detect crime.

In this *Kelly Case* there was also a Federal statute[4] pleaded setting forth that a person may be arrested and imprisoned according to the usual method in that state. But the courts said that statute did not apply to fingerprinting an accused.[5]

The New Jersey court is in accord with the Federal court in holding that the fingerprinting of an individual is not a violation of his constitutional rights. In *Bartletta* v. *McFeeley*,[6]

[2] 51 F. (2) 263, 1931.

[3] 153 App. Div. 216 (N. Y.); 137 N. Y. S. 1090.

[4] 18 U. S. C. A. sec 591, United States Rev. Stats., sec. 1014. An offender against any law of the United States may be arrested, imprisoned, and bailed agreeably to the usual mode of process against offenders in such State.

[5] See also *People* v. *Les,* 255 N. W. 407, Mich. (1934), in which there are dicta to the same effect. In *Duree* v. *United States,* 1924, 297 F. 70, a train was robbed and the mail car blown open with nitroglycerin. Fingerprints found on bottle which contained nitroglycerin were identified as the accused's. Court held, "The fingerprints on the bottle as shown by the photographs were important, the same comparing with the recorded fingerprints of Babe Downer." 16 A. L. R. 370.

[6] 107 N. J. Eq. 141 (1931), 152 Atl. 17. Affirmed 109 N. J. Eq. 241, 156 Atl. 658.

Bartletta sought to recover his fingerprints from the police commissioner. He was arrested for possession of lottery tickets and fingerprinted. The court held:

The police are charged with the duty of preventing crime, apprehending criminals, and gathering evidence upon which they may be brought to trial. In the performance of this duty, they may use any apt and reasonable means which do not invade the rights of the accused or of other persons. Fanciful rights of accused persons cannot be allowed to prevent the functioning of the police and so to jeopardize the safety of the public. . . . The right of the police to fingerprint and photograph is powerfully supported by the argument for convenience and for the public interest in permitting the courts to learn the truth of the question at issue. This right is also upheld by custom.

There is a close analogy between searching the person of a prisoner and fingerprinting him. Both acts have for their purpose the obtaining of evidence against him; in both is his person subjected to some handling beyond what is required for preventing escape.[7]

In *Garcia* v. *State* [8] a constitutional provision that a defendant in a criminal case cannot be compelled to give testimony

[7] *Schulman* v. *Whitaker* (La.) 42 So. 227. 7 L. R. A. (N. S.) 274. *Downs* v. *Swann* (Md.), 73 Atl. 653, 23 L. R. A. (N. S.) 739, *State* v. *Clausmeier* (Ind.), 57 N. E. Rep. 541. 50 L. R. A. 73. *Shaffer* v. *United States*, 24 App. D. C. 417. In 176 *Law Times*, p. 25, there is a discussion of an unnamed case which came before the Justiciary Appeal Court of Edinburgh where the question arose of taking the fingerprints of an untried prisoner, without his consent. The court decided that it was permissible, and not violative of the liberty of the subject. Stone's *Justices' Manual*, sixty-fifth edition, 1933, p. 1342, says that a prisoner may be measured, his picture taken, and his description secured, according to the Prevention of Crime Act 1871, 34 and 35 Vict. C. 112, and the Penal Servitude Act 1891, 54, and 55, Vict. C. 69, and a dissenting judge in the Justiciary Appeal Court was of the opinion that these acts did not include fingerprinting because they were passed before fingerprinting of prisoners was generally adopted. Therefore, the court's act in ruling that the taking of the prisoners' fingerprints did not constitute an assault upon the person of a citizen which infringed his common-law rights, was judicial legislation.

[8] 26 Arizona 597. 229 Pac. 103. 80 U. Pa. L. R. 887, p. 890.

against himself, was not violated by introducing evidence of fingerprint impressions of the defendant. The court was cognizant of the fact that the prints had been obtained from the defendant by subterfuge and he did not know they were to be used against him.[9]

In New York in 1917, where there was a state statute which provided that no person could be convicted until fingerprint records were searched, the defendant in *People* v. *Sallow*[10] contended that she had to testify against herself. She was fingerprinted and the record revealed that she was a fourth-time offender, which incurred an additional penalty. The court sustained the conviction, saying that there was no violation of her constitutional rights, as there was no willing act on the part of the mind of the defendant required because the prints spoke for themselves.

Subsequently the New York court had before it in *People* v. *Hevern*[11] the law[12] providing that no person charged with a felony or certain other specified offenses, should be admitted

9 *State* v. *Chin Lung* (1927), 106 Conn. 701. 139 Atl. 91. Fingerprints on revolver showing defendant was an accomplice to the murderer as he handed the gun to the principal. *State* v. *Martinez* (1926), 43 Idaho 180. 250 Pac. 239. Fingerprints of first wife introduced in court when defendant was charged with bigamy. *Hopkins* v. *State* (1927), 174 Ark. 391. 295 S. W. 361.

10 100 Misc. Rep. 447. 165 N. Y. S. 915.

11 215 N. Y. S. 412, 127 Miss. Rep. 141. "Fingerprinting before conviction involved prohibited compulsory self-incrimination. . . . Concededly there may not be a compulsory written examination of a defendant as to his past career, and in my judgment he may not be compelled to make disclosure of his past life by the nod or nay of the head or the lines of his hands." In *People* v. *Fine,* 251 N. Y. S. 187, 140 Misc. Rep. 592, the court held that fingerprint records, though admissible, are not sufficient proof of the defendant's prior conviction without original or certified copies of the records. In *Bernier* v. *Lawrensen,* 283 N. Y. S. 452, 1935, defendant, a peace officer, came into the plaintiff's room, arrested him, and fingerprinted him. The plaintiff recovered in an action for false arrest.

12 New York Laws 1926, C. 419, amending Code Cr. Proc., secs. 552-554, 557, 558, and enacting new sec. 552-a.

to bail until such persons forthwith on arrest be fingerprinted. The court held it was a violation of Art. 1, Section 6, New York Constitution, prohibiting self-incrimination. No specific mention was made of the case of *People* v. *Sallow*.[13]

The weight of authority seems to be with the Kelly[14] case, holding that fingerprinting is not a violation of the accused's constitutional rights against compulsory self-incrimination. The prohibition against such compulsion relates primarily to testimonial utterances, that is, communications which involve the active cooperation of the intellect and will. Submitting to fingerprinting is a passive act in which the person makes no communication concerning a matter within his knowledge.

In the case of *State* v. *Kuhl*, 42 Nev. 185; 175 Pac. 190 (1918), it was held that evidence of experts as to identity of palm prints of the defendant in a homicide case with that found upon a blood-smeared envelope found at the place of crime was promptly admitted. The court in this case stated in part:

Were we dealing here with a fingerprint impression, or the question of the comparison or identity of fingerprint impressions, our course would be easy, for the courts of this country, and of England as well, have paved the way for the recognition of this science as an evidentiary element of criminal prosecution. The main contention here is that the experts who testified were not qualified to give an opinion as to the identity of palm-print impressions; and, as we understand the contention of appellant, it is that science has not yet developed this question sufficiently to bear out the conclusion of an expert on the subject. Will the same rule which led the court to recognize experts of fingerprint identification permit such experts to testify as to their conclusions upon palm-print identification? This is the vital question here.

The court, after referring to decisions, textbooks, and other authorities, continued (p. 192):

13 See note 10 supra.
14 Cited supra.

All of the learned authors, experts, and scientists on the subject of fingerprint identification . . . agree that these patterns, formed by the papillary ridges on the inner surface of the human hand and the sole of the foot, are persistent, continuous, and unchanging from a period in the existence of the individual extending from some months before birth until disintegration after death. While most of the experts on fingerprint identification deal most extensively with impressions of the human fingers, we find that some, of whom Mr. Galton is first and foremost, have divided the palmar surface of the human hand into what they term well-marked systems of ridges. . . .

In the following three murder cases photographs of palm prints found at the crime scene on weapons used in the crime were admitted in evidence for comparison with the palm prints of the accused:

Louisiana—*State v. Dunn,* 100 So. 56, 161 La. 532 (1926), writ of error dismissed, 47 S. Ct. 344, 273 U.S. 656, 71 L.Ed. 825 (1927).

Nebraska—*Sharp v. State,* 214 N.W. 643, 115 Neb. 737 (1927).

Vermont—*State v. Lapan,* 146 A. 686, 101 Vt. 124 (1928).

The admissibility of infant footprints as evidence of the child's identity was established in New York courts as a consequence of two unrelated kidnapping cases which were both tried in 1959: New York—*People v. Iavarone,* Co. Ct., Brooklyn, (1959) and New York—*People v. Ortiz,* Co. Ct., Manhattan (1959). In the former case the testifying expert, Detective Arthur Mandella of the New York Police Department, relied mainly on the flexure creases for the identification. The creases, according to Mandella's testimony, would have remained unchanged during the period of time that had elapsed between the recording of the footprints at the hospital shortly after the child's birth and the recording of the footprints following the infant's recovery. Thirteen points of identification were shown in the hospital footprint to correspond to a similar set of thirteen points in the footprint of the recovered baby. The absence of any inconsistencies was emphasized: the flexure creases were identical with respect to relative location, trend, and formation.

Quantum of Evidence Necessary in Latent Fingerprint Cases

State v. *Steffen,* 230 N. W. (Iowa) 536, holds the expert may not testify to the ultimate fact that the latents are identical with the fingerprints of the defendant, but the ultimate conclusion that the fingerprints are identical is the province of the jury to determine. It has, however, been held proper to permit an expert opinion to the effect that a given print could not have been made by any person other than the accused. [Texas —*Grice* v. *State,* 151 S.W. 2d 211, 142 Tex.Cr.R. 4 (1941)] Actually, whether the expert makes the identification in the form of an opinion or as a direct conclusion is a matter of words [Nevada—*State* v. *Kuhl,* 175 P. 190,42 Nev. 185 3 A.L.R. 1694 (1918)], since the jury in either event determines the weight given his testimony.

As a guide in identifications from impressions, the views of Edmond Locard still retain a special interest:

(1) Where there are more than 12 evident points and the impression clear, identification is absolute.

(2) Where there are 8 to 12 points, identity depends upon (*a*) clearness of impression; (*b*) rarity of the type; (*c*) presence of the core or of the delta in the part that is decipherable; (*d*) the presence of pores; (*e*) the perfect and evident identity of the breadth of the ridges and furrows. In these cases certainty of the identification is to be established only after the discussion of the case by one or more competent experts.

(3) Where there are few points: In this case the print, taken by itself, does not furnish certain identity but only a presumption proportional to the number and clearness of the points. Should a number of prints of the third class be available, their

can scarcely be claimed without at least 12 homologous points of comparison. However, the said authors express the opinion that 6 or 8 points well grouped, defining a center of exceptional form, constitute such perfect proof of identity as to give no grounds for argument. Prevailing pertinent court decisions should be consulted when doubt may exist as to the exact evidence required.

A related but less difficult question is posed by the fragmentary fingerprint found at the crime scene: Is such a print sufficient for a conclusive comparison with the known fingerprint of the accused? An affirmative view of the weight and sufficiency of such an identification has been expressed by a Texas court (Texas—*Grice v. State,* cited above):

"The entire fingerprint . . . was not shown on the glass, but only one fourth or one fifth. It is argued by appellant that not a sufficient print was on the glass to furnish a conclusive comparison with the known thumbprint of appellant. Here we must look to the evidence of the expert. . . . He testified as follows: 'Yes, more than a sufficient number of characteristics as shown by the known print appeared in the other to afford *positive identification.* All of the ridge characteristics within that area were present in both of these impressions. *It is not necessary that we have the entire pattern to identify a finger print.'* " (Italics by court.)

APPENDIX
PALMS AND FOOTPRINTS

Any area of the body which bears a permanent and complex set of ridges or lines can be used for identification. In particular, the palm of the hand and the sole of the foot are adaptable to this purpose.

Palm prints are not infrequently found in criminal investigations, on window sills and the like. Ridges are sometimes found on the outer side of the heel of the palm. The major area will usually consist of a complex of fine lines, some of which are obviously crease lines. If the palm print is visible without development, it should be photographed at once. If developed with black powder on a white surface, the lines of the palm may appear white, while the ridges appear black. This should present no difficulty, however, since the palm print is compared rather than classified. A suspect's palm prints can be obtained by inking the palms and pressing them against a card.

The importance of infant footprints has been repeatedly emphasized in civil and criminal cases. Accidental baby "switches" can be easily rectified by a comparison of the baby's footprints with the recorded prints in the hospital records. In two cases of kidnapping a positive comparison of the child's footprint with a hospital record was accepted by the court as conclusive proof of the child's identity.

Both the ridge areas and the flexure lines serve to identify an infant. When ridge areas are present, there is a tendency to structure the identification about the ridges. This does not imply that flexure lines are invalid as identification. Indeed, the child's foot may not possess legible ridge areas, but the flexure lines of the sole are sufficient in number, complexity, and variance in distribution to be considered individual.

At birth two kinds of flexure lines are observable on the child's foot. One group of lines tends to disappear after seven months. The other group is more permanent—the same set of lines, together with the same relative location, have been observed to remain for a period of years. These latter lines constitute the basis of foot identification in infants, since they will not change during the period in question. Naturally, the case is further strengthened by the existence of a distinct ridge area. See illustration facing page 327.

A prerequisite in any attempt at infant identification is the maintenance of adequate footprint records at the hospital. In some jurisdictions private as well as public hospitals are now required to record infant footprints. The records of many hospitals, however, have been found to be inadequate, because of poor printing methods.

Inadequate records of this nature are attributable to failure in training a group of hospital employees in the elements of inking and recording. The designated employees should first be instructed in the nature of their task so that they will recognize a properly recorded footprint. The importance of using a limited amount of ink and the correct pressure should then be stressed. Finally, the records should be regularly inspected by an experienced hospital supervisor.

Police departments can aid considerably in a hospital's identification program by instructing personnel in the requisite techniques, periodically reviewing the hospital's file, and conducting an informal critique to demonstrate aspects of the records reflecting excellent and inadequate techniques.

INDEX

Accidental patterns, 84, 120

Aerosol spray, 254

Amputation, deformities or injuries, 24, 107-109, 144

Arches, 29; exceptional, 52, 58-64, 148; plain, 52, 212; tented, 52-64, 119, 148-50

Barlow single-fingerprint system, 204-206

"Battley glass," 145

Battley single-fingerprint system, 145-55

Bertillon, Alphonse, 16-17; system of fingerprinting, 163; system of measurements, 16-17

Bifurcation, 39

Biological significance of skin patterns, 1-18

Borgerhoff single-fingerprint system, 196-97

Borgerhoff system, 172-73

Born single-fingerprint system, 198-200

Bromine vapor in fuming process, 270

Brushes, suitable for powdering prints, 246

Brussels system, 164-65

Budapest or Hungarian system, 162-63

Cabezas system, 175-76

Cameras, fingerprint, 313-14

Castings of latent prints, 281-83

Central pocket loops, 75-78, 119

Classification of prints (*see Henry system*)

Coding in data processing, 213

Collins single-fingerprint system, 181-86; coding, 184-85

Color photography, 320-21

Communications, 213

Comparison prints, taking, 238

Composites, 31

Conlay system, 180-81

Cores, 37-38

Court decisions, 353-68 (*see also Precedent Court decisions*)

Daae system, 164

Deceased persons, fingerprinting of, 299-308

Deltas, 38; open and closed, 44

Developing latent prints, fuming, 262-72; heat treatment, 275-76; ink process, 272-74; silver nitrate method, 276-79

Distortion of fingerprints, 249-50

Divergence, 39

Dot, 4, 6

Dresden single-fingerprint system, 201-202

Ektalith, 214

Electronic data processing, 209ff

Enclosure, 4, 6

Enlargements of photographs, 320, 325-27

Epidermis, 2-4

Equipment for fingerprinting, 19-20; for field kit, 232

Exceptional arches, 52-58

Exhibits, Court, 325-27, 344

371